Introductory Guide to NHS Finance in the UK

This Guide was finalised in March 2011 and looks at how the NHS will be structured for the next year or so. It also highlights at the end of each chapter how things will change if the coalition government's planned reforms go ahead as they are set out in the *Health and Social Care Bill 2011*. The Guide does not take account of any amendments that may be agreed during the Bill's passage through parliament.

Contents

Foreword

Welcome to the tenth edition of the HFMA's *Introductory Guide to NHS Finance* in the UK. This version follows the same format as the 2008 Guide but has been updated to take account of the many developments and challenges that the NHS has faced over the intervening period. For the first time in its history, this Guide also looks to the future by seeking to identify at the end of each chapter the key changes that will be introduced subject to any amendments that are agreed as the *Health and Social Care Bill 2011* makes its way through parliament.

The *Introductory Guide* is designed to give readers a solid grounding in – and practical understanding of – all key aspects of NHS finance. It also provides some contextual background that helps explain why the NHS is as it is today and gets to grips with the jargon that has built up around NHS finance over the years. Although the Guide focuses on the policy and organisational framework for the NHS in England, it includes chapters that highlight the key differences in Northern Ireland, Scotland and Wales.

As always, the chapters have been written in a simple, straightforward style by NHS finance practitioners and include practical examples wherever possible to help explain often complicated financing rules and regulations. Further reference sources for those who want to delve into a subject in more detail are also provided along with a glossary and list of abbreviations.

Given the significant changes planned for the NHS over the coming years, the next edition is likely to look very different but the HFMA's commitment to producing an easy to understand Guide to NHS finance remains as will our determination to improve the awareness of finance and financial management across the NHS and beyond.

We trust that you find this Guide useful, informative and easy to read – if you have any comments we would be pleased to hear from you.

Keith Wood,
Chair, HFMA Financial Management and Research Committee

Acknowledgements

The production of the *Introductory Guide to NHS Finance in the UK* involves a large number of people who contribute their time and expertise to the production of one or more chapters. It has been prepared primarily by members of the HFMA's Financial Management and Research Committee. The main contributors to this edition – either as chapter authors or 'quality assurors' – are:

Keith Wood (Chair)
Les Allen
Pen Andersen
Sarah Bence
Phil Bradley
Steve Brown
Andy Colledge
Tarryn Lake
Steve Elliot
Keely Firth
Nick Gerrard
Kavita Gnanaolivu
Anna Green
Andy Goor
Edmund King
Emma Knowles
John Loftus
Andy Lund
Richard Mellor
Adrian Murphy
Tracey Paton
Janet Perry
Mary Pettman
Carol Potter
Sheenagh Powell
Chris Reid
Neil Robson
Pippa Ross-Smith
Paul Skillen
Karl Simkins
Paul Taylor
Huw Thomas
Andrew Treherne
Robert White

Editorial work was undertaken by Anna Green.

The HFMA is grateful for the contributions of all those listed above, who give their time free of charge, often in addition to the long hours routinely worked by most senior NHS finance staff.

1. Introduction

Purpose

For more than twenty years, the *Introductory Guide to NHS Finance* has sought to provide an easy to read, accessible guide to the workings and language of NHS finance for the benefit of practitioners and observers. The Guide is produced by The Healthcare Financial Management Association (HFMA), a charity established 60 years ago to support those working within the NHS finance function. By improving financial literacy both within and outside NHS finance, the HFMA hopes it can inform and improve the debate on healthcare finance issues.

The Guide has been developed to provide a self-contained source of advice and guidance for readers from an array of backgrounds. There are many aspects of NHS finance that are unique to the service, and a language laden with jargon, abbreviations and acronyms has developed that to many outsiders or newcomers can appear impenetrable. This Guide aims to provide advice to all levels of finance staff from finance directors (who often use the guide as an aide memoir to more recent changes) to accounts assistants, governors, non-executive and executive directors (who may not be finance specialists but still have shared corporate responsibility for understanding and managing the financial position), clinicians, budget holders and service managers, and people who need an understanding of NHS finance for academic study purposes.

Over the years the Guide has grown in size so that it can provide both an overview of the current finance regime and a sense of how it has developed over the years. It remains as its title suggests an introductory guide; a reasonably straightforward but comprehensive description of the structures and processes of the varying health economies of England, Northern Ireland, Scotland and Wales.

The last version of the *Introductory Guide* was produced in 2008 in the aftermath of a period of structural change within the NHS. This edition is released as the coalition government is beginning to implement a programme of proposals first set out in its June 2010 white paper *Equity and Excellence: Liberating the NHS* that will change the structure and approach of the NHS more dramatically than any other reforms since the NHS was established in 1948. This Guide therefore aims to fulfil two functions: firstly it looks at the NHS as it is working now and for the next year or so and secondly it highlights at the end of each chapter how things are expected to change once the coalition government's reforms are implemented. The HFMA intends to issue a further version of the Guide in time for the start of the new structure.

Contents

This version of the *Introductory Guide* follows the approach readers will be familiar with – namely that each chapter treats its topic in a largely self-contained way. Cross-references are included where they are helpful and sources of further advice and technical guidance are listed at the end of each chapter. There are also appendices containing a glossary of terms and abbreviations.

The greater part of the Guide concentrates on the financial arrangements for the NHS in England for 2011/12 with an indication in each chapter of how things will change over the coming years (subject to any amendments agreed to the *Health and Social Care Bill, 2011* which is currently making its way through Parliament). There are also chapters highlighting key differences in Northern Ireland, Scotland and Wales – these differences will become even more marked once the coalition government's proposals for England are implemented. Separate introductory guides covering NHS finance in Scotland and in foundation trusts are also available.

The Authors

The *Introductory Guide* is produced by the HFMA's Financial Management and Research Committee. Members of the committee are finance staff from across the NHS who give up their time voluntarily to help improve financial management standards and control in the NHS, and to promote an understanding of NHS finance both inside and outside the finance department.

The Introductory Guide as a Training Tool

The copyright for the Guide is held exclusively by the HFMA. Further copies can be obtained directly from the HFMA or via the website at www.hfma.org.uk

The Guide is designed as both a reference source and a training tool. Although normal copyright restrictions apply, in recognition of the Guide's training role, the HFMA allows the reproduction of diagrams, statistics and quotes.

The Introductory Certificate to NHS Finance

In addition to the *Introductory Guide*, the HFMA has produced a modular e-learning course that allows individuals to address their NHS finance training needs in a tailored way. The e-learning modules are aimed at non-finance professionals, governors, non-executive directors and finance staff that are new to the NHS and can also be used as a 'refresher' for existing staff.

Although modules can be studied individually, there is an *Introductory Certificate* that involves learners selecting five modules from an ever expanding list of topics. These cover both the structure of the NHS (for example, NHS finance, primary care finance and the foundation trust financial regime) and processes (for example, payment by results, budgeting and costing). Each training session takes approximately one and a half hours to complete and includes an assessment test. On successful completion of the fifth module, a certificate is awarded. The *Introductory Certificate* is fast becoming an industry standard; a means of assessing an individual's basic competence in NHS finance. Further details are available from the HFMA website at www.hfma.org.uk

2. Background to the NHS

Introduction

The scale and complexity of the NHS should not be underestimated – at present, it is the largest employer in Europe, with more than 1.3 million staff. Since its formation in 1948, the NHS has been reorganised, reformed and modernised. The structural changes can appear in many cases to be cyclical and each iteration brings with it new terminology that can become entrenched to such an extent that even a decade after the structures and processes have moved on, finance professionals quote the acronyms and terms of yesteryear. Understanding a little more about the history of the NHS and why it has got to where it is today is therefore often helpful and instructive. It is also invaluable for individual members of staff – both those who spend their entire careers working within the NHS and those that bring in skills from other industries and graft on NHS experience.

This chapter aims to provide a brief outline history of key policy developments in the NHS over the last twenty years – it follows a broadly chronological approach so that readers can see how and why the NHS has grown in the way it has.

NHS Finance in Context – Key Policy Developments

The internal market, 1980s

In the late 1980s it was decided that the NHS should be reconfigured along purchaser and provider lines. This required the NHS to operate a 'quasi-market', known as the internal market. The key feature of this approach was the separation of the provision of hospital/community services from the commissioning or purchasing function – the so-called 'purchaser/provider split'. Hospitals were encouraged to apply for self-governing trust status, creating organisations quite separate from the health authorities from which they were devolved. To achieve trust status, and formally separate from the health authorities, provider organisations had to follow an application process that assessed viability and robustness – this has parallels with the current foundation trust application process.

There was also an optional scheme to give general practitioners (GPs) the ability to hold budgets for the purchase of hospital services for their patients (known as GP fund holding). At the same time, trusts were encouraged to invest in and develop services and to compete with each other to win patient service contracts with purchasers.

There were a number of criticisms associated with the internal market. In particular, it was argued that it led to fragmentation and a lottery in service provision, with competition proving a weak lever for improvement. It also led to overall increases in administration costs to the NHS as 'losing' organisations had to be sustained to ensure that services could be maintained.

In 1997, the change of government resulted in plans to dismantle the internal market.

The New NHS – Modern, Dependable, 1997

In 1997 the White Paper *The New NHS – Modern, Dependable* set out a programme for reform of the NHS. These proposals became law with the *1999 Health Act* and the focus shifted away from competition to a collaborative model, where NHS organisations worked together and with local authorities to refocus healthcare on the patient. By removing the competitive nature of the internal market the changes in policy sought to ensure the seamless delivery of services.

Key changes were an end to GP fund holding and the introduction of new organisations for primary care. Primary care organisations (either groups or trusts) were formed from groups of local GP practices, or 'natural communities'. Boundaries were encouraged to coincide where possible with local authority borders to simplify the integration of health and social care. In their initial stages these groups were sub-committees of health authorities, used to inform the commissioning process. As they found their feet, these new organisations were able to apply for trust status, creating bodies independent from the health authority and managing increasingly significant portions of former health authority budgets.

The *1999 Health Act* also established the Commission for Health Improvement (to be succeeded by the Commission for Healthcare Audit and Inspection, then by the Healthcare Commission and now the Care Quality Commission) and the National Institute for Health and Clinical Excellence (NICE) as special health authorities.

There was also a renewed emphasis on cutting management costs – a challenging objective given the increase in the number of NHS organisations, and greater involvement of management at a local level. The shared services initiative was, at least to an extent, an attempt to mitigate the pressure on management costs by reducing the cost of providing support services. National shared service centre pilots were established and there are now four shared business services centres in Wakefield, Bristol, Southampton and Portsmouth run as a joint venture between the Department of Health and Steria. Alongside these national centres, there are many other shared service arrangements within local health communities that aim to provide efficient, cost-effective services.

The purchaser/provider split created by the internal market was retained. Initially health authorities remained and continued to purchase healthcare using service and financial framework agreements (SaFFs). These health authorities were then abolished but the division between commissioning and provision continued with primary care trusts (PCTs) taking over responsibility for commissioning hospital services. At their inception, many PCTs also had a provider role for community services.

The 1997 White Paper also heralded a move towards longer planning time frames, promising the replacement of annual contract negotiations with three-year resource announcements. This was delivered at a Department of Health level, with the budget announcement including levels of funding for the next three years. Three-year allocations to PCTs were introduced from 2003/04 to help improve the service planning process and most organisations committed to three-year local development plans (LDPs) – although the level of detail incorporated in years two and three was limited.

The NHS was encouraged to form partnerships with both private and public sector partners, including local authority social services. The *1999 Health Act* (since superseded by the *NHS Act 2006*) broadened the scope for pooling of health and social services budgets. Partnership working with the private sector was formalised in a 'concordat' agreement, which highlighted scope for partnerships in elective, critical and intermediate care. New independently run diagnosis and treatment centres or independent sector treatment centres (ISTCs) were established so extending the role of the private sector in the NHS.

The NHS Plan: a Plan for Investment, a Plan for Reform, 2000

In July 2000 the *NHS Plan* was presented to Parliament. The plan consisted of a vision of the NHS first outlined in the 1997 White Paper – modernised, structurally reformed, efficient and properly funded. Much of the document was dedicated to identifying new targets and milestones on wide ranging issues (from waiting lists to implementation of electronic patient records) and measures that needed to be taken to facilitate the achievement of those targets.

The Health Act 2002

In April 2002 a further tranche of changes came into effect. At the end of March 2002, the 95 health authorities in England were abolished and replaced by 28 strategic health authorities (SHAs). At the same time the eight regional offices were replaced by four directorates of health and social care (DHSCs) which were themselves dissolved in 2003. The changes, first outlined in April 2001 in the policy paper *Shifting the Balance of Power (StBoP)*, were designed to transfer management resource and control closer to the locality, and hence to the patient.

The establishment of PCTs was also completed in 2002 – a key change here was the fact that PCTs were allowed to expand primary care services beyond those traditionally provided by GPs. This prompted a growth in 'GPs with special interests' and in services provided in the community by PCTs where previously they had been delivered in an acute hospital setting.

Many of the monitoring and planning processes were devolved from the old regional offices to the new SHAs, while commissioning functions were transferred to PCTs.

The structure that was introduced in 2002 for the NHS in England (and which will remain in place until the coalition government's reforms are implemented) is shown over the page. This includes foundation trusts that came into being following the *Health and Social Care (Community Health and Standards) Act 2003* (see later in this chapter).

Comprehensive spending reviews and budgets

In 1997, the government committed to increasing NHS funding to a level that would bring the UK's health spending in line with the average for the rest of Europe. The first step toward this target was taken in the 2000 budget, with a further significant increase in 2001. However, it was the 2002 budget that gave the first indication of the substantial and long-term increases required for that promise to be delivered. Funding for these increases was achieved by the introduction of employer and employee national insurance surcharges at a rate of 1%, and from the release of funds from other sources, enabled by the government's comprehensive spending review (CSR). The three-year CSR process is designed to assess critically the spending of government departments in the light of changing government priorities.

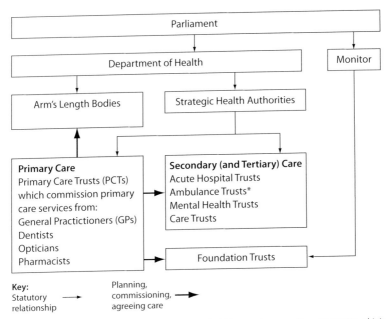

```
                        ┌─────────────────────────────────────┐
                        │              Parliament               │
                        └─────────────────────────────────────┘
         ┌──────────────────────────────────────┐   ┌──────────────┐
         │        Department of Health           │   │   Monitor    │
         └──────────────────────────────────────┘   └──────────────┘
    ┌────────────────────┐   ┌──────────────────────────────┐
    │  Arm's Length Bodies│   │  Strategic Health Authorities │
    └────────────────────┘   └──────────────────────────────┘
```

Primary Care
Primary Care Trusts (PCTs)
which commission primary
care services from:
General Practictioners (GPs)
Dentists
Opticians
Pharmacists

Secondary (and Tertiary) Care
Acute Hospital Trusts
Ambulance Trusts*
Mental Health Trusts
Care Trusts

Foundation Trusts

Key:
Statutory relationship →
Planning, commissioning, agreeing care →

Ambulance trusts also work with NHS Direct and via the 999 system to respond to emergencies – this is regarded as part of primary care

Successive budgets maintained the commitment to longer-term budgeting. However, the 2007 CSR process led to more modest increases for the three year period from 2008/09 compared with the preceding period, averaging 3.9% growth in real terms, compared with 7.5% for the previous CSR period.

The impact of the economic downturn following the banking crisis in 2008 led to warnings about the future funding of the NHS. The *Pre-Budget Report 2009*, the 2010/11 *Operating Framework* and the *Budget 2010 – Securing the Recovery* began to highlight the extent of the challenge.

In preparation for tighter times ahead, efficiency savings targets steadily moved upwards. To help achieve these targets and in line with a renewed emphasis on quality, the Department of Health expected NHS organisations to meet the 'quality, innovation, productivity and prevention (QIPP) challenge'. In practice, this meant organisations had to follow 'lean management principles' of avoiding duplication, preventing errors that need to be corrected, and stopping ineffective practices. Inevitably this involved a focus on reducing back office functions and (from a finance perspective) re-ignited the debate about the relative advantages and disadvantages of shared services.

The most recent spending review took place in October 2010 and reflected the need to reduce significantly the public sector borrowing requirement. However, the health budget was protected with the result that revenue spending in NHS England will rise to £109.8bn by 2014/15 (see chapter 3 for details).

Payment by results

A key element of the Labour government's modernisation plans was reforming the financial framework and the way funding flowed around the NHS. The proposal for bringing about this change was set out in 2002 in *Delivering the NHS Improvement Plan* and involved the introduction of a system of payment by results (PbR). This was designed to ensure that money flowed with patients as:

- PCTs commission from a plurality of providers on the basis of a standard national tariff, which reflects the complexities of the cases commissioned (the 'casemix')
- Instead of block contracts, hospitals (and other providers) are paid for the actual activity they undertake.

The main driver behind this initiative was patient choice – by introducing standard tariffs, the need for local negotiation on price was removed and instead the focus was shifted to quality and responsiveness, the things that are important to the patient. The combination of patient choice and PbR was expected to drive an increase in healthcare capacity and deliver shorter patient waiting times.

Both patient choice and the new financial framework were phased in over a period of years. Key milestones in the development of patient choice included:

- Providing patients waiting for elective surgery for over six months with the choice of an alternative provider (summer 2004)
- Patients requiring a routine elective referral offered a choice of four or five providers (including one private sector provider) at the point of referral (i.e. at their GP) by the end of December 2005
- Patients needing to see a specialist able to choose to go to any hospital in England, including many private and independent sector hospitals (from April 2008).

The first steps to introduce the new PbR financial framework were taken in the 2003/04 contracting process. Cost and volume contracts were required in six surgical specialties and the new tariff was introduced for growth activity in 15 surgical procedures. The scope has been extended progressively over the years that have followed. Most secondary sector acute activity is now commissioned on the basis of tariff. Plans are well advanced to implement PbR within the mental health setting, while work is underway at the Department of Health on a PbR-like solution for ambulance services. Chapter 13 looks in detail at PbR.

NHS foundation trusts

NHS foundation trusts (FTs) were created as new legal entities in the form of public benefit corporations by the *Health and Social Care (Community Health and Standards) Act 2003* – now consolidated in the *NHS Act 2006*. They were introduced to help implement the labour government's 10-year *NHS Plan* which set out a vision for the NHS in England to be responsive, effective and high quality. By creating a new form of NHS trust that had greater freedoms and more extensive powers, the government hoped to liberate the talents of frontline staff and improve services more quickly.

Initially, applications for foundation status were restricted to a number of 'three-star' trusts with the first wave of FTs coming into being in April 2004. Since then there has been a steady growth in the number of FTs. However, during 2009/10, the number of new FTs slowed as organisations struggled to demonstrate their long-term financial viability in the light of the deteriorating economy, and the increased expectation of efficiency. In addition, the application process increased its focus on clinical quality in the light of high profile governance failures, such as that identified in Mid-Staffordshire.

As part of its reform programme, the coalition government expects all remaining NHS trusts to achieve foundation status by March 2014 (see chapter 8 for more about foundation trusts).

Commissioning a Patient-led NHS (CPLNHS), 2005

Following a consultation process in 2005, a reconfiguration of SHAs, PCTs and ambulance trusts was launched by the Department of Health. Its implementation resulted in a significant reduction in their numbers. The aim was that the reconfiguration of organisations would reduce management overheads and generate cost savings that could be re-invested in the provision of healthcare.

The reduction in PCT numbers was consistent with the simplification of the commissioning process inherent in the patient choice and PbR initiatives. Increasingly patients were able to select their preferred healthcare provider, thereby refocusing the commissioning role on assessing overall supply levels, negotiating provider standards, and managing demand.

Implementation of CPLNHS resulted in a reduction in the number of SHAs from 28 to 10. The structure of SHAs was based on the assumption that, by reflecting the geographical span of the government offices for the regions, working with other public sector partners would be easier – chapter 5 looks more closely at SHAs.

Ambulance trust merger was designed to achieve purchasing and management economies of scale and to allow them to develop greater resilience than was possible with smaller scale operations. The aim was for all ambulance trusts to be coterminous with SHAs. This has almost been achieved – at present, only the Avon, Gloucester and Wiltshire and Isle of Wight ambulance services do not match SHA boundaries.

Practice based commissioning

Practice based commissioning (PBC) was introduced in 2005/06 with a view to enabling primary care clinicians to take commissioning decisions themselves, thereby providing patients with higher quality services that better suit their needs and circumstances. The underlying presumption was that primary care professionals were in the best position to decide what services their patients needed and to redesign them accordingly. Unlike GP fund holding, which was a feature of the original purchaser/provider split of the 1990s, PBC covered both emergency services and elective activity.

Under PBC, responsibility for commissioning along with an associated budget from the PCT is allocated to primary care clinicians. However, because PCTs remain legally responsible for managing the money and negotiating and managing all contracts with providers, the budget is notional or 'indicative'. In practice this means that although primary care clinicians determine the range of services to be provided for their population, the PCT acts as their agent to undertake any required procurements and to carry out the administrative tasks that underpin these processes.

The Darzi Review – High Quality Care for All, 2007

In July 2007, the government asked the then health minister Lord Darzi to carry out a wide ranging review of the NHS. An interim report was issued in October 2007 and recommended a number of changes to the provision of healthcare services within the primary/secondary sector, including the development of 'poly-clinics' where appropriate – a primary healthcare equivalent of the 'one-stop shop'. The final report – High Quality Care for All – was issued in June 2008 (in time for the 60th anniversary of the NHS on 5th July 2008) and set out a vision of an NHS that 'gives patients and the public more information and choice, works in partnership and has quality of care at its heart'.

The NHS Constitution, 2010

In January 2010, the first ever NHS Constitution came into effect with all providers and commissioners of NHS care now under a statutory duty to have regard to the Constitution in all their decisions and actions. As the Department of Health's website states: 'This means that the Constitution, its pledges, principles, values and responsibilities need to be fully embedded and ingrained into everything the NHS does.'

Equity and Excellence: Liberating the NHS, 2010 and the Health and Social Care Bill, 2011

In July 2010, following the formation of the coalition government, the Secretary of State for Health issued a series of consultation papers that signalled far-reaching changes for the NHS in England. In December 2010, a comprehensive response to the consultation responses was issued setting out how the proposals would be taken forward in the Health and Social Care Bill 2011. The Bill itself was published in January 2011 and is currently (March 2011) making its way through Parliament. The proposals include:

- Abolishing strategic health authorities (in 2012) and primary care trusts (in 2013)
- Establishing a new NHS Commissioning Board, responsible for commissioning primary medical services, allocating budgets to GP consortia and determining the structure of the payment system
- Handing the bulk of commissioning to GP consortia which will be accountable to the NHS Commissioning Board for their management of public funds
- Allowing consortia to decide which activities they provide in-house, and which they buy in from public or independent sectors (including aspects of financial management and contract negotiation)
- Extending Monitor's role to that of economic regulator for the health and social care sectors with responsibility for licensing healthcare providers, promoting competition, setting and regulating prices and (with the Commissioning Board) ensuring continuity of services
- Strengthening the role of the Care Quality Commission as 'an effective quality inspectorate'

- Requiring all remaining NHS trusts to attain foundation status within three years with the NHS trust legislation repealed in 2014
- Setting up a 'Provider Development Authority' within the Department of Health to oversee NHS trusts and support the FT 'pipeline' once SHAs cease to exist in April 2012
- Introducing more best practice tariffs 'so that providers are paid according to the costs of excellent care rather than average price'
- Allowing commissioners to pay quality increments and impose contractual penalties
- Moving to a value-based pricing system for drugs after the expiry of the current payment scheme
- Giving NHS employers the right to determine pay for their own staff
- Continuing QIPP (quality, innovation, productivity and prevention) with a 'stronger focus on general practice leadership'
- Giving foundation trusts greater freedom on income, governance and mergers
- Handing responsibility for public health (with an associated ring fenced budget) to local authorities with 'Public Health England' set up within the Department of Health
- Setting up 'health and wellbeing boards' in every upper tier local authority to 'join up commissioning across the NHS, social care, public health and other services ... directly related to health and well-being'
- Developing local 'HealthWatch' from existing local involvement networks (LINks) to ensure that the views of patients, carers and the public are taken into account. Local HealthWatch will be funded by local authorities and supported and led by 'HealthWatch England', an independent committee within the CQC
- Requiring 'unprecedented efficiency gains' (estimated at between £15bn–£20bn over the next four years)
- Requiring a reduction in management costs of 'more than 45%' across SHAs, PCTs and arms' length bodies over the next four years.

As far as timing is concerned, the first group of GP consortia 'pathfinders' was announced in December 2010 with more being established during 2011/12. Subject to any amendments that may be agreed to the *Health and Social Care Bill 2011*, early implementer/pathfinder health and wellbeing boards and local HealthWatch will also appear during 2011/12 and shadow arrangements for the NHS Commissioning Board, 'new' Monitor and the changes to public health will be put in place. The Provider Development Authority will also be set up during 2011/12 ready to take over the management of NHS trusts and the FT pipeline from SHAs when they are abolished in April 2012. As part of the preparations for the new Commissioning Board, SHAs are working with PCTs to establish 'cluster arrangements'.

April 2012 will see the introduction of new Monitor, the Commissioning Board, Public Health England, health and wellbeing boards and local HealthWatch. PCT clusters will remain but will be accountable to the Commissioning Board. The Board will also authorise GP consortia and notify them of their 2013/14 allocations.

2013/14 will be the first full year of the new system with PCTs abolished and GP consortia and health and wellbeing boards assuming their statutory responsibilities. New Monitor's licensing regime will also be operating.

The diagram that follows shows what the NHS is likely to look like once the coalition government's proposals (as set out in the *Health and Social Care Bill 2011*) have been implemented:

Proposed NHS Structure

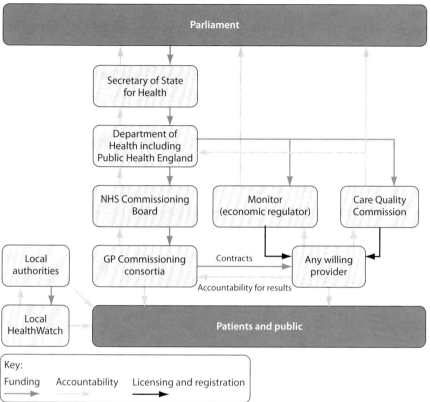

Conclusion

This chapter has shown clearly that government policy on the NHS changes constantly. However, many features have remained unaltered since its inception in 1948 – for example:

- The underlying principle that the service remains free at the point of delivery (or use)
- The need to manage within overall resource limits determined by the government each year
- The need to match finite resources to what is essentially infinite demand for health services
- The expectation that continued efficiency savings can be made, often as a result of structural or technological advances
- Intense public and media interest in, and scrutiny of, the NHS.

References and Further Reading

The New NHS: Modern, Dependable (1997 White Paper) – Department of Health archived web pages: www.archive.official-documents.co.uk/document/doh/newnhs/forward.htm

Care Quality Commission: www.cqc.org.uk/

National Institute for Health and Clinical Excellence (NICE): www.nice.org.uk

NHS Shared Business Services: www.sbs.nhs.uk/

The NHS Plan: a Plan for Investment, a Plan for Reform, Department of Health, 2000: www.dh.gov.uk/en/Publicationsandstatistics/Publications/PublicationsPolicyAndGuidance/DH_4002960

HM Treasury – Comprehensive Spending Reviews and Budget Reports: www.hm-treasury.gov.uk/spend_index.htm

NHS Act 2006: www.opsi.gov.uk/Acts/acts2006/pdf/ukpga_20060041_en.pdf

Shifting the Balance of Power, Department of Health, 2001: www.dh.gov.uk/en/Publicationsandstatistics/Publications/PublicationsPolicyAndGuidance/DH_4008424

Quality, innovation, productivity and prevention (QIPP), Department of Health: www.dh.gov.uk/en/Publicationsandstatistics/Lettersandcirculars/Dearcolleagueletters/DH_104239

Creating a Patient-led NHS: Delivering the NHS Improvement Plan, Department of Health, 2002: www.dh.gov.uk/en/Publicationsandstatistics/Publications/PublicationsPolicyAndGuidance/DH_4106506

Patient Choice – Department of Health archived web pages: http://webarchive.nationalarchives.gov.uk/+/www.dh.gov.uk/en/Healthcare/PatientChoice/index.htm

Payment by Results: www.dh.gov.uk/en/Managingyourorganisation/NHSFinancialReforms/index.htm

Commissioning a Patient-led NHS, Department of Health, 2005: www.dh.gov.uk/en/Publicationsandstatistics/Publications/PublicationsPolicyAndGuidance/DH_4116716

Practice Based Commissioning – Department of Health archived web pages: http://webarchive.nationalarchives.gov.uk/+/www.dh.gov.uk/en/Managingyourorganisation/Commissioning/Practice-basedcommissioning/index.htm

Our NHS Our Future: NHS Next Stage Review (the Darzi review), 2007: www.dh.gov.uk/en/Publicationsandstatistics/Publications/PublicationsPolicyAndGuidance/DH_079077

High Quality Care for all: NHS Next Stage Review final report, Department of Health, 2008 – archived web pages: http://webarchive.nationalarchives.gov.uk/+/www.dh.gov.uk/en/Healthcare/Highqualitycareforall/index.htm

The NHS Constitution for England, Department of Health, 2010: www.dh.gov.uk/en/Publicationsandstatistics/Publications/PublicationsPolicyAndGuidance/DH_113613

Equity and Excellence: Liberating the NHS (and associated consultation papers), Department of Health, 2010: www.dh.gov.uk/en/Publicationsandstatistics/Publications/PublicationsPolicyAndGuidance/DH_117353

Health and Social Care Bill, 2011: http://services.parliament.uk/bills/2010-11/healthandsocialcare.html

3. Funding the NHS

Introduction

Health spending has always been a topic of political and public interest and in the last decade spending on health has increased at a significantly higher rate than many other government programmes. This chapter focuses on how resources are allocated nationally for health and how they are divided up amongst the different areas of health spending. However, before looking at the allocation process in detail it is helpful to get an idea of the scale of UK spending on health compared with other countries.

UK Spending Levels

The Organisation for Economic Cooperation and Development (OECD) health data for 2010 shows that during 2008, the United Kingdom spent 8.7% of gross domestic product (GDP) on health expenditures. This compared with an average across the 30 OECD countries of 9% although this figure is made up of national spending well in excess of the average – for example, 16% in the US, 11.2% in France and 10.5% in Germany. The data also indicated that in 2008, 82.6% of total spending on health in the UK came from general government expenditure – well above the average for OECD countries. Although the percentage of GDP spent on health in the UK has been rising steadily since 2002/03 when it was 7.7%, constraints on public spending following the economic downturn in 2008/09 mean that future spending in the UK is now expected to plateau.

The Role of the Treasury

The responsibility for allocating and managing the finances of national government lies with the Chancellor of the Exchequer, who leads the Treasury. The Treasury also draws up public service agreements (PSAs), which define the key improvements that the public can expect to see from these resources.

To promote better planning of public spending the Treasury undertakes periodic spending reviews to set firm and fixed three-year 'departmental expenditure limits' for each government department. In recent years, these reviews have been carried out every two years on a rolling basis, meaning there is one year of overlap. Each spending review confirms (or occasionally revises) the figures for the first year and then announces new figures for the following two years. A special case was made for health in 2002 when a five-year settlement was announced. This followed on from a major review of funding needs for the UK health system undertaken by former NatWest Chief Executive Derek Wanless (see later in this chapter) and was intended to put the NHS on a sustainable, long-term financial footing.

There have been six spending reviews since they were first introduced in 1998. These spending reviews are themselves reviewed twice a year – in the budget and the pre-budget report, where the government sets out how it will finance its spending commitments and makes any necessary or technical adjustments to its spending plans. The most recent review was in October 2010 and set out the coalition government's departmental spending plans for the next four years – up until 2014/15.

Public expenditure falls into one of two categories:

- Departmental expenditure limit (DEL) spending, which is planned and controlled on a three year basis in spending reviews
- Annually managed expenditure (AME), which is expenditure that cannot reasonably be subject to firm, multi-year limits in the same way as DEL. Examples of such spending would be social security benefits which are subject to fluctuation depending on the level of unemployment.

Together, DEL plus AME sum to 'total managed expenditure' (TME).

A key issue for any government is the relative level of public spending compared to national wealth. The following graph shows how the percentage of public spending compared to GDP has fluctuated over the years. Relative to GDP (which itself fluctuates from year to year), spending since 1970 has varied from 48.9% in 1975, 34.8% in 1989 and 36% in 1999. The predicted position for 2010 is 46.4% of GDP spent in the public sector.

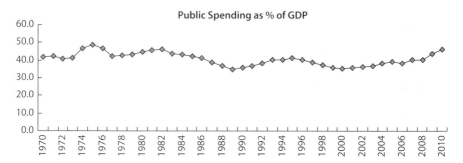

The Treasury allocates DELs for revenue and capital spending. Revenue spending is for day-to-day items such as salaries and running costs, while capital spending is for buying larger items such as buildings and equipment, which have a usable life of over one year.

The Treasury's 2010 spending review resulted in the following pattern of allocations of revenue ('resource') and capital DELs to government departments:

Total Department Programme and Administration Budgets – revenue DEL excluding depreciation and capital				
	2011/12 £bn	2012/13 £bn	2013/14 £bn	2014/15 £bn
NHS (Health)	101.5	104.0	106.9	109.8
Education	51.2	52.1	52.9	53.9
Energy and Climate Change	1.5	1.4	1.3	1.0
CLG Communities and Local Government	28.1	26.1	25.8	24.1
Defence	24.9	25.2	24.9	24.7
Home Office	8.9	8.5	8.1	7.8
Foreign and Commonwealth Office	1.5	1.5	1.4	1.2

Total Department Programme and Administration Budgets – revenue DEL excluding depreciation and capital – Continued				
	2011/12 £bn	2012/13 £bn	2013/14 £bn	2014/15 £bn
Justice	8.1	7.7	7.4	7.0
Business, Innovation and Skills	16.5	15.6	14.7	13.7
Transport	5.3	5.0	5.0	4.4
International Development	6.7	7.2	9.4	9.4
Work and Pensions	7.6	7.4	7.4	7.6
Scotland	24.8	25.1	25.3	25.4
Wales	13.3	13.3	13.5	13.5
Northern Ireland	9.4	9.4	9.5	9.5
Other Departments and Reserve	17.4	17.4	17.4	15.9
TOTAL DEL	**326.7**	**326.9**	**330.9**	**328.9**

Source: Spending Review, 2010, HM Treasury.

Total Department Capital DEL				
	2011/12 £bn	2012/13 £bn	2013/14 £bn	2014/15 £bn
NHS (Health)	4.4	4.4	4.4	4.6
Education	4.9	4.2	3.3	3.4
Energy and Climate Change	1.5	2.0	2.2	2.7
CLG Communities and Local Government	3.3	2.3	1.8	2.0
Defence	8.9	9.1	9.2	8.7
Home Office	0.5	0.5	0.4	0.5
Foreign and Commonwealth Office	0.1	0.1	0.1	0.1
Justice	0.4	0.3	0.3	0.3
Business, Innovation and Skills	1.2	1.1	0.8	1.0
Transport	7.7	8.1	7.5	7.5
International Development	1.4	1.6	1.9	2.0
Work and Pensions	0.2	0.3	0.4	0.2
Scotland	2.5	2.5	2.2	2.3
Wales	1.3	1.2	1.1	1.1
Northern Ireland	0.9	0.9	0.8	0.8
Other Departments and Reserves	4.3	3.2	2.8	3.0
TOTAL Capital DEL	**43.5**	**41.8**	**39.2**	**40.2**

Source: Spending Review, 2010, HM Treasury.

For the NHS in England the position over the spending review period (including percentage growth rates) is summarised in the table that follows:

	2011/12 £bn	2012/13 £bn	2013/14 £bn	2014/15 £bn
DEL Settlement				
Total DEL is the sum of resource DEL (excluding depreciation) and capital DEL				
NHS (Health) REVENUE	101.50	104.00	106.90	109.80
annual growth	2.8%	2.5%	2.8%	2.7%
NHS (Health) CAPITAL	4.40	4.40	4.40	4.60
annual growth	−13.7%	0.0%	0.0%	4.5%
NHS (Health) TOTAL	105.90	108.40	111.30	114.40
annual growth	2.0%	2.4%	2.7%	2.8%
GDP deflator	**1.9%**	**2.3%**	**2.6%**	**2.7%**
Real growth	**0.1%**	**0.1%**	**0.1%**	**0.1%**
AME Forecast				
NHS (Health) RESOURCE AME forecast	−1.60	−1.00	−0.40	0.20
NHS (Health) CAPITAL AME forecast	–	–	–	–

Source: Spending Review, 2010, HM Treasury

Funding for health services in other UK nations is included in the separate Northern Ireland, Scottish and Welsh block grants. Any changes in planned spending in the NHS in England are matched by relative increases within these block grants. However, the individual administrations may spend less or more than these amounts on health services depending on their own priorities.

Adequacy of Funding

The 'adequacy' of NHS funding has been the subject of heated political debate since the NHS was formed in 1948. At that time it was believed that once the initial backlog of ill health had been treated NHS funding levels could reduce. Clearly this has never been the case for a variety of reasons.

In 2001, the former Chief Executive of NatWest Bank, Derek Wanless was commissioned to undertake a review of the funding mechanisms for the NHS and to establish the levels of investment required to meet the objectives of the *NHS Plan: a Plan for Investment, a Plan for Reform* and the labour government's election manifesto commitments.

Securing Our Future Health: Taking a Long-Term View (the Wanless report) was published in April 2002 and concluded that public funding was a 'fair and efficient' way to provide a comprehensive, high quality service based on need, not the ability to pay. In addition it set out a number of major influences on the resources needed to provide such a service. These included:

- The commitments already made in relation to the improvements expected in the NHS (including the NHS Plan and the various national service frameworks setting standards in key service areas)
- Rising patient and public expectations
- Improvements in medical technologies and pharmaceuticals – particularly the potential expansion in genetics
- The demands of an ageing population that is living longer.

The report set out a number of scenarios which made different assumptions about the take-up of services and the extent to which the public assisted or otherwise in their own health improvement. Wanless concluded that, assuming that private health expenditure remained constant at around 1.2% of gross domestic product, total UK health spending would need to rise to between 10.6% and 12.5% of national income in 20 years time. The report anticipated that the growth in workforce required could be managed if 20% of GPs' and junior doctors' work could be carried out by nurse practitioners and 12.5% of nurse workload could shift to healthcare assistants.

At the time of the Wanless report the labour government was projecting that investment in health would reach 9.4% by 2007/08 – however, as we saw earlier in this chapter, this target was not met with UK spending reaching only 8.7% of GDP in 2008.

The Role of the Department of Health

At present, the he Department of Health is responsible for the NHS in England, personal social services and the Food Standards Agency. It also decides how the funding it receives from the Treasury is allocated. Health and social services in Northern Ireland, Scotland and Wales is the responsibility of devolved administrations (see chapters 18, 19 and 20).

Spending split

Most of the NHS settlement is spent on hospital, community and family health services (HCFHS) – this includes general medical services (GMS) expenditure through the GP contract and general dental services. There are also much smaller budgets for:

- Central health and miscellaneous services (CHMS), covering some centrally administered services including some public health functions and support to the voluntary sector
- The Department's own running costs.

NHS funding allocated by the Department of Health

At present (2011/12), the vast majority of NHS funding (over 80%) is allocated directly by the Department of Health to the commissioners of healthcare – primary care trusts (PCTs). This is looked at in more detail later in this chapter. In line with the three year spending review settlement, the Department has been making three year allocations to assist the service in its medium term planning and investment decisions.

Disposition of Department of Health resources in 2009/10

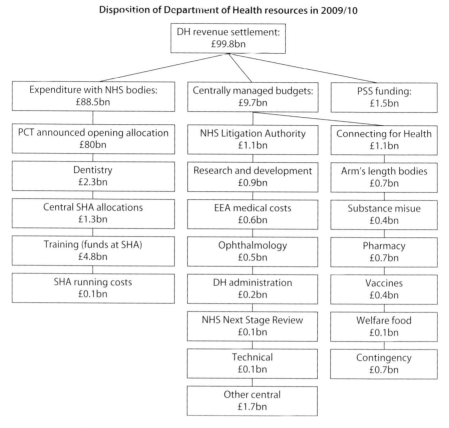

Source: Department of Health Departmental Report, 2009.

The diagram above shows how NHS resources were allocated in 2009/10 – PCTs controlled over 80% of the total NHS revenue budget.

Centrally managed budgets

As mentioned above, HCFHS includes a number of centrally managed budgets that are sometimes referred to as 'centrally funded initiatives, services and special allocations (CFISSA)'. These are budgets for initiatives where the Department of Health specifically allocates the resources to statutory bodies, education, training and research activities – for example:

- Common services – a range of services and projects managed centrally for the benefit of the NHS (for example, clinical negligence)
- A range of statutory and other bodies funded centrally including the NHS Business Services Authority, the Care Quality Commission and the Information Centre for Health and Social Care
- Research and development.

In addition to the budgets held and allocated centrally by the Department of Health, there are also a number of central initiative budgets that are devolved to strategic health authorities (SHAs) for local management – see chapter 5 for more about the role of SHAs.

Primary Care Trusts

Allocations to PCTs

Recurrent revenue allocations to PCTs are resource and cash-limited and PCTs have a statutory duty not to exceed these limits. The allocations cover hospital and community health services (HCHS), GP prescribing and 'primary medical services' (i.e. general and personal medical services – see chapter 6 for more details). Under the current regime, resources are allocated to each individual PCT by the Department of Health using a 'weighted capitation formula'. This is designed to determine PCTs' target (or 'fair') shares of available resources to enable them to commission similar levels of healthcare for populations with similar healthcare needs. The weighted capitation formula is used to set targets which then inform allocations. There is also a 'pace of change policy' that determines actual allocations – this dictates how quickly PCTs are moved from their historic funding level to their target allocation.

Elements of resource allocation

There are four elements that affect PCTs' actual allocations:

By far the most important is a PCT's **recurrent baseline** (a) – this is the prior year's allocation.

Weighted capitation targets (b) – targets are set according to the national weighted capitation formula, which calculates PCT 'fair shares' of available resources based on the health needs of their populations. These targets are recalculated regularly prior to the allocation of resources to take account of changes such as the latest census data. Changes in the targets do not immediately lead to changes in actual allocations.

Distance from target (DFT) – this is the difference between (a) and (b); if (b) is greater than (a) a PCT is said to be under target; if (b) is less than (a) it is said to be over target. These are expressed in monetary and percentage terms.

Pace of change – this is the speed at which PCTs are moved closer to target (or 'levelled up') and is a policy that has been operating for some years. Levelling up is achieved through the distribution of extra resources – a process known as differential growth, where all PCTs receive some growth funds, but higher levels of growth are targeted at PCTs most under target. PCTs do not receive their target allocation immediately but are moved to it over a number of years. For example, in 2009/10 and 2010/11 the average increase nationally was 5.5% but minimum growth (allocated to those PCTs most over target) was 5.2% in 2009/10 and 5.1% in 2010/11.

The weighted capitation formula

Healthcare is provided to people and so the primary determinant of a PCT's funding allocation is the size of its population. However, because a simple capitation formula (i.e. an amount per head) would provide the same level of funding for every person in the population, adjustments are needed to reflect the fact that the healthcare requirements of an individual depend on a range of factors including their age and needs. The makeup of each PCT's population will vary and so the population for a PCT needs to be 'weighted' (or adjusted) for:

- Age related need – recognising that levels of demand for health services vary according to the age structure of the population
- Additional need – reflecting relative need for healthcare over and above that accounted for by age
- Unavoidable costs – taking account of unavoidable geographical variations in the cost of providing services.

PCTs then receive the same level of funding per weighted head of population.

PCTs are responsible for funding the healthcare provision of all patients registered with GPs in practices forming part of the PCT. This means that patients registered with a GP in one PCT area who are resident in a neighbouring or other PCT area remain the responsibility of the PCT with which their GP of registration is associated. PCTs are also responsible for residents within their geographical boundaries who are not registered with a GP. The population for which the PCT is responsible is referred to as the 'relevant population'.

To ensure that (when combined) the sum of individual PCT populations adds up to the total population for England, a 'scaling factor' is applied to give a 'normalised population' for each PCT. This involves scaling GP registered populations to the resident populations from the Office for National Statistics (ONS) Census.

Components of the formula

The weighted capitation formula considers relative need in separate areas with each component given a relative weighting to reflect the makeup of overall health spending. A new formula was introduced for the 2009/10 and 2010/11 allocation rounds following a review by the Advisory Committee on Resource Allocation (ACRA). There are three components as set out below along with their relative weights (they do not total 100% due to roundings):

- Hospital and community health services (HCHS) (76%)
- Prescribing – the drugs bill (12%)
- Primary medical services (11%).

A similar approach is followed for each component – in effect a weighted population is calculated for each component and these individual weighted populations are combined in the set proportions (76%, 12% and 11%) to create a unified weighted population.

How of funds from PCTs

Once a PCT has been notified of its resource position for the forthcoming year, it plans how to use the funding across the full range of NHS services that it commissions with the overall aim of improving the health and well-being of its population. A PCT commissions services from a range of providers including NHS trusts and foundation trusts, the private and voluntary sectors (see chapter 11 for more on commissioning).

Practice based commissioning

Under the current regime, a proportion of a PCT's budget will be allocated to those practices in its area that have decided to take part in practice based commissioning (PBC). PBC is designed to make the NHS more patient centred through the use of choice in elective (i.e. planned) care, and by empowering primary care professionals to commission more specifically on behalf of patients.

Essentially, PBC involves allocating responsibility for commissioning along with an associated 'indicative' (or 'notional') budget to primary care clinicians on the basis that they are best placed to decide what services their patients need. Chapter 11 looks at PBC in more detail.

Foundation and NHS Trusts

Funding secondary care

The majority of acute, specialist and mental health care in England is provided by either NHS trusts (see chapter 7), or NHS foundation trusts (see chapter 8). These trusts meet the costs of providing healthcare services (staff salaries are normally the biggest element) and receive income from PCTs mostly via contracts that specify the quantity, quality and price of services to be provided (for activity covered by PbR the unit price is the nationally set tariff). Each PCT is responsible for meeting the cost of services provided to its population in line with the contract's or agreement's terms. PCTs and providers have a joint responsibility for ensuring that patient treatments are clinically appropriate and provided in a cost effective way.

Additional sources of funding

Trusts also get a small proportion of their total income from other sources such as private patient income, research, car park receipts and leasing of buildings. In addition some trusts get substantial sums from the monies earmarked in the centrally held budgets referred to earlier in this chapter. In particular teaching trusts receive funding to support the cost of teaching and research – for example, at present SHAs manage and disperse budgets for multi-professional education and training (MPET), the service increment for teaching (SIFT) which supports the additional costs incurred in providing clinical placements for medical undergraduates and the medical and dental education and training levy (MADEL).

Many trusts also have access to funds donated on a charitable basis – for example, by members of the public. However these can be used only for the purpose for which they were given – for more about charitable funds see chapter 17.

Community Services

Community services encompass a wide range of care including district nursing, health visitors and allied health professionals such as speech therapists and community physiotherapists.

The 'Transforming Community Services' programme initiated by the Labour government and continued by the coalition government is designed to improve the quality and efficiency of these services and the patient's experience. However, the focus so far has tended to be on which organisation provides these services.

Prior to 2009/2010, the majority of community services were delivered by PCT 'provider arms'. However, the situation has now changed with the coalition government requiring PCTs to separate commissioning from the provision of services by April 2011 'even if this means transferring services to other organisations while sustainable medium-term arrangements are identified and secured'. In practice this will mean that in future, community services could be delivered by a wide range of organisation types including foundation, acute and mental health trusts; social enterprise organisations and the independent sector.

Primary Care Services

The majority of primary care services are provided by independent contractors such as general medical practitioners (GPs) or general dental practitioners (GDPs). While they are an integral part of the NHS, these contractors currently operate as small businesses that contract with the NHS to provide primary care services. Contracts with GPs and GDPs are designed to reward the quality of treatment rather than paying on a piece-work basis.

PCTs reimburse GPs and GDPs according to nationally negotiated contracts – although extensions to the basic contract are negotiated locally. For example, under the practice based contract to GPs, practices receive a global sum to cover the provision of core services to their registered practice list and additional 'quality' payments for achieving goals set out in the quality and outcomes framework (QOF).

The interface between primary and secondary care is not always clear and GPs with specialist interests are increasingly playing a significant part in delivering patient care outside of the traditional hospital routes.

What is the Money Spent on?

Since 2003/04, the Department of Health has collected information about how the billions invested in the NHS are spent and what is achieved for that investment. The idea is to collect information in a consistent manner about the clinical areas (or 'programme budgets') in which NHS resources are being spent.

The main aims of programme budgeting are to provide:

- A way of monitoring where NHS resources are invested
- A way of assisting in evaluating the effectiveness of the pattern of resource deployment
- A tool to support and improve the process for identifying the most effective way of commissioning NHS services for the future.

The latest figures for 2009/010 across programme budget categories are shown over the page in diagrammatic form:

Programme Budgeting – estimated expenditure 2009/10

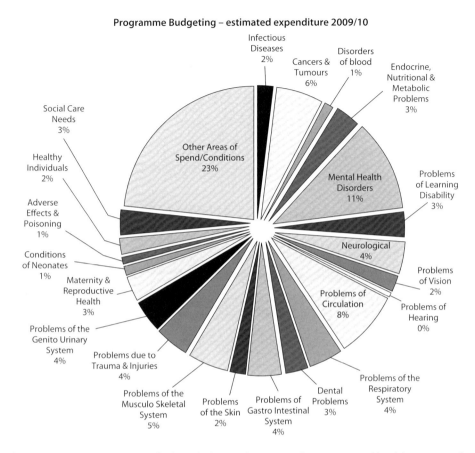

Of the programme areas identified (excluding 'other'), spending on mental health accounts for the largest single proportion of NHS spending at 11% of the total. Note that the 'other' category includes expenditure on primary medical services.

What the future holds for NHS Funding

Subject to any amendments agreed to the *Health and Social Care Bill 2011*, the coalition government's plans for the NHS over the coming years will see a radical change in the flow of funds from taxpayer to front line healthcare services. Although the Treasury will still allocate DELs to the Department of Health in line with spending reviews, a newly formed NHS Commissioning Board will take over responsibility for allocating the funding previously received by PCTs directly to GP consortia. This allocation will be made to consortia for the first time for 2013/14. The methodology that the Board will use is being developed by the Department of Health with ACRA and will involve a 'formula at practice level which will form the building block for consortia allocations'.

It is likely that the approach will be based on the current weighted capitation model used to allocate resources to PCTs in which case, the key factor affecting the budget each consortium receives will be the number of patients registered with its constituent practices. If this approach is adopted, the weighted capitation formula will give a 'target' amount or 'fair share' for each consortium – in other words, the amount of money that would enable all consortia to commission the same level of healthcare for their population regardless of its makeup.

GP consortia will then use the funding they receive to commission the majority of NHS services for their patients including:

- Planned hospital care
- Rehabilitative care
- Urgent and emergency services including out-of-hours services
- Community health services
- Maternity services
- Mental health services
- Learning disabilities services.

In practice, this means that consortia will agree contracts with 'any willing providers' of acute, specialist and mental health care.

GP consortia will not be responsible for all commissioning – instead, the NHS Commissioning Board will itself commission the primary medical services provided by GPs, dentists, community pharmacists, primary ophthalmic practitioners and national and regional specialised services. There will also be special arrangements made for high security psychiatric facilities.

Public health will be covered by a separate ring fenced budget that will be managed by local authorities with a new public health service – Public Health England – set up within the Department of Health.

It is unclear at present exactly how the funding streams for MPET, SIFT and MADEL will be managed once SHAs are abolished although the general principle set out in the White Paper is that education and training are to be aligned with the commissioning of patient care. The government's consultation paper *Developing the Healthcare Workforce* proposes that local 'skills networks' will take on SHAs' current workforce functions with a new 'autonomous statutory board' – Health Education England – set up to focus on issues that need to be managed nationally and to support healthcare providers in their workforce planning, education and training.

On programme budgeting, it is expected that over the coming years data will be developed further so that GP consortia will have more accurate, timely and detailed information on spending levels and patterns. The Department of Health is also planning to move to a price based programme budgeting return that will analyse costs across care settings.

References and Further Reading

OECD Health at a Glance: Europe 2010: www.oecd.org/document/19/0,3746,en_2649_34631_46460563_1_1_1_1,00.html#exec_sum

HM Treasury Spending Review: www.hm-treasury.gov.uk/spend_index.htm

Securing Our Future Health: Taking a Long-Term View (the Wanless Report) – archived web pages: http://webarchive.nationalarchives.gov.uk/+/http://www.hm-treasury.gov.uk/consultations_and_legislation/wanless/consult_wanless_final.cfm

Departmental Report, Department of Health, 2009: www.dh.gov.uk/en/Publicationsandstatistics/Publications/PublicationsPolicyAndGuidance/DH_100667

NHS Allocations (including the weighted capitation formula), Department of Health: www.dh.gov.uk/en/Policyandguidance/Organisationpolicy/Financeandplanning/Allocations/index.htm

Office for National Statistics: www.statistics.gov.uk/default.asp

Advisory Committee on Resource Allocation (ACRA): www.dh.gov.uk/en/Managingyourorganisation/Financeandplanning/Allocations/index.htm

Transforming Community Services, Department of Health: www.dh.gov.uk/en/Healthcare/TCS/index.htm

Programme Budgeting, Department of Health: www.dh.gov.uk/en/Policyandguidance/Organisationpolicy/Financeandplanning/Programmebudgeting/index.htm

Developing the Healthcare Workforce, Department of Health, 2010: www.dh.gov.uk/en/Aboutus/Features/DH_122974

4. The Department of Health

Introduction

The NHS was established under the *National Health Service Act of 1946*. This and other subsequent Acts of Parliament relating to the NHS set out the duty of the Secretary of State for Health to provide a comprehensive health service in England. Parliament holds the health secretary to account for the functioning of the NHS and the use of resources and the Department of Health sets policy on health and social care issues with the overall aim of improving the health and well-being of the people of England.

The Secretary of State and Ministers

The Department of Health operates with a team of ministers, including the Secretary of State who is a Cabinet minister. The ministers are appointed by the government and are either MPs elected by the public, or members of the House of Lords.

The Secretary of State for Health has overall responsibility for the activities of the Department of Health, and works closely with the junior ministers for health, the permanent secretary, the NHS Chief Executive and the Chief Medical Officer.

The junior ministers each have individual responsibility for different aspects of the Department of Health's work. The portfolios attached to the ministerial posts often change, depending on the priorities at that point in time and the personal interests of the individuals. Further information on ministerial portfolios is available on the Department's website.

Parliamentary Scrutiny

The work of the Department of Health is examined by the cross party House of Commons Health Committee on behalf of the House of Commons. The members of this committee are appointed by the House of Commons and examine the expenditure, administration and policy of the Department of Health and its associated bodies. The committee's constitution and powers are set out in *House of Commons Standing Order No. 152*.

The committee has a maximum of eleven members and the quorum for any formal proceedings is three. The members of the committee are appointed by the House and, unless discharged, remain on the committee until the next dissolution of Parliament.

Within its remit, the committee has complete discretion to decide which areas to investigate and has the power to require the submission of written evidence and documents, and to send for and examine witnesses. The committee's oral evidence sessions are usually open to the public and are often televised. Deliberative meetings are held in private.

When an inquiry ends, a report is agreed by the committee and then published by the Stationery Office. The report is usually published in two volumes: the findings of the committee and the background (memoranda and oral) evidence. The government is committed to responding to such reports within two months of publication.

The committee is supported in its work by a team of staff and by part-time specialists, usually academics or experts from professions relevant to the committee's inquiries.

Two other Parliamentary committees scrutinise the Department of Health and the health service:

- The Public Accounts Committee (PAC)
- The Public Administration Select Committee (PASC).

The PAC keeps a check on all public expenditure including money spent on health. Its remit takes it far wider than a view on the annual accounts, with the results of National Audit Office value for money studies usually being considered by the committee. In these instances, the committee takes evidence on health issues, usually questioning the NHS Chief Executive, before publishing its own report and making recommendations.

The PASC examines the reports of the Parliamentary and Health Service Ombudsmen and considers matters relating to the quality and standards of civil service administration.

Other select committees may from time to time conduct inquiries into government policies that impact upon the Department of Health.

The Department of Health

The Department of Health supports the Secretary of State and ministers in carrying out their ministerial responsibilities for health and social care services. It sets policy on all health and social care issues (including public health matters) and is responsible for ensuring provision of a comprehensive health service through the NHS.

The Department also sets national standards, policy and priorities for the NHS and (under the current regime) manages the performance of the ten strategic health authorities (SHAs) through the NHS Chief Executive.

The Department of Health operates through a number of arm's length bodies, such as the Care Quality Commission and the National Institute for Health and Clinical Excellence (NICE). These organisations regulate the health and social care system, improve standards, protect public welfare and support local services.

The Department of Health currently (2011) employs around 2,400 people, with headquarters staff based in Leeds and London. At present, public health teams are co-located within each of the government offices in the English regions, headed by a Regional Director of Public Health, who is also Director of Public Health in the relevant SHA.

Role, aims, and objectives

The Department of Health's website states that 'its work centres around three strategic objectives:

- Better health and well-being for all: helping people stay healthy and well; empowering people to live independently; and tackling health inequalities

- Better care for all: the best possible health and social care that offers safe and effective care, when and where people need it; and empowering people in their choices
- Better value for all: delivering affordable, efficient and sustainable services; contributing to the wider economy and the nation.'

Within the context of these aims, the Department of Health currently has three distinct but inter-related roles:

- The effective national headquarters of the NHS
- The lead Department of State for a broad and complex range of governmental activity
- Setting policy on public health, adult social care and a swathe of related topics extending from genetics to international work.

These roles are translated into a number of 'deliverables' for the NHS. While the emphasis is increasingly moving towards the establishment of 'locally-appropriate' priorities, the context and direction of travel are set out each year in the *NHS Operating Framework*. This is available on the Department's website.

Financial Role of the Department of Health

Negotiations with the Treasury

The Treasury sets the Department of Health's budget for a three-year period in a budgetary exercise known as the spending review, which takes place across government. The Department submits evidence to the Treasury setting out its proposals for expenditure plans covering the three-year period, in line with its public service agreement (PSA) objectives. The plans are discussed and challenged over several months before being finalised. The outcome of the most recent spending review was released in October 2010 and covers the years 2011/12 to 2014/15 (see chapter 3 for more details).

Allocating resources

Once the Treasury has set the overall budget total, the Department determines how this should be allocated. Under the current arrangements, the vast majority of funding is allocated to primary care trusts (PCTs) via the revenue allocations but some is retained in central budgets. For example, in 2009/10, the total investment in the NHS was £102.7 billion of which £80 billion was given in allocations to PCTs.

As we saw in chapter 3, the spending review in October 2010 reflected the need to reduce significantly the public sector borrowing requirement. However, the health budget was protected with the result that there will be a 0.1% real terms increase in each of the next four years.

Payment by results – setting the tariff

Payment by results (PbR) is based around the use of a prospective, tariff-based system that links a preset price to a defined measure of output or activity. At present (2011/12), the Department is responsible for setting the tariff each year based on reference cost returns for example, the 2011/12 tariff, published in January 2011, was based on reference costs for 2008/09. The setting of the tariff takes account of pay and price pressures, investment in quality improvements, technical changes and other cost pressures as well as making assumptions for efficiency savings between the year of the underpinning costs and the year the tariff is put into operation. See chapter 13 for more about PbR.

Monitoring the NHS

Once resources have been allocated, the Department of Health has an on-going responsibility to ensure that the NHS lives within its resources, and that its objectives are achieved as efficiently as possible. Under the current arrangements (2011/12), PCTs and NHS trusts are accountable to their SHAs for their performance, which includes providing activity and financial data. On a monthly basis, financial monitoring information is collected from NHS bodies on the Financial Information Management System (FIMS).

NHS foundation trusts (FTs) are regulated by Monitor, a non-departmental public body that is directly accountable to Parliament. Information relating to FTs is shared between Monitor and the Department of Health so that the Department has a comprehensive understanding of the overall financial position of the NHS.

Arm's Length Bodies

Arm's length bodies (ALBs) are stand-alone national organisations sponsored by the Department of Health to undertake executive functions to facilitate the delivery of its agenda. They range in size but tend to have boards, employ staff and publish accounts.

Currently (2011) ALBs are categorised by function as follows:

Regulatory – ALBs that hold the health and social care system to account:

- Care Quality Commission
- Council for Healthcare Regulatory Excellence
- Human Fertilisation and Embryology Authority
- Human Tissue Authority
- Medicines and Healthcare Products Regulatory Agency
- Monitor.

Public welfare – ALBs that focus primarily on safety and the protection of public and patients:

- Alcohol Education and Research Council
- Health Protection Agency
- National Patient Safety Agency
- General Social Care Council
- National Treatment Agency for Substance Misuse.

Standards – ALBs that focus primarily on establishing national standards and best practice:

- National Institute for Health and Clinical Excellence (NICE).

Central services to the NHS – ALBs that provide cost-effective services and focused expertise across the health and social care system:

- NHS Appointments Commission
- NHS Business Services Authority
- Information Centre for Health and Social Care
- NHS Blood and Transplant
- NHS Institute for Innovation and Improvement
- NHS Litigation Authority.

What the future holds for the Department of Health

Subject to any amendments agreed to the *Health and Social Care Bill 2011*, the coalition government's plans for the NHS over the coming years see the Department of Health reducing in size and assuming a more strategic role. The Secretary of State will remain politically accountable for the NHS and for the resources allocated to the health and social care system; system design; the legislative framework; overall strategic direction and progress against national outcomes. However, the Secretary of State's role will be constrained by a new duty to 'maximise the autonomy' of commissioners and providers by 'limiting his general powers of direction'.

There will also be significant changes for the way in which the Department of Health relates to the NHS as a whole. Although its overall objectives will remain broadly the same (namely to improve the health and well-being of the people of England and ensure that they have a comprehensive health service), it will no longer be supported by SHAs or allocate funding to PCTs. Instead the Department will allocate the resources it receives from the Treasury to an independent NHS Commissioning Board that will then decide on funding levels for GP consortia and commission some services itself. To ensure consistency and facilitate the production of its overall resource account, the Department of Health will specify to the Commissioning Board the 'precise form and content of the accounting information it requires' with the Board doing the same in relation to GP consortia.

The Department's role in relation to public health will also change with the introduction of a new public health service – Public Health England. Although Public Health England will be established within the Department to lead health protection and harness efforts to improve the public's health, it will work closely with local authorities who will take on primary responsibility at local level for health improvement and reducing health inequalities.

One other area of responsibility that the Department will assume once SHAs are abolished in April 2012 is to support the remaining NHS trusts as they work towards foundation status by the deadline of March 2014. This will be achieved via a new Provider Development Authority that will be located within the Department – it will be wound up in March 2014.

The Department of Health's role in relation to PbR will also change with Monitor and the NHS Commissioning Board assuming joint responsibility for setting prices with Monitor focusing on designing the pricing methodology and using it to set prices and the Commissioning Board developing the pricing structure. See chapter 13 for more on PbR and how it is expected to develop in future.

The other major area of change for the Department relates to its arm's length bodies (ALBs) which will reduce from 18 to 6. Those that will remain are:

- Monitor
- The National Institute for Health and Clinical Excellence (NICE)
- Care Quality Commission (CQC)
- Information Centre for Health and Social Care
- Medicines and Healthcare Products Regulatory Agency
- NHS Blood and Transplant.

A further two ALBs – the NHS Litigation Authority and NHS Business Services Authority – will be retained in the short term but undergo a commercial review to identify opportunities for efficiencies through outsourcing, divestment and contestability and/or employee ownership.

The Council for Healthcare Regulatory Excellence (the body that scrutinises the UK's nine healthcare professional regulators) will also be retained, but not as an ALB. It will become self-funding through a levy on the bodies it regulates.

The Human Fertilisation and Embryology Authority and the Human Tissue Authority will remain as ALBs in the short term but the intention is that their functions will transfer to the CQC by the end of this parliament in order to achieve greater synergies.

The Health Protection Agency and the National Treatment Agency for Substance Misuse will be abolished as ALBs but their functions will transfer to the Secretary of State as part of the new public health service.

The NHS Appointments Commission will be abolished with remaining appointments moving to the Department of Health.

The Alcohol Education and Research Council will be abolished.

The NHS Institute for Innovation and Improvement and National Patient Safety Agency will disappear but activities relating to quality improvement (in the case of the Institute) and safety functions (in the case of the Agency) will transfer to the Commissioning Board. The possibility of other Institute functions being delivered through commercial models will be explored. The National Clinical Assessment Service (currently part of the NPSA) will become self funding over 2/3 years.

The General Social Care Council will cease to exist but the regulation of social workers will transfer to the Health Professions Council.

A new research regulator may also be established to rationalise the regulation and governance of all health research (currently carried out by a number of ALBs), as recommended by the Academy of Medical Sciences in its January 2011 report *A new pathway for the regulation and governance of health research*.

References and Further Reading

Department of Health website: www.dh.gov.uk

Office of Public Sector Information (for details of legislation including Health Acts): www.opsi.gov.uk/legislation/about_legislation.htm

Select Committees: www.parliament.uk/business/committees/

Department of Health Strategic Framework: www.dh.gov.uk/en/Publicationsandstatistics/Publications/PublicationsPolicyAndGuidance/DH_085928

The NHS in England: Operating Frameworks, Department of Health: www.dh.gov.uk/en/Managingyourorganisation/Financeandplanning/Planningframework/index.htm

Public services agreements, spending reviews and budgets – details available from the treasury's website: www.hm-treasury.gov.uk/spend_index.htm

NHS allocations: www.dh.gov.uk/en/Managingyourorganisation/Financeandplanning/Allocations/index.htm

Payment by Results: www.dh.gov.uk/en/Managingyourorganisation/NHSFinancialReforms/index.htm

Department of Health Arm's Length Bodies (includes links to all those referred to in the chapter): www.dh.gov.uk/en/Aboutus/OrganisationsthatworkwithDH/Armslengthbodies/index.htm

A new pathway for the regulation and governance of health research, Academy of Medical Sciences, January 2011: www.acmedsci.ac.uk/index.php?pid=47&prid=88

5. Strategic Health Authorities

Introduction

Strategic health authorities (SHAs) were introduced in 2002 to manage the local NHS on behalf of the Secretary of State for Health. Originally, there were 28 SHAs but since July 2006 there have been ten covering the following geographical areas:

- East Midlands
- East of England
- London
- North East
- North West
- South Central
- South East Coast
- South West
- West Midlands
- Yorkshire and the Humber.

The coalition government plans to abolish SHAs from April 2012 so this chapter will apply only for 2011/12.

Roles and Responsibilities

Under the current arrangements, 'SHAs are responsible for:

- Developing plans for improving health services in their local area
- Making sure local health services are of a high quality and are performing well
- Increasing the capacity of local health services so they can provide more services
- Making sure national priorities (for example, programmes for improving cancer services) are integrated into local health service plans.'[1]

Although SHAs do not themselves provide services, they give leadership, coordination and support to NHS organisations across their geographical area and are accountable to their local populations. The *Statement of NHS Accountability for England* makes this clear when it states that a SHA is 'responsible for ensuring that patients have access to high quality services in its area'. The *Operating Framework 2010/11* is also helpful as it made clear that SHAs 'are the system managers and thus have a critical role in ensuring that local plans stack up and do not have undesirable consequences when considered in the round'.

Governance, Accountability and Financing

Under the current regime, SHAs are accountable to the Secretary of State through the NHS Chief Executive. In effect, they are the local headquarters of the NHS – the key link between

---

[1] NHS choices website: www.nhs.uk/NHSEngland/thenhs/about/Pages/authoritiesandtrusts.aspx#strategic

the Department of Health and the NHS at the local level. However, it is important to note that they are statutory organisations in their own right as opposed to outposts of the Department of Health.

Each SHA is managed by a Health Authority Board comprising executive and non executive directors in a similar way to NHS trusts and PCTs. As mentioned above, SHAs have a legal status in law and are governed by law and their own standing orders and standing financial instructions.

As far as their financing is concerned, SHAs are allocated budgets by the Department of Health for two main purposes:

- Their own management – to cover staffing, accommodation, office expenses and some development support for NHS organisations within their boundaries
- Workforce development (see later in this chapter).

SHAs also hold what is known as the 'SHA bundle' – this is money for central initiatives devolved to SHAs for local management. For 2011/12, the total value of this bundle is £6.2 million.

Financial Duties

Like all NHS bodies, SHAs are required to meet a number of financial duties and targets. They must:

- Keep expenditure, measured on an accruals basis, within revenue resource limits. The revenue resource limit (RRL) is set by the Department of Health for accrued revenue expenditure. SHAs are required to stay within this limit when measuring gross revenue expenditure less miscellaneous income
- Keep expenditure, measured on an accruals basis, within capital resource limits. The CRL is set by the Department of Health for accrued capital expenditure in year. SHAs are required to stay within this limit when measuring gross capital expenditure less the book value of assets disposed of during the year
- Remain within cash limits. There is a combined cash limit for both revenue and capital.

In addition, the Department of Health holds the SHAs responsible for delivering an agreed aggregate financial position (or control total) in any one year for both itself and the PCTs and NHS trusts within its area.

SHAs must also apply the *Better Payment Practice Code* and achieve a public sector payment standard of valid invoices paid within 30 days of the receipt of the invoice. A target is set at the start of the year by the Department of Health for the value and volume of invoices that must be paid within 30 days (currently the target is 95%).

Key Functions

To fulfil their responsibilities, SHAs carry out a number of functions including:

- Developing coherent strategic frameworks
- Performance management
- Supporting improvement
- Workforce planning and development
- Setting strategic financial frameworks.

Coherent strategic frameworks

One area where SHAs currently play a key role is in creating a coherent strategic framework for the development of services across the full range of local NHS organisations. SHAs carry out this role in consultation with stakeholders, balancing the needs and concerns of local people.

As part of creating this strategic framework, SHAs are responsible for ensuring strong and coherent professional leadership and the involvement of all relevant professional groups. SHAs also develop and support the delivery of cohesive strategies for capital investment and information management.

Performance management

Another key function is the performance management of local non-foundation NHS trusts and PCTs. SHAs manage their performance across organisational boundaries and networks to secure the best possible improvements for patients. At present, SHAs also lead on the creation and development of public health networks and help ensure sound clinical performance and that adequate arrangements for patient safety are in place. Where conflicts occur between local NHS bodies or problems arise that threaten the delivery of objectives, SHAs intervene and broker solutions as necessary.

SHAs have no direct responsibility for foundation trust (FT) performance as FTs report to Monitor – see chapter 8 for details.

During the year SHAs hold NHS trusts and PCTs to account for their performance against national targets and their use of public funds. The SHA ensures that the service delivery and financial position of these NHS bodies is fairly and accurately reported to government throughout the year. Where it sees that performance differs from plan, the SHA ensures that the NHS locally takes appropriate remedial action.

SHAs also monitor other financial performance indicators, including capital expenditure compared to plan, external financing requirements (performance against the external financing limit or EFL) and how promptly NHS bodies are paying bills under the *Better Payment Practice Code* – the target is to pay 95% within 30 days (see chapter 14 for more on financial and performance reporting).

Where there are wider concerns about performance, SHAs intervene in line with the guidance set out in the *NHS Performance Framework*. This Framework is administered by the Department and applied quarterly. It involves measuring provider trusts' performance through national indicators and rating them as either:

- Performing
- Performance under review
- Underperforming
- Challenged.

If a provider is categorised as 'underperforming', the SHA must intervene although the Framework does not prescribe what that intervention should involve – only that there should be 'a remedial action plan with defined timescales for improvement'.

Supporting improvement

Under the current regime, SHAs support the improvement of the NHS by working with local PCTs and NHS trusts to enhance the involvement of patients, the public and health and social care professionals in developing services. SHAs also support the implementation of clinical governance programmes to improve the quality and consistency of care through the development of clinical networks across organisations.

At present, SHAs also work with:

- NHS trusts as they prepare for foundation status by helping them develop a 'robust and credible' FT application during the 'SHA/trust development phase' (see chapter 8 for more on FTs and the application process)
- The Care Quality Commission, the National Clinical Assessment Authority and other bodies to ensure local PCTs and NHS trusts are equipped to meet national standards and improve performance.

Workforce planning and development

As part of Lord Darzi's Next Stage Review, the future of the NHS workforce was considered with the key conclusions set out in the 2008 report *A High Quality Workforce*. In line with this report's recommendations, the Department's Workforce Directorate is currently responsible for 'developing all policy that impacts on the working lives of NHS staff, including pay, pensions, education and training and health and well-being'. The directorate is also committed to:

- Ensuring that the four pledges to staff set out in the *NHS Constitution* are met
- Developing the workforce needed for the future success of the service.

As far as education and training are concerned, SHAs currently determine how to invest the £5billion central budget.

Strategic financial frameworks

Revenue

In spite of their limited budgets, SHAs currently have enormous managerial influence, typically overseeing between £5bn to £10bn spent in their local health communities. Their influence is exercised through their responsibilities for ensuring coherent services and financial plans, robust business processes, and the performance management of NHS bodies in meeting their service targets and financial duties. For example, although PCTs are required to produce operational plans showing how they will deliver targets and priorities within available resources, it is the SHA that reconciles these plans across the local health community. The SHA then submits them to the Department of Health so that plans for national priorities, activity plans and financial plans can be reviewed before the start of the financial year.

SHAs must also meet the targets set out in the *Operating Frameworks* in relation to revenue surpluses. For example, SHAs and PCTs are expected to end 2010/11 with an 'aggregate surplus of £1 billion' (equivalent to about 1% of NHS allocations).

Each SHA must agree with the Department what level of surplus its area is expected to achieve and how that will be spread amongst PCTs and itself.

Capital

Since 2007/08 each NHS trust has been set an annual prudential borrowing limit – this is derived in a similar way to the approach used by FTs. The approach to capital for PCTs also changed in 2008/09 with capital scheme funding being allocated on the basis of their capital plans as agreed with their SHA. These plans had to be robust and affordable – in other words, sustainable from a revenue consequences perspective. See chapter 16 for more details about the capital regime.

Under the current regime, SHAs are responsible for assessing, approving and monitoring individual capital schemes that have already been funded from strategic capital (i.e. as part of the 'old' capital regime), and for managing the CRL. This involves a number of activities including:

- Advising NHS bodies on the development of business cases and project management
- Advising on the selection of the most appropriate procurement process (see chapter 10) and the provision of support in the procurement process
- Formally appraising business cases, focusing on value for money and technical robustness
- Performance managing and monitoring the implementation of schemes
- Liaising with the Department of Health on scheme development and final approvals for schemes in excess of SHA delegated limits (currently £35m)
- Managing the CRL, EFL and capital cash limit within the SHA area.

SHAs also approve outline and full business cases for investment from PCTs and NHS trusts, where the scheme value is above trusts' delegated limits. The current limits are set out in the Department of Health's 2010 guidance – *Delegated Limits for Capital Investment*. In summary:

- SHAs can approve trust and PCT business cases up to £35m
- PCTs have a delegated limit of zero
- NHS trusts have a delegated limit of £3m but this can be reduced to £1m if a trust goes into financial deficit or suspended if a case is 'complicated and contentious'.

SHA Performance

Financial performance

As mentioned earlier in this chapter, each SHA reports to the Department of Health on the overall financial position of the organisations within its area. Where an organisation flags a deviation from its agreed financial plan, the SHA may request a financial recovery plan to demonstrate how a return to financial balance will be achieved. The SHA will then closely monitor delivery of the plan and meet regularly with the organisation to provide advice and support in relation to the achievement of financial balance.

Since April 2006, some SHAs have operated a bank system whereby PCTs are required to hold reserves at levels agreed with the SHA. These reserves are 'banked' with the SHA to ensure that the overall financial control totals can be met. The 2011/12 *Operating Framework* states that 'SHAs will determine and agree with the Department of Health the level of aggregate PCT/SHA sector surplus for their area to be delivered in 2011/12 and how that agreed surplus is distributed between their PCTs and themselves.'

SHAs also have a role in two key areas as set out in the *Revision to the 2010/11 Operating Framework* and re-iterated in the *2011/12 Operating Framework* – namely to:

- Achieve in aggregate savings in management costs across SHAs and PCTs of at least £222 million in 2010/11 and a further £350 million by the end of 2011/12
- Ensure that within each SHA area at least 2% of recurrent funding 'is only ever committed non-recurrently' between 2010/11 and 2013/14. To 'reinforce financial control', this 2 per cent is held by SHAs with PCTs required to submit business cases that show that planned expenditure is non recurrent in order to access the funding.

Other Functions

SHAs are required to perform a range of other supporting functions. These include:

- Case work in support of parliamentary questions and parliamentary business
- External communications, media handling and public relations
- Complaints, appeals and dispute resolution for delayed discharges, continuing care funding and similar matters
- Ad hoc investigations into serious incidents or providing support/information for national investigations
- Dispute resolution between commissioners and providers.

What the future holds for SHAs

Subject to any amendments agreed to the *Health and Social Care Bill 2011*, the coalition government has announced that SHAs will be abolished from April 2012 with their functions being taken on by a variety of organisations. For example:

- Instead of SHAs 'performance managing' PCTs and NHS trusts, the NHS Commissioning Board will hold the new GP consortia to account for their management of public funds and monitor their activities

- All remaining NHS trusts are expected to attain foundation status by March 2014 and after SHAs are abolished, their functions in this area will be assumed by a new Provider Development Authority that will be set up within the Department of Health
- The NHS Commissioning Board will take on responsibility for managing financial risk across GP consortia with Monitor fulfilling the same role for NHS trusts
- Local authorities will have a statutory responsibility to join up commissioning of NHS services, social care and health improvement and will jointly appoint a Director of Public Health in conjunction with the newly established Public Health Service (Public Health England)
- Responsibility for workforce planning, education and training will pass to providers of NHS funded care with support from an 'autonomous statutory board' called Health Education England.

Between now and when they are abolished (i.e. for 2011/12), SHAs will remain accountable at regional level for operational delivery. During this transition period, the coalition government also expects SHAs to pave the way for the new structure. Their responsibilities in this area were set out in 'transition letters' issued by Sir David Nicholson in July and December 2010 which identified the following key functions:

- Separating their commissioner and provider oversight functions
- Overseeing the development of 'clusters' of PCTs that will oversee delivery and closedown of the 'old' regime and support emerging consortia
- Ensuring coherence across the developing architecture of the new approach – for example, relationships between consortia pathfinders and health and wellbeing board early implementers
- Being accountable for the regional elements of the transition process, working with partners in public health and social care
- Ensuring the sustainability of local operational delivery and QIPP plans
- Redeveloping QIPP plans as 'QIPP and reform plans' with clear timelines
- Overseeing the completion of the Transforming Community Services process and driving the foundation trust pipeline
- Providing support to commissioners in the transition to GP consortia
- Working with colleagues within the agreed HR framework to support people through the transition period – in particular, working with PCTs and emerging GP consortia to assign staff
- Working with colleagues to ensure the sustainability of key systems and processes through the transition period and that organisational memory is not lost.

References and Further Reading

NHS Choices website: www.nhs.uk/NHSEngland/thenhs/about/Pages/authoritiesandtrusts.aspx

Statement of NHS Accountability for England, Department of Health: www.dh.gov.uk/en/Publicationsandstatistics/Publications/PublicationsPolicyAndGuidance/DH_093422

Operating Frameworks for the NHS in England: www.dh.gov.uk/en/Managingyourorganisation/Financeandplanning/Planningframework/index.htm

Better Payment Practice Code: www.payontime.co.uk/

NHS Performance Framework: www.dh.gov.uk/en/Publicationsandstatistics/Publications/
PublicationsPolicyAndGuidance/DH_098525

A High Quality Workforce: NHS Next Stage Review, Department of Health, 2008:
www.dh.gov.uk/en/Publicationsandstatistics/Publications/PublicationsPolicyAndGuidance/
DH_085840

Department of Health workforce web pages: www.dh.gov.uk/en/Managingyourorganisation/
Workforce/index.htm

NHS Constitution for England, Department of Health, 2010: www.dh.gov.uk/en/
Publicationsandstatistics/Publications/PublicationsPolicyAndGuidance/DH_113613

Delegated Limits for Capital Investment, Department of Health, 2010: www.dh.gov.uk/
prod_consum_dh/groups/dh_digitalassets/@dh/@en/@ps/documents/digitalasset/
dh_122842.pdf

Dear Colleague letter on managing the transition, Department of Health, July 2010:
www.dh.gov.uk/prod_consum_dh/groups/dh_digitalassets/documents/digitalasset/
dh_117406.pdf

6. Primary Care Trusts

Introduction

At present (2011/12), there are 151 primary care trusts (PCTs) in England responsible for managing around 80% of the national NHS budget. PCTs are key to all aspects of the NHS as they commission services from across all sectors including public health; primary care (including GPs, dentists, and pharmacists); acute and non-acute secondary care hospital providers (both in the NHS and independent sector); community health and mental health.

Policy Context

Under the current regime, PCTs are expected to ensure that decisions about services are made at a local level by those best placed to make them, and that those services reflect the needs and views of their population. Over recent years there have been a number of policy initiatives that have been designed (in one way or another) to ensure that this happens. Before looking in detail at what PCTs currently do, it is therefore helpful to look at this policy context.

Commissioning a Patient-led NHS

As well as reducing the number of PCTs (there were 303 before October 2006), the Department of Health's 2005 strategy paper – *Commissioning a Patient-led NHS* – strengthened the focus on the way health services were commissioned. These changes were designed to complement the policies of patient choice, payment by results and the labour government's expectation (at that time) that all acute and mental health activity would be provided through foundation organisations by around 2011.

PCTs were expected to develop their role to:

- Better engage with local clinicians in the design of services
- Implement the roll out of practice based commissioning (PBC)
- Manage performance via contracts with all providers.

Strategic health authorities (SHAs) were also reduced in number (from 28 to 10) and their role strengthened to that of 'system managers' within their areas, supporting and 'performance managing' commissioning and contracting activity. See chapter 5 for more about SHAs.

World Class Commissioning

The focus on commissioning was strengthened further by the introduction in 2008 of World Class Commissioning (WCC) which was designed to transform the way health and care services were commissioned by delivering 'a more strategic and long-term approach to commissioning services, with a clear focus on delivering improved health outcomes'.

There were four main elements to the WCC framework:

- A vision – that WCC would deliver better health and well-being for all; better care for all and better value for all

- A set of organisational competencies defined in terms of what world class commissioners should do – namely that they:
  - locally lead the NHS
  - work with community partners
  - engage with public and patients
  - collaborate with clinicians
  - manage knowledge and assess needs
  - prioritise investment
  - stimulate the market
  - promote improvement and innovation
  - secure procurement skills
  - manage the local health system
  - make sound financial investments
- An annual assurance system that reviewed PCTs' progress towards achieving better health outcomes for their populations by assessing three elements – outcomes (the rate of improvement); competencies (as listed above and using a rating of 1 to 4) and governance (using a red, amber, green traffic light score)
- A support and development framework that gave PCTs 'access to the tools they needed to become world class commissioners, either by sharing services and good practice, developing internal resources, or buying in external expertise, for example through the Framework for Securing External Support for Commissioners (FESC)'.

For more about commissioning, see chapter 11.

PCTs as service providers

As the focus on their commissioning role grew, there was some discussion about whether or not PCTs should also provide healthcare services. In 2009, the Department of Health issued *Transforming Community Services: enabling new patterns of provision* which set out plans to improve services, develop the workforce, and reform the system to build on other policies including the results of the Darzi review (see below). *Transforming Community Services* gave new impetus to the original proposal in *Commissioning a Patient-led NHS* to separate PCT providing and commissioning roles and the *Operating Framework 2011/12* took this to its conclusion with PCTs required to dispose of their provider functions by 31st March 2011.

Primary care and 'care closer to home' services

National policy, reflected in commissioning intentions, is to encourage the transfer of services to the community from hospital settings wherever this improves patient care and is practical. The success of this initiative will, in large part, be determined by the provision of sufficient numbers of trained, highly skilled community-based staff to support clients in their own homes or other community accommodation.

The current GP contract also offers incentives to GPs to develop enhanced services from their practices, which may help with the long term monitoring and clinical management of patients within the community.

The key policy document in this area was *Our Health, Our Care, Our Say – A New Direction for Community Services* which was issued by the Department of Health in 2006. More recently, the funding included in PCTs' 2011/12 allocations for 're-ablement' reflects the close linkages between community services and social care and the importance of PCTs and local authorities working together.

Focus on quality

High Quality Care for All: Next Stage Review (2008)

During 2007 and 2008, the then health minister Lord Darzi carried out a wide ranging review of the NHS which recommended a change of focus for the NHS to a service that 'gives patients and the public more information and choice, works in partnership and has quality of care at its heart'. The Darzi review also recommended a number of changes to the provision of healthcare services within the primary/secondary sector, including the development of 'poly-clinics' where appropriate – a primary healthcare equivalent of the 'one-stop shop'. The themes and focus of the Darzi review were re-iterated in the *Operating Framework 2010/11* which emphasised that quality should be the 'organising principle' that underlies all that the NHS does.

Quality innovation productivity and prevention

In the light of constraints in public sector funding from 2010/11, the Department of Health launched an initiative in 2009 known as 'quality, innovation, productivity and prevention' or QIPP. In many ways, the QIPP initiative is founded on the principles in the 2008 Darzi Report – however, the worsening economic outlook made the need for change more pressing and profound. International evidence has shown that it is possible to improve the quality of care (and patient experience as a by product) while reducing costs. This 'right first time' philosophy now applies throughout the NHS.

Roles and Functions

At present (2011/12), PCTs are responsible for the planning and securing of health services and improving the health of their local population. The precise population size covered by each PCT varies, but ranges from around 250,000 to above 1,000,000. PCTs must make sure that there are enough GPs to meet the needs of their population and that they are accessible to patients. PCTs must also ensure the provision of other health services including hospitals, dentists, mental healthcare, walk-in centres, NHS Direct, patient transport, population screening, pharmacies and opticians. In addition, they are responsible for integrating health and social care so that the two systems work well together for the benefit of patients.

PCT objectives can be summarised as being to:

- Improve health/reduce inequalities
- Commission health services (see chapter 11 for more on commissioning)
- Develop primary care and community services
- Promote partnership working (see chapter 9 for more on working with local authorities).

To be able to secure health services for their population, PCTs enter into contractual arrangements with service providers. Since 2008/09 a standard contract has been in use to manage the major contractual relationships a PCT has with its providers of acute care. In 2010/11 this contract was extended to cover mental health and community providers. These contracts are designed to allow PCTs to manage key elements of their spending within a logical formal framework of review and agreement. The contracts used by PCTs will be looked at more closely later in this chapter.

In 2008 a national Co-operation and Competition Panel was established to ensure that the NHS operated within an appropriate procurement framework. This was prompted by the policy of 'plurality' whereby all providers of healthcare are treated equitably subject to quality and financial considerations. As part of the *Operating Framework 2008/09*, the Department of Health issued *Principles of Co-operation and Competition* which outlined how PCTs and other NHS organisations should operate in a competitive situation.

As far as their public health responsibilities are concerned, PCTs currently commission a wide range of health and well-being services, often in partnership with local authorities (see chapter 9).

Governance and Accountability

The board

Each PCT has a board which consists of up to seven non-executives and seven executive directors plus a Chair. The executive members must include the Chief Executive, the Finance Director, the Chair of the professional executive committee (PEC), a GP and a nurse.

The professional executive committee

Each PCT must also have a professional executive committee or PEC which provides clinical leadership and is made up of a variety of clinical professionals. As far as the PEC's roles and responsibilities are concerned, PCTs follow guidance set out on the Department of Health's 2007 guide *Primary Care Trust Professional Executive Committees – Fit for the Future*. Although PCTs have the freedom to determine how PECs operate in line with local circumstances, the guiding principles for all PECs are that they need to:

- Be patient focussed and promote the health and well-being of communities as well as addressing health inequalities
- Be drivers of strong clinical leadership and enablers of clinical empowerment
- Be decision-making and firmly part of the governance and accountability framework of the PCT
- Reflect a range of clinical professions and the wealth of experience this brings.

Line of accountability

PCTs are financially accountable to the Department of Health and the public and are 'performance managed' by their SHA.

Planning

PCTs are required to produce annual 'operational plans' that outline how the PCT intends to meet national and local priorities within the allocation period. PCTs must also:

- Make an annual service plan available to the public
- Set out a clear medium term 'commissioning strategy' which reflects public health needs and expectations
- Produce a current year 'commissioning prospectus'.

These documents are supported by underpinning delivery strategies including a medium term financial strategy, procurement strategy and manpower strategy.

The Department's *Operating Frameworks* set out in detail what is expected of NHS organisations each year and in particular the national priorities against which they are expected to improve. For 2011/12 the indicators and milestones for planning and assessing delivery of PCT and SHA plans are grouped under three domains:

- Quality (safety, effectiveness and experience)
- Resources (finance, workforce, capacity and activity)
- Reform (commissioning, provision, partnership building, putting patients first and developing the new public health infrastructure).

Financial monitoring

All PCTs must hold board meetings in public at which regular financial reports on progress towards achieving financial targets are presented. Most PCTs provide the following information in these reports:

- Operating cost statement
- Statement of financial position (formerly known as the balance sheet)
- Statement of cash flows
- Workforce information
- Forecast performance against statutory duties
- Commentary highlighting any significant issues.

All PCTs are subject to monthly financial monitoring by their SHA. In addition PCTs report to the Department of Health on a regular basis throughout the year through their SHAs.

Annual report and accounts

PCTs must publish an annual report and audited accounts as one document and present it at the annual public meeting. It must also be made available (if requested) to a member of the public. In addition, PCTs can (if they wish) prepare and distribute an annual report and summary financial statements.

The annual report is similar to a commercial annual report and gives an account of the PCT's operations over the last financial year. The annual accounts give a financial picture of the PCT over the year and comprise:

- Foreword to the accounts
- Directors' statement of responsibilities
- External auditors' report
- Statement on internal control
- The four primary statements (operating cost statement, statement of financial position, statement of cash flows, statement of changes in taxpayers' equity)
- Notes to the accounts.

A *Manual for Accounts* is issued annually by the Department of Health and sets out the accounting statements to be completed by PCTs. The HFMA has also produced (in conjunction with the Audit Commission) *PCT accounts: a Guide for Non-executives* and *NHS Annual Accounts Planning Guide*, aimed at practitioners new to the process.

PCTs are required to submit a set of accounting statements for external audit in the prescribed format in accordance with the Department of Health's timetable. Failure to do so results in audit criticism and forms part of the SHA performance assessment.

See chapter 14 for more about financial reporting.

PCT Funding

PCTs receive funding in two forms – revenue and capital. Revenue funding covers costs for the commissioning of health services in primary, community and secondary care settings and general day to day running costs. Capital funding, which is relatively small for most PCTs, provides for expenditure on items with a useful life expectancy in excess of one year and with a value greater than £5,000, such as land, buildings and larger pieces of equipment.

Chapter 3 looks in detail at how the NHS is funded but the key elements relating to PCTs are summarised below.

Revenue

Under the current (2011/12) regime, the main source of funding that PCTs receive is their revenue resource limit (RRL) which is a 'unified allocation' which includes allocations for hospital and community health services (HCHS), the GP contract, dental services and prescribing. These unified allocations are determined by the Department of Health using an allocation process based on a weighted capitation formula.

There are four elements of resource allocation which affect the level of funding received by PCTs in their unified allocations:

- By far the most important is a PCT's **recurrent baseline** (a) – for each year the recurrent baseline is the prior year's allocation adjusted as necessary
- **Weighted capitation targets** (b) – targets are set according to the national weighted capitation formula, which calculates PCT 'fair shares' of available resources based on the

health needs of their populations. These targets are recalculated regularly prior to the allocation of resources to take account of changes such as the latest census data. Changes in the targets do not immediately lead to changes in actual allocations

- **Distance from target (DFT)** – this is the difference between (a) and (b); if (b) is greater than (a) a PCT is said to be under target; if (b) is less than (a) it is said to be over target. These are expressed in monetary and percentage terms
- **Pace of change** – this is the speed at which PCTs are moved closer to target (or 'levelled up') and is a policy that has been operating for some years. Levelling up is achieved through the distribution of extra resources – a process known as differential growth, where all PCTs receive some growth funds, but higher levels of growth are targeted at PCTs most under target.

PCTs may also receive funding from NHS central budgets or the 'central bundle' – these are funds allocated to SHAs or resources held centrally by the Department of Health for specific development initiatives. The level of funds held centrally has significantly reduced over the last few years with more resources being included in unified allocation baselines.

PCTs can also seek funding from non-NHS sources such as the European Community and charitable trusts in order to meet their overall objectives.

For more details about the resource allocation process (including the weighted capitation formula and what is covered by HCHS), see chapter 3.

Capital

Many PCTs hold significant levels of capital assets, including GP premises and multi-functional health centres used by a range of providers. Some of these assets have been funded via the private finance initiative (PFI) or local improvement finance trust (LIFT) schemes – see chapter 10 for more details.

Given the impending abolition of PCTs any capital expenditure must be discussed with their SHA as (from 2011/12), PCTs have a zero delegated limit.

Financial Duties and Targets

Like SHAs and NHS trusts, PCTs are required to follow international financial reporting standards (IFRS) except where departures are allowed under the *NHS Manual for Accounts*.

PCTs have a range of financial duties:

- Contain expenditure, measured on an accruals basis, within the revenue resource limit set by the Department of Health for accrued revenue expenditure. PCTs are required to stay within this limit when measuring gross revenue expenditure less miscellaneous income
- Contain expenditure, measured on an accruals basis, within a capital resource limit. The CRL is set by the Department of Health for accrued capital expenditure in year. PCTs are required to stay within this limit when measuring gross capital expenditure less the book value of assets disposed of during the year

- Cash limit – a statutory duty not to spend more than the cash allocated to them. PCTs have a combined cash limit for both revenue and capital
- PCTs have flexibility to transfer any amount of resource limit from revenue to capital but transfers from capital to revenue (to allow for 'capital grant' payments to non-NHS organisations) are subject to SHA control totals
- A requirement to pay capital charges on their assets. These include a depreciation charge to reflect the use of fixed assets (other than land) and a 3.5% cost of capital charge on net relevant assets (see chapter 16)
- Apply the *Better Payment Practice Code*. PCTs have to achieve a public sector payment standard of valid invoices paid within 30 days of the receipt of the invoice. A target is set at the start of the year by the Department of Health for the value and volume of invoices that must be paid within 30 days (currently the target is 95%).

See chapter 14 for more about financial and performance reporting.

Commissioning Health Services

At present, PCTs use their resources to ensure that a full range of primary and secondary care services are available for their populations. PCTs also commission 'well-being' services (often in partnership with local authorities) in line with their public and community health responsibilities.

The approach followed for each key primary and secondary care provider is discussed in turn below.

Primary care services

Payments for primary care services are funded almost entirely through PCTs' unified allocations. Primary care includes a wide range of services provided principally by independent contractors, as discussed below:

GP services

At present, there are two main contract types for GP services – General Medical Services (GMS) or Personal Medical Services (PMS). Across England, about 60% of GP practices have a GMS contract. However, within any one PCT, this percentage will vary. Both GMS and PMS are funded from the unified allocations that PCTs receive.

General Medical Services (GMS)

The 'new' GMS contract (also known as the GP contract) came into effect in April 2004. This practice-based contract (the 'old' GMS was with individual GPs) provides practices with three main income streams, all of which are funded from the unified allocation:

- A global sum to cover running costs and the provision of essential and additional services
- Enhanced service payments for practices which expand the services they provide
- The Quality and Outcomes Framework (QOF) to reward improved standards in both clinical and non clinical areas.

The global sum is calculated through a resource allocation formula based on the age/sex of the practice's population, additional needs, list turnover, nursing home patients and rurality. In addition to general running costs, this global sum covers the provision of essential and additional services. Essential services, which have to be provided by every practice, cover the care of patients during an episode of illness, the general management of chronic disease and care for the terminally ill. Additional services, such as contraceptive services, child health surveillance and out of hours services are voluntary. Practices that opt out of additional services have their global sum reduced by a nationally agreed percentage rate.

Practices and other providers are able to apply to PCTs for additional funding to meet the costs of specialised or enhanced services commissioned by the PCT (for example, extended minor surgery and childhood immunisations). These are usually paid to practices on an activity basis at locally set rates. PCTs also have to commission a number of 'directed enhanced services' that are agreed at a national level and which usually reflect national policy – for example covering access or 'choose and book' initiatives and targets. These are subject to annual review and change. PCT unified allocations have also contained a guaranteed minimum expenditure level for the development of these enhanced services.

At present, a significant proportion of money is available to reward practices for providing higher quality services. This is achieved via the QOF which sets out a range of standards across four headings – clinical, organisational, additional services and patient experience. Practices are awarded points for achieving these standards, set out in some 150 indicators, and receive a set payment per point. PCTs initially make 'aspiration payments' to practices throughout the year based upon 70% of their previous year's QOF achievement levels. Full QOF payments are made once it is known how successful a practice has been in delivering the QOF. Final achievement payments are made in the first quarter of the following financial year.

Practices that might have lost out under the resource allocation formula are currently protected by a minimum practice income guarantee (MPIG). This guarantees a practice's level of income based on rates achieved prior to the implementation of the new GMS contract in April 2004. From 2009/10, the value of the MPIG is gradually being eroded as a result of changes to the methodology used in the GP contract and moves to introduce a more equitable system of funding core GP services.

There are also separate funding streams for:

- Premises: under the terms of the contract, PCTs reimburse practices for their premises costs. This includes rent and rates charges incurred. A notional rent payment is made to practices that own their premises
- Seniority pay: this is paid at nationally agreed rates and is dependent upon the number of years a GP has worked in the NHS
- Locum cover: PCTs may also make a contribution to practices towards the costs of employing a locum to cover maternity, paternity and sickness of a partner
- Information communications and technology (ICT): funding the purchase, maintenance, future upgrades and running costs of ICT within primary care is the responsibility of PCTs, rather than practices.

Personal Medical Services (PMS)

Under PMS GPs are paid contract sums to deliver a defined service to give PCTs and providers freedom to develop innovative options for meeting primary care needs. This forms part of a PCT's normal primary care commissioning budget.

PMS continues side-by-side with the 'new' GMS contract and PMS practices are also able to receive quality payments and are eligible for enhanced services (if these are not already in their PMS contract) plus the premises, ICT and seniority pay. PMS practices can opt to switch into the new GMS contract.

Prescribing

The costs of drugs prescribed by GP practices are calculated by NHS Prescription Services (formerly the Prescription Pricing Authority but now part of the NHS Business Services Authority) and charged to the cash-limited budget held by the relevant PCT. PCTs fund prescribing expenditure from their unified allocations.

The rising cost of primary care prescribing is a significant cost pressure for PCTs with drug inflation regularly outstripping inflation on other budgets by significant amounts. Prescribing costs have always risen faster than general inflation as new, more effective and more expensive drugs become available. However, this has become even more pronounced in recent years with the introduction of national service frameworks (NSFs) which have led to increased prescribing in areas such as coronary heart disease. Guidance from the National Institute for Health and Clinical Excellence (NICE), which assesses the clinical and cost-effectiveness of new drugs and technologies, is also driving both prescription volume and cost. The impact of these rising costs is mitigated to an extent by securing efficiencies from improvements in prescribing practice.

Dental services

Since April 2006 a 'new' general dental services (nGDS) contract has paid dentists a set value for an agreed number of units of dental activity (UDAs). A reform of patients' charges also came into effect in April 2006 with the introduction of three bands depending on the type of treatment received.

Some practices have a personal dental services (PDS) contract. These practices are paid a set contract value in return for having an agreed number of patients on their list. The contract is designed to give a 10% decrease in working time to allow dentists to use 5% for PCT access slots for unregistered patients to be seen urgently, and 5% to take them off the 'treadmill' of items of service payments.

Under the GDS and PDS contracts, PCTs are required to gain the budgeted level of patients' charge revenue via the dentists. If national estimates are above actual patient charges collected by dentists from patients, PCTs suffer a shortfall in income.

The budget for primary dental services is devolved to PCTs and from 2011/12 included within PCT baselines. Under the current regime, PCTs are also responsible for dental public health and commissioning suitable 'high street' specialised dental services to meet local health needs.

The coalition government intends to introduce a new dental contract with a pilot programme in 2011/12 that will test three different contract models.

Pharmacy services

Under the *NHS (Pharmaceutical) Regulations 1992*, payments are made to pharmacists and some doctors for supplying and dispensing certain drugs (net of prescription charges collected) and for items such as rota services, the supply and maintenance of oxygen concentrators and providing services to residential homes. In sparsely populated country areas, essential small pharmacy allowances may also be payable. Normally payments are made monthly by PCTs.

In relation to the supply and dispensing of drugs, NHS Prescriptions Services receives details of all prescriptions dispensed in England, and then calculates the amounts payable, allowing for the drug and container cost and a service fee.

In April 2005, a 'new' pharmacy contract came into effect. This enables community pharmacies to carry out four main roles:

* Self care
* Management of long term conditions
* Public health
* Improving access to services.

These roles are split into the following services:

* Essential services – such as: dispensing; disposal of unwanted medicines; promoting healthy lifestyles; signposting; support for self care; support for people with disabilities; and clinical governance
* Enhanced/local services – commissioned by PCTs to meet local needs, including: out-of-hours service; minor ailments schemes; anticoagulant monitoring; stop smoking schemes
* Advanced services – accreditation of a pharmacy is required to allow medicine use reviews (MURs) and prescription intervention.

From 2011/12, the funding for pharmacy services is included within PCT baselines.

An electronic prescription service (EPS) is also being developed by NHS Connecting for Health – this allows prescribers (such as GPs and practice nurses) to send prescriptions electronically to a dispenser of the patient's choice, thus making the prescribing and dispensing process safer and more convenient.

Ophthalmic services

Payments are made to ophthalmic medical practitioners, dispensing opticians and ophthalmic opticians for NHS eye tests (where a fee or reduced fee is payable by the recipient of the test) and for the supply, repair or replacement of spectacles. Sometimes a fee is paid for home visits. From 2011/12, the budget for these payments is included within PCT baselines.

Hospital and community health services

PCTs assess the needs of their populations and commission hospital and community services from local and national providers. A national contract drawn up by the Department of Health has been in use since 2008/09 – this is used by all PCTs and their provider acute trusts including foundations trusts (FTs). In 2010/11 this contract was extended to cover mental health and community providers. During 2011/12 and 2012/13, these standard contracts will be revised to prepare for the coalition government's new regime.

NHS trusts are paid for the activity they undertake (and which is commissioned by PCTs) in a number of ways. Acute trusts receive the bulk of their income through payments for a spell of activity according to a nationally set tariff rate, meaning that variations in activity are generally paid for at full cost either by the PCT for 'over performance' or repaid by the trust as 'under performance'. This system is called payment by results (PbR) and provides tariffs for groups of treatments/ procedures known as healthcare resource groups (HRGs).

PbR means that money moves with the patient and allows patients to choose in which hospital they receive their treatment. The PCT pays the set national tariff to whichever provider is used so that competition is focussed on quality not price. Payments are also made by PCTs for services provided on a non-tariff basis at local negotiated prices or agreed values. For more information about PbR see chapter 13.

Practice Based Commissioning

Under the current arrangements, GP practices are encouraged to operate practice based commissioning (PBC) and hold indicative budgets for all services commissioned by the PCT. This initiative was designed to engage clinicians in making decisions about the most appropriate and cost effective treatment for their patients.

Just as PbR was designed to incentivise hospitals to use capacity productively and efficiently, so PBC incentivises GPs and local clinicians to manage demand for hospital care and therefore balance the system. Savings made by GP practices from operating their indicative budgets can be used for investment in other services provided by the practices with the agreement of the PCT. The PCT remains accountable for the overall budget and entering into contracts with providers, as well as meeting the operational targets set down by the Department of Health. For more on PBC see chapter 11.

Partnership Working

At present, PCTs have a general responsibility to maximise partnership working for the benefit of patients. In particular, flexibilities exist to allow pooling of budgets – for example, so that a PCT and its local social services department can pool their resources for mental health and social care services. This enables PCTs to commission and provide services through a joint pool so that services may be delivered more flexibly. Children's trusts also promote much closer working between health and local authorities. Chapter 9 looks in more detail at the current relationship with local authorities.

What the future holds for PCTs

Subject to any amendments agreed to the *Health and Social Care Bill 2011*, the coalition government has announced that PCTs will be abolished from April 2013. At that point, GP consortia will take over responsibility for agreeing what care the patients registered with their constituent practices need, negotiating contracts with healthcare providers and monitoring their implementation. These contracts will set out the level and quality of the services required and their cost and will follow the new NHS Commissioning Board's model contract (the existing suite of contracts is to be reviewed between 2011 and 2013 in preparation). These healthcare services may be provided by foundation trusts or other public or private sector providers (i.e. 'any willing provider').

Although GP consortia will commission the majority of NHS services for their patients (including, planned hospital care; rehabilitative care; maternity services; urgent and emergency services including out-of-hours services; community health services; mental health services and learning disabilities services), they will not be responsible for commissioning primary medical services provided by GPs, dentistry, community pharmacy, primary ophthalmic services and national and regional specialised services. These will instead be commissioned by the NHS Commissioning Board. There will also be special arrangements made for high security psychiatric facilities.

GP consortia will receive their funding from the NHS Commissioning Board which will be required to remain within an 'NHS commissioning revenue limit' for which the Board's Chief Executive (the accountable/accounting officer) will be held to account by the Department of Health. The Board will also be required to prepare a consolidated annual account for all consortia which will be a key element in the Department of Health's overall resource account. To be able to fulfil these requirements, the Commissioning Board will itself hold GP consortia to account for their stewardship of resources and outcomes achieved. In particular, each consortium will have a duty to achieve financial balance. The Board will also specify the form and content of accounting information that consortia must provide and a timetable for submission.

Consortia budgets will include a maximum allowance to cover management costs but it will be for each consortium to decide how to spend this funding. Some may choose to undertake some or all of these roles themselves, others may use the money to buy in the services needed including data analysis and contract monitoring – roles which are currently undertaken by PCTs.

As far as governance arrangements are concerned, each consortium will be a statutory body with an accountable officer (AO) with an accountability line to the NHS Commissioning Board. Consortia will also have a Chief Financial Officer. Under the current arrangements, the PCT Chief Executive is the AO and it is expected that under the new structure it will be the 'senior official' within each consortium. It is also assumed that the inclusion of an AO in the structure means that he or she will need to comply with the Treasury's requirements for all other AOs in the public sector, namely that the AO will have to ensure that:

- The consortium operates efficiently and to a high standard of probity
- Governance, decision making and financial management standards (as set out in the Treasury's guide *Managing Public Money*) are met
- Value for money is demonstrated.

In future, local authorities will lead the joint strategic needs assessment (at present this a joint responsibility with PCTs), which will inform healthcare commissioning. Local authorities will provide strategic co-ordination to commissioning of NHS services, social care and health improvement through newly established health and wellbeing boards. GP consortia members will be represented on these boards.

Between now and when they are abolished, the coalition government expects PCTs to help pave the way for the new structure while remaining statutorily accountable. In particular 'clusters' of PCTs will be set up in all regions by June 2011. Each cluster will have a single executive team and their role will be to:

• Oversee delivery during the transition and close down of the 'old' system
• Support emerging consortia
• Develop commissioning support providers.

PCTs' detailed responsibilities were set out in 'transition letters' issued by Sir David Nicholson in July and December 2010 which identified the following key functions:

• Supporting and enabling the new GP consortia
• Working with colleagues within the agreed HR framework to support people through the transition period
• Working with colleagues to ensure the sustainability of key systems and processes through the transition period
• Completing the separation of commissioning from provision
• Strengthening links with local authorities, particularly on the integration of health and social care and health improvement
• Creating more choice for patients.

When the Commissioning Board becomes a statutorily accountable body from April 2012 and SHAs are abolished, PCTs (through clusters) will be accountable to the Commissioning Board. During 2012/13, the Commissioning Board will authorise consortia which will assume their statutory status in April 2013 – at that point, PCTs will be abolished.

References and Further Reading

Commissioning a Patient-led NHS, Department of Health, 2005: www.dh.gov.uk/en/Publicationsandstatistics/Publications/PublicationsPolicyAndGuidance/DH_4116716

World Class Commissioning – Department of Health archived web pages: http://webarchive.nationalarchives.gov.uk/+/www.dh.gov.uk/en/Managingyourorganisation/Commissioning/Worldclasscommissioning/index.htm

Framework for Securing External Support for Commissioners (FESC): www.dh.gov.uk/en/Publicationsandstatistics/Publications/PublicationsPolicyAndGuidance/DH_065818

Operating Frameworks, Department of Health: www.dh.gov.uk/en/Managingyourorganisation/Financeandplanning/Planningframework/index.htm

Transforming Community Services: enabling new patterns of provision, Department of Health, 2009: www.dh.gov.uk/en/Publicationsandstatistics/Publications/PublicationsPolicyAndGuidance/DH_093197

Our Health, Our care, Our Say: a new direction for Community Services, Department of Health, 2006 – archived web pages: http://webarchive.nationalarchives.gov.uk/+/www.dh.gov.uk/en/Healthcare/Ourhealthourcareoursay/index.htm

High Quality Care for All: NHS Next Stage Review (the Darzi review) – Department of Health archived web pages: http://webarchive.nationalarchives.gov.uk/+/www.dh.gov.uk/en/Healthcare/Highqualitycareforall/index.htm

Quality, innovation, productivity and prevention (QIPP): www.institute.nhs.uk/cost_and_quality/qipp/cost_and_quality_homepage.html

Principles and Rules of Co-operation and Competition, Department of Health, 2010: www.dh.gov.uk/en/Publicationsandstatistics/Publications/PublicationsPolicyAndGuidance/DH_113746

PCT Professional Executive Committees – Fit for the Future, Department of Health, 2007: www.dh.gov.uk/en/Publicationsandstatistics/Publications/PublicationsPolicyAndGuidance/DH_073508

Manual for Accounts, Department of Health: www.info.doh.gov.uk/doh/finman.nsf

Primary Care Trust Accounts: a Guide for Non-executives, HFMA/ Audit Commission, 2010: www.hfma.org.uk or www.audit-commission.gov.uk

Annual Accounts Planning Guide, HFMA, 2010: www.hfma.org.uk

NHS allocations (including the weighted capitation formula): www.dh.gov.uk/policyandguidance/organisationpolicy/financeandplanning/allocations/fs/en

Primary medical care contracting and legislation, Department of Health: www.dh.gov.uk/en/Healthcare/Primarycare/PMC/contractingroutes/index.htm

Quality and Outcomes Framework: www.dh.gov.uk/en/Healthcare/Primarycare/PMC/QualityOutcomesFramework/index.htm

Fairer Funding of GP Services, Department of Health: www.dh.gov.uk/en/Publicationsandstatistics/Lettersandcirculars/Dearcolleagueletters/DH_097506

NHS Prescription Services: www.nhsbsa.nhs.uk/prescriptions

National Institute for Health and Clinical Excellence: www.nice.org.uk/

Dental Contract – details available via the Chief Dental Officer's website: www.dh.gov.uk/AboutUs/HeadsOfProfession/ChiefDentalOfficer/fs/en

Contractual framework for community pharmacy: www.dh.gov.uk/en/Healthcare/Primarycare/Communitypharmacy/index.htm

Electronic Prescription Service: www.connectingforhealth.nhs.uk/systemsandservices/eps

Eye care (ophthalmic) services, Department of Health: www.dh.gov.uk/en/Healthcare/Primarycare/Optical/index.htm

The Standard NHS Contract for Acute Hospital Services and Supporting Guidance: www.dh.gov.uk/en/Publicationsandstatistics/Publications/PublicationsPolicyAndGuidance/DH_081100

Payment by Results: www.dh.gov.uk/en/Managingyourorganisation/NHSFinancialReforms/index.htm

Practice Based Commissioning – Department of Health archived web pages: http://webarchive.nationalarchives.gov.uk/+/www.dh.gov.uk/en/Managingyourorganisation/Commissioning/Practice-basedcommissioning/index.htm

7. NHS Trusts

Introduction

NHS trusts were formed from 1991 onwards under the *NHS and Community Care Act 1990*. All NHS hospitals in England providing acute and mental health services form part of an NHS trust and in some areas they also host community services. NHS trusts provide mainly, but not exclusively, hospital-based (secondary care) services.

Although managerially independent, all NHS trusts are statutory bodies and as such are accountable to the Secretary of State for Health through the Department of Health via strategic health authorities (SHAs).

Types of NHS Trust

There is a wide range of NHS trusts covering the population's different health needs:

- District acute general hospital trusts
- Specialist hospitals that provide regional or national services – for example, Great Ormond Street Hospital for Children NHS Trust
- Combined teaching, specialist and district general hospitals – for example, Leeds Teaching Hospitals NHS Trust
- Mental health and learning disability services – for example, Derbyshire Mental Health Services NHS Trust
- Care trusts – organisations that work in both health and social services and may carry out a range of services including social care, mental health services, learning disability and primary care services – for example, Sandwell Mental Health NHS and Social Care Trust
- Ambulance services, including paramedical and patient transport services – for example, the London Ambulance Service NHS Trust.

There are also over 120 NHS foundation trusts (FTs) which first came into being in April 2004. Although they are part of the NHS, FTs operate under different governance and financial arrangements – see chapter 8 for more details. The coalition government is expecting all remaining NHS trusts to achieve foundation status by March 2014.

Governance Arrangements

Primary legislation under *The NHS Trusts (Membership and Procedure) Regulations 1990* stipulates the makeup of NHS trust boards but does give some flexibility over the number of non-executive members.

The maximum number of directors of an NHS trust was set originally at eleven. However, since 1998, each board can have a maximum number of twelve directors excluding the Chair – up to seven non-executive members (although the majority have five) and no more than five executive directors.

Within the executive directors, each trust must have:

- A chief officer
- A chief financial officer
- A medical or dental practitioner and registered nurse or midwife (except in the case of ambulance trusts).

In 2000, the board structure of mental health trusts was set at a maximum of 14, excluding the Chair, to include no more than seven non-executive directors (NEDs) and seven executive directors. This structure was extended to care trusts in 2001.

Other executive directors may attend board meetings but do not hold the full range of responsibilities – for example, they do not have the right to vote on board decisions. While the medical and nursing professions must be represented at board level, this can be through a Chief Executive with a medical or nursing background.

The Role of Boards and NEDs

An NHS trust board is collectively responsible for promoting the success of the organisation by directing and supervising its affairs. This involves:

- Setting the organisation's values and standards and ensuring that its obligations to patients, the local community and the Secretary of State are understood and met
- Providing active leadership of the organisation within a framework of prudent and effective controls which enable risk to be assessed and managed
- Setting the organisation's strategic aims
- Ensuring that the necessary financial and human resources are in place for the organisation to meet its objectives
- Reviewing management performance.

Over recent years, increased emphasis has been placed on the board's role in improving financial management and on the part played by NEDs.

Accountability and Responsibilities

At present (2011/12), NHS trusts are accountable to the Secretary of State through the Department of Health via SHAs. They are also required to produce annual accounts and reports and are subject to audit and regulation. The key 'accountability tools' are discussed in the sections that follow, namely:

- The planning process
- The annual report on the previous year's performance
- The annual accounts
- Quality accounts
- Performance management and monitoring (and in particular, monitoring returns against trust financial duties)
- The Care Quality Commission's registration and review processes.

Planning process

The planning process is designed to:

- Ensure efficient and effective delivery of services
- Demonstrate public accountability
- Ensure congruence with national and local commissioning plans and targets.

At present, NHS trust plans must be consistent with the level of resources negotiated in PCTs' 'operational plans'. These operational plans cover three years and are designed to show how PCTs intend to address health inequalities, improve health outcomes and improve the targeting of healthcare provision in accordance with national and local priorities and targets and in line with PCT commissioning strategies.

Plans are reviewed regularly (for example, at performance meetings held with the SHA) and if there are significant issues changes may be needed – for example, if serious financial problems develop in the health economy.

Annual report

NHS trusts are required to produce annual reports which must be published with the full set of audited accounts as one document and presented to the trust's annual general meeting. Trusts may also produce summarised versions to aid communication with stakeholders.

The annual report is primarily a narrative document similar to the directors' report described in the *Companies Act*, but with additional information reflecting the trust's position in the community, the impact on the environment and emergency preparedness. The report gives an account of the trust's activities and performance over the last financial year.

Although the overall layout of the annual report is at each trust's discretion, there are mandatory items that must be included. These are set out in the *Manual for Accounts* which is available on the Department of Health's website. For example, in addition to the financial statements, the report must include a directors' statement of responsibilities and the auditor's report on the accounts. Trusts also use the annual report as an opportunity to set out their achievements in the year and highlight the challenges ahead.

Since 2005/06, it has been best practice to prepare an 'operating and financial review' (OFR) as part of the annual report. An OFR focuses on matters that are of interest to the public and gives a comprehensive picture of the trust's business incorporating future plans and aspirations as well as past performance. Guidance on preparing an OFR is available from the HFMA's website.

The annual report must be approved by the trust's Board of Directors before presentation at a public meeting. This meeting must be held before 30th September following the end of the relevant financial year.

Annual accounts

The annual accounts must comprise:

- A foreword and notes to the accounts
- The four primary statements:
    - Statement of comprehensive income (formerly the income and expenditure statement)
    - Statement of financial position (formerly the balance sheet)
    - Statement of changes in taxpayers' equity (formerly the statement of total recognised gains and losses)
    - Statement of cash flows
- Directors' statements of responsibilities
- The statement on internal control
- Independent auditors' report, giving an opinion on the accounts.

The accounts give a financial picture of the trust over the year and since 2009/10 have been produced in line with international financial reporting standards (IFRS). The *Manual for Accounts* gives details of the full set of accounting statements to be completed by NHS trusts, including trust financial monitoring and accounting forms (TRUs), together with detailed guidance for their completion.

Trusts are required to submit a set of accounting statements for external audit in the prescribed format in accordance with the Department of Health's timetable. Failure to do results in audit criticism and forms part of the SHA performance assessment.

Quality accounts

Since April 2010, all providers of acute care (including mental health, ambulance and disability learning trusts) are required by statute (the *Health Act 2009*) to produce a 'quality account' – an annual report to the public about the quality of services delivered.

The Department of Health has set out six areas that a quality account should cover:

- An overall statement of accountability from the board
- Three to five priorities for improvement
- A review of quality performance (including at least three indicators from each of the three 'domains of quality' – safety, effectiveness and patient experience)
- Research and innovation
- What others say about the provider
- Data quality.

More details are available on the Department's website.

Performance management and monitoring

All NHS trusts are subject to financial (and non financial) performance monitoring against plan at least on a quarterly basis. At present, this is carried out by the SHA which collates and acts upon monitoring returns and evaluates progress against key national and local targets. Current practice is for these returns to be collected on a monthly basis. The returns include as a minimum:

- Income and expenditure – both capital and revenue covering year to date and forecast outturn
- Statement of financial position (formerly the balance sheet)
- Cash flow
- Current period and forecast outturn 'run rate' (variance between income and expenditure)
- Update on delivery of cost improvement (savings) plans
- Performance against the *Better Payment Practice Code*
- Break-even duty
- Performance against the capital cost absorption and external financing limit duties
- Provisions for liabilities and charges
- A commentary on variances against plan and previous expenditure levels
- A written narrative summary of the financial position.

Trusts are also subject to monthly workforce monitoring which includes an analysis of pay expenditure.

Trusts' financial duties and targets are discussed in more detail later in this chapter.

Care Quality Commission

The Care Quality Commission (CQC) took over the regulation of health and social care from April 2009 and its regime includes periodic reviews of providers to assess performance. See chapter 14 for more about the role of the CQC.

Financing of NHS Trusts

NHS trusts are financed in two main ways:

- Revenue financing for their day to day running
- Capital financing to fund the purchase of new and replacement assets (buildings and equipment).

Revenue financing

At present, NHS trusts receive revenue income from five main sources:

- Through the commissioning process with PCTs and other NHS trusts – this usually represents 75% to 90% of total income
- Specific funding to NHS trusts providing nursing, medical and non-medical staff education and training services (generally based on numbers in training)
- Through research and development allocations to trusts undertaking agreed research and development

- Charges to staff, visitors or patients for services provided, such as catering or the provision of private patient facilities
- Grants from other government bodies or charitable organisations
- The NHS injury cost recovery scheme – this allows the NHS to reclaim the cost of treating injured patients in all cases where personal injury compensation is paid.

Capital financing

Prior to 2007/08, the majority of public capital was allocated on a formulaic basis to trusts as 'operational capital' (for buildings and equipment replacement and renewal). These allocations took the form of public dividend capital (PDC) which attracted dividend payments. An element of capital funding was also managed centrally to target particular investment objectives.

In 2007/08, the capital allocation process for NHS trusts changed to an approach similar to that followed by FTs. This means that access to capital and working capital[2] is now linked to financial performance and affordability with a 'prudential borrowing limit' or PBL set for each trust.

NHS trusts have two main sources of capital funding:

- Internally generated funds (via retained surpluses, depreciation and proceeds from the sale of capital assets)
- Capital investment loans from the Department of Health (within the PBL).

The PBL is set by the Department on the assumption that the trust can afford the costs of borrowing to this level both in terms of the interest payments and the principal repayments, and taking into consideration any working capital loans a trust may already have. At present, access to capital investment loans is controlled through both the PBL and the SHA business case approval process. Once SHA approval is secured, the loan must be approved by the Department. The loan interest is set in accordance with the National Loans Fund rate and fixed over the period of the loan, which in the case of a capital investment loan is generally the same as the life of the asset to which it relates. The loan and the associated interest (calculated on the outstanding balance) are repaid in equal instalments in September and March each year. Trusts must generate the cash (for example, through surpluses) to repay the principal and interest on any loans, the interest being charged to revenue expenditure.

The PBL for each trust is not an annual limit – instead it indicates the maximum cumulative borrowing that a trust may take on to fund additional capital investment and to finance operations generally. Following a system that mirrors arrangements for FTs, the PBL is calculated using information from the previous year's financial accounts and financial plan and applying a series of financial ratios to calculate an overall financial risk rating for each trust. PBLs are reviewed at least annually when the latest accounts data becomes available.

---

[2] Working capital is the money and assets that an organisation can call upon to finance its day-to-day operations (it is the difference between current assets and liabilities and is reported in the statement of financial position (balance sheet) as net current assets (liabilities)). If working capital dips too low, organisations risk running out of cash and may need a working capital loan to smooth out the troughs.

Exceptionally, loans may be approved even if they are not supported by a trust's PBL – for example, where the capital investment itself will lead to future income streams that will enable repayment of the loan.

NHS trusts may also have access to other forms of capital including:

- Charitable donations
- A private finance initiative (PFI) contract with the private sector (see chapter 10).

FTs have different capital funding opportunities – see chapter 8 for more details.

Financial Duties and Targets

NHS trusts have a number of statutory financial duties – i.e. duties that are a formal requirement as laid down in statute through Parliament. The principal financial duty is to achieve a break-even position on income and expenditure taking one year with another (see break-even duty below).

Secondary duties are to:

- Manage within a preset external financing limit (EFL)
- Meet the capital resource limit (CRL) – in other words manage capital expenditure within a preset limit
- Achieve a capital cost absorption rate of 3.5%
- Comply with the *Better Payment Practice Code*
- Produce a set of annual accounting statements in the prescribed format.

Break-even duty

Section 10 (1) of the *NHS and Community Care Act 1990* requires trusts to achieve break-even. This means that a trust must ensure that its revenue is not less than sufficient, taking one financial year with another, to meet outgoings properly charged to the statement of comprehensive income or SOCI (formerly the income and expenditure account). 'Taking one financial year with another' has been interpreted to mean that over a three year period, trusts are required to achieve break-even position in their SOCI. This is to allow some flexibility where exceptional costs are incurred and when managing the financial recovery of a trust with serious financial difficulties.

There is also an 'annual' break-even requirement that is sometimes referred to as an 'administrative duty'. This is monitored by the SHA. An administrative duty is not the same as a statutory duty – rather it is an additional rule and regulation set down by the Department of Health that clarifies or specifies how a trust will operate. Trusts must report on the achievement of their financial duties in the annual report and accounts.

Given its importance, break-even (and related issues) is discussed in more detail overleaf:

Break-even, Deficits and Working Capital Loans

Break-even

Trusts' statutory duty to break-even taking one year with another has been interpreted within the NHS as meaning breaking even over three rolling years, allowing trusts to make deficits in one year as long as they are recovered within the next two years. In the past, trusts' real financial position was not always completely clear as break-even was at times achieved through the use of brokerage (financial support from other trusts, sometimes treated as revenue rather than a loan). However, since the introduction in 2006/07 of working capital loans, trusts have been able to manage cash shortfalls caused by SOCI deficits. These loans are shown in the accounts and trusts pay interest on the borrowing. This means that any deficit is shown clearly on the SOCI, with the cash consequences of that deficit dealt with through a working capital loan, reported on the statement of financial position.

It is important to note that the objective of the break-even duty is to protect a trust's liquidity. Events such as an impairment (a reduction in an asset's value compared with the value recorded in the statement of financial position), which may result in a reported loss do not affect liquidity. The Department of Health has recognised this in its guidance and such events do not affect the achievement of the break-even duty.

In-year financial performance

This is the outcome of revenue compared with expenditure in any one year.

Underlying or 'normalised' financial position

This is in effect the financial position a trust would be in if one-off sources of income and/or non-recurrent expenditure are discounted. A trust could break-even in-year (for example, by taking a number of one-off measures such as leaving vacancies unfilled or delaying initiatives) but still have an underlying deficit that needs to be addressed if it is to continue to deliver a balanced position in future years.

Projected financial position

A trust may start the year planning, or 'projecting', to break-even. Throughout the year it will re-analyse its original plans and estimates on the basis of the actual activity and expenditure that is occurring. At various points throughout the year, it will review and revise its projected year-end position. A trust that is projecting a year-end deficit mid-year will not necessarily end the year in deficit. The projection may simply be highlighting the need to take action to avoid such an outcome – for example, by identifying further cost savings or 'stalling' planned service developments.

Working capital loans

In 2006/07, the informal and 'un-transparent' system of cash brokerage that had previously operated across the NHS to assist trusts with temporary cash flow difficulties was replaced by a formal system of interest bearing loans and deposits. This brought trusts more closely in line with the approach operated by FTs, which borrow for their working capital needs. Trusts requiring cash to manage temporary cash flow problems take out interest bearing loans from the Department of Health, which are disclosed in the statement of financial position (unlike the cash brokerage system where brokerage received was treated as income with the income and expenditure balance distorted as a result).

Under the current regime (2011/12), an affordable repayment strategy must be identified, agreed and formally approved by the host SHA before a working capital loan to a trust can be sanctioned by the Department of Health. In order to repay the loan the trust must generate sufficient surplus in its SOCI to cover the capital repayments over the duration of the loan term – therefore the request for a loan must form part of the trust's overall recovery plan. Loan repayments must be managed in this way and must not be funded through retained depreciation, cash from asset sales or extending payment terms to creditors. Interest is charged at a rate equivalent to the National Loans Fund rate and is a charge to the SOCI. Loan repayments and interest payments are currently made on a bi-annual basis.

External financing limit

The external financing limit (EFL) was originally established to control the amount a trust could spend on capital in a year and included all sources of finance (internal, external or from the Department of Health). However, over time the EFL came to be seen as a 'financing limit' – i.e. the maximum amount that a trust could draw from the Department over and above what it could generate from its own operations. Since 2008/09, the EFL has been set to include cash provided for capital purposes from:

- The Department (PDC and loans – although new PDC is available only in exceptional circumstances)
- Internal generation
- External sources.

The EFL is an absolute financial duty. There is no tolerance above the EFL target. The purpose of the EFL is to control the cash expenditure of the NHS as a whole to the level agreed by Parliament in the public expenditure control totals.

The EFL sets a limit on the level of cash that an NHS trust may:

- Draw from either external sources or its own cash reserves (a positive EFL) **OR**
- Repay to external sources to increase cash reserves (a negative EFL)

A target EFL is set at the start of the financial year by the Department of Health and the trust is expected to manage its resources to ensure it achieves the target – they must not overshoot the EFL as it is a departmental duty.

External financing requirement

The external financing requirement (EFR) is the difference between the cash an NHS trust plans to spend in a year and the amount it can generate through its own operations. EFR can therefore be positive (a net requirement for cash) or negative (a trust generates more cash than it needs). If the EFR exceeds a trust's EFL this is an EFL overshoot – as mentioned above, trusts must not overshoot their EFL as it is a departmental duty.

Capital resource limit

NHS trusts must control capital expenditure to meet their capital resource limit (CRL). The CRL is set by the Department of Health and is the total of the following:

- SHA-agreed amounts brought-forward from the previous year
- Depreciation as charged to the SOCI
- Proceeds from asset sales
- Capital loans
- Funding from central funds (provided as PDC).

The charge against the CRL is calculated as follows:

Gross capital expenditure
Less: book value of assets disposed
Plus: loss on disposal of donated assets
Less: capital grants and donations.

Capital cost absorption duty

The financial regime of NHS trusts recognises that there is a cost associated with the maintenance of the capital of the organisation. NHS trusts are required to absorb the cost of capital (effectively the dividend paid on PDC) at a rate of 3.5% of average relevant net assets (the average of the asset values held at the beginning and end of the year). See chapter 16 for more details.

The PDC dividend paid by trusts for a particular year is calculated based on the average of the trust's opening and closing statement of financial position. It is paid in two instalments. The first in September – an estimated 50% of annual dividend based on the average of opening statement of financial position and forecast year end prepared in June. The second 50% similarly estimated based on the opening and December statements of financial position. Any variance with the 3.5% absorption is recorded in the accounts as either a debtor (or 'receivable') or creditor (or 'payable') with the Department of Health.

There is no requirement to absorb the cost of capital in relation to assets purchased using capital investment ('interest bearing') loans.

Better Payment Practice Code

NHS trusts must comply with the *Better Payment Practice Code*. The target is set at the start of each year by the Department of Health for the value and volume of invoices that must be paid within 30 days of receipt. The target is currently 95%. Trusts may be unable to meet the target if they have inefficient internal systems or have short-term cash problems.

Other Issues

NHS trusts need to be aware of a number of other issues, including:

- **Clinical litigation**. The costs to the NHS of clinical litigation are rising rapidly as result of changes in court procedures and increased awards made by courts. There is also some evidence of an increased willingness by patients to resort to litigation. NHS trusts join a central scheme, the Clinical Negligence Scheme for Trusts (CNST), aimed at 'smoothing' the cash flow implications of unpredictable claims over a period. Through this process, trusts contribute to a 'risk pool', which is managed by a special health authority, the NHS Litigation Authority (NHSLA). Since April 2002 all cases have been managed by, and have become the financial responsibility of, the NHSLA. Individual trusts pay an annual premium (which they build into their costs and prices), but trusts do not need to include a provision for the expected settlement liability in their accounts above the excess. The extent to which an NHS trust has implemented best practice in risk management is assessed and discounts awarded for achieving certain pre-determined risk management levels
- **Reference costs**. NHS trusts are required to produce reference costs each year. The information is used for cost comparison purposes and to calculate the national tariff, which is used in payment by results (see chapters 12 and 13).

What the future holds for NHS trusts

Subject to any amendments agreed to the *Health and Social Care Bill 2011*, the key change for NHS trusts as a result of the coalition government's plans is that they are all expected to achieve foundation status by March 2014 at which point the NHS trust legislation will be repealed. Sir David Nicholson's July 2010 transition letter emphasised the importance of all trusts achieving this goal and also highlights the need for them to:

- Build relationships with prospective GP commissioners
- Further strengthen clinical leadership
- Focus on measurable improvements in outcomes and get ready for increasing amounts of information about those outcomes to be available
- Focus on how to provide more integrated care and support the completion of Transforming Community Services.

A new Provider Development Authority in the Department of Health will be set up during 2011 in time to take over SHAs' responsibilities in relation to driving progress in the foundation trust pipeline and overseeing providers. This Authority will be established as a time limited special health authority reporting directly to Parliament – it will be wound up in 2014.

To find out more about the regime NHS trusts will operate under when they become foundation trusts see the next chapter.

References and Further Reading

NHS and Community Care Act 1990: www.opsi.gov.uk/ACTS/acts1990/ukpga_19900019_en_1

The NHS Trusts (Membership and Procedure) Regulations, 1990: www.opsi.gov.uk/SI/si1990/Uksi_19902024_en_1.htm

Manuals for Accounts, Department of Health: www.info.doh.gov.uk/doh/finman.nsf

A Guide to Good Practice on the Annual Report/ Review incorporating requirements under Reporting Standard 1 (RS 1) for NHS Organisations including the Operating and Financial Review (OFR) – available from the HFMA: www.hfma.org.uk

Quality Accounts, Department of Health: www.dh.gov.uk/en/Healthcare/Qualityaccounts/index.htm

NHS Injury Cost Recovery Scheme: www.dh.gov.uk/en/Managingyourorganisation/NHSInjuryCostRecovery/index.htm

HSC 1999/146 Guidance to Health Authorities and NHS Trusts on Break-Even Duty; Provisions and Accumulated Deficits. Available via the HSC pages of the Department of Health's website: www.dh.gov.uk/PublicationsAndStatistics/LettersAndCirculars/HealthServiceCirculars/fs/en

Better Payment Practice Code: www.payontime.co.uk

NHS Litigation Authority: www.nhsla.com/home.htm

Reference costs: www.dh.gov.uk/en/Managingyourorganisation/NHScostingmanual/index.htm

8. Foundation Trusts

Introduction

NHS foundation trusts (FTs) were created as new legal entities in the form of public benefit corporations by the *Health and Social Care (Community Health and Standards) Act 2003* – now consolidated in the *NHS Act 2006*. They were introduced to help implement the labour government's 10-year *NHS Plan* which set out a vision for the NHS in England to be responsive, effective and high quality. By creating a new form of NHS trust that had greater freedoms and more extensive powers, the government of the day hoped to liberate the talents of frontline staff and improve services more quickly.

Initially, applications for foundation status were restricted to a number of 'three-star' trusts with the first wave of FTs coming into being in April 2004. Since then there has been a steady growth in the number of FTs and the coalition government expects all remaining NHS trusts to achieve foundation status (or be integrated into an existing foundation trust) by 31 March 2014.

How FTs differ from other NHS trusts

The FT structure represents a model of local management where central government involvement is reduced. FTs are run by boards of directors and governors and have new freedoms to develop in line with local priorities and raise funds directly from the private sector. In practice, this means that in many ways FTs operate on a similar basis to commercial organisations.

FTs possess a number of characteristics that distinguish them from NHS trusts:

- Freedom to decide locally how to meet their obligations – they can tailor their governance arrangements to suit the local circumstances of their community and health economy, while reflecting the range of diverse relationships (for example, with patients and other stakeholders)
- Accountability to local people, who can become members and governors
- Authorisation and ongoing regulation by the Independent Regulator of NHS Foundation Trusts – Monitor. Monitor also has powers to intervene if an FT fails to comply with the terms of its authorisation
- A duty to engage with local communities and encourage local people to become members of the organisation. This duty is central to the mutual model on which the constitution of FTs is based.

In spite of these differences, it is important to remember that FTs remain part of the NHS with the primary purpose of providing NHS services to NHS patients according to NHS principles and standards. In particular, the public continues to receive healthcare according to core NHS principles – free care, based on need and not ability to pay.

To ensure that NHS patients did not lose out as a result of the introduction of FTs, there were statutory provisions set out in the *NHS Act 2006*, which placed a 'lock' on the purpose of any FT. In particular, 'mandatory goods and services' are currently specified in an FT's terms of authorisation – these are those goods and services that an FT must provide unless a variation is agreed first with commissioners and then with Monitor. Two other key safeguards or restrictions were also established:

- *Protected assets*

Any proposed change in the use (including sale) of scheduled or protected non-current assets must be authorised by Monitor. Protected assets are identified at the time of application as assets essential for the delivery of mandatory services. When authorising an FT, Monitor takes due regard of the protected assets for subsequent monitoring. In addition, protected assets cannot be pledged as security for loans.

- *Private patient income cap*

To ensure that the estate and future growth in services of an FT benefit NHS patients, the Act placed a cap on the growth in private patient activity. Specifically, the Act required that the level of income from private activity as a proportion of total income must be no greater than it was for the predecessor NHS trust. In other words if private income was 3% of defined income in 2002/03 (in most circumstances the 'base financial year'), then it must not exceed 3% of defined income in each subsequent year.

During 2008/09, the way in which FTs were applying the private patient income (PPI) cap was challenged by UNISON, the public sector trade union, which was concerned that FTs were 'treating increasing numbers of private patients'. This challenge culminated in judicial review at the High Court in December 2009 which upheld the limit on the amount of income FTs can receive for treating private patients and found that Monitor's previous interpretation of the income that should be included as private patient income for the purposes of the PPI cap was not valid.

In response, Monitor issued revised rules and guidance which came into effect from April 2010. These made clear that 'income receivable by an FT as an entity which is derived from and has its origins in private patient activity is what is important, irrespective as to whether that activity is delivered directly by the FT or indirectly through another entity'.

For mental health FTs, the cap on private income was amended by the Health Act 2009 so that it is currently the proportion of total income derived from such charges in 2002/03 (which for many trusts was 0%) or 1.5% if greater.

The coalition government regards the private patient income cap as 'arbitrary and unfair' and plans to remove it.

Governance Arrangements

The most significant feature of FTs is that they are released from direct Department of Health control, which is currently exercised through strategic health authorities (SHAs). Instead their functions are managed and executed through a Board of Governors and a Board of Directors. This means that while FTs are not required to seek approval from their SHA or the Department for proposed developments, there is no safeguard provided by these bodies in the event of financial or other difficulties.

The Board of Governors

Unlike other NHS organisations, the FT structure includes governors to represent local interests and to 'bind a trust to its patients, service users and stakeholders'.[3] These governors consist of both elected and appointed individuals who represent FT members and other stakeholder groups (including the public, patients and staff). When applying to be a member of an FT, an individual applicant can also confirm an interest in becoming a governor.

Legislation provides for each FT to decide on the size and shape of its Board of Governors in the light of their local circumstances, within certain minimum parameters set out in legislation:

- More than half of the members of the Board of Governors must be elected from the public and, where applicable, patient membership (FTs must have public and staff membership categories but can choose whether or not they have a patient membership category)
- There must be at least three staff governors elected from the staff membership, or where there are classes within the staff constituency at least one governor from each class
- There must be at least one local authority governor, one PCT governor and (where applicable) at least one university governor, all via nomination.

Monitor's *Code of Governance* also emphasises that 'the Board of Governors should not be so large as to be unwieldy' and recommends that its role, structure, composition and procedures be reviewed regularly.

The Board of Governors represents the interests of the members and partner organisations in the local health economy in the governance of the FT and is responsible for feeding back information to them about the trust's performance and key decisions. Individual governors are eligible to serve for a term of up to three years and to stand for re-election.

The Chair of the FT is both the Chair of the Board of Governors and the Board of Directors. This ensures that views from governors are considered by the directors and gives the Chair a pivotal role in the organisation.

A key role of the Board of Governors is to work closely with the Board of Directors to help set the FT's strategic direction. At the same time, Monitor's *Code of Governance* states that the Board of Governors is expected to 'hold the Board of Directors to account for the performance of the trust, including ensuring the Board of Directors acts so that the FT does not breach its terms of authorisation'.

The Board of Governors is also responsible for appointing the FT's Chair and non-executive directors (NEDs) and the external auditors. In addition, the Board of Directors must obtain the approval of the Board of Governors before they can appoint a chief executive officer.

Monitor's *Code of Governance* gives more details about the role of governors and emphasises that they 'must act in the best interests of the FT and should adhere to its values and code of

---

[3] *Your Statutory Duties: a Reference Guide for NHS Foundation Trust Governors*, Monitor, 2009.

conduct'. It also states that 'the roles and responsibilities of the Board of Governors should be set out in a written document'.

The Board of Directors

Every FT must have an effective Board of Directors that consists of executive directors (which must include the Chief Executive and Finance Director) and non-executive directors (NEDs). The Chair of the board must be a NED. NEDs should have particular experience or skills that help the board function well. They are appointed by the Board of Governors based on recommendations made by a 'nominations committee'.

The Board of Directors takes full responsibility for the governance of the FT and should present a balanced and understandable assessment of the FT's position and prospects. This responsibility extends to all public statements and reports to regulators and inspectors, as well as information presented under statutory requirements.

The Board of Directors is collectively responsible for every decision it takes regardless of individual directors' skills or status. In particular, the Board of Directors must set the FT's strategic aims (taking account of the views of the Board of Governors) and is responsible for 'ensuring compliance by the NHS foundation trust with its terms of authorisation, its constitution, mandatory guidance issued by Monitor, relevant statutory requirements and contractual obligations'.[4]

The role of NEDs on the Board of Directors is different from their traditional role in NHS trusts. This is due in part to representation of local communities on the Board of Governors. As members of a unitary board, NEDs must take equal responsibility and accountability for the function and success of the business. They also have a duty to ensure appropriate challenge is made – particularly in relation to the FT's executive management.

One particularly important duty placed on the Board of Directors and stated in Monitor's *Code of Governance* is that it 'must notify Monitor and the Board of Governors without delay and should consider whether it is in the public interest to bring to public attention all relevant information which is not public knowledge concerning a material change:

- in the NHS foundation trust's financial condition
- in the performance of its business; and/or
- in the NHS foundation trust's expectations as to its performance which, if made public, would be likely to lead to a substantial change to the financial well-being, healthcare delivery performance or reputation and standing of the NHS foundation trust.'

The Role of the Independent Regulator of NHS Foundation Trusts – Monitor

Application process

At present (2011/12), external monitoring and regulation of FTs is undertaken by Monitor in accordance with FTs' terms of authorisation which set out the basis for their establishment and

---

[4] *The NHS Foundation Trust Code of Governance*, Monitor.

future operation. To qualify for authorisation to operate as an FT, applicants must meet stringent criteria set by the Department of Health and pass Monitor's rigorous assessment process.

Under the current approach, before an NHS trust can apply to Monitor to become an FT it must first work with its SHA to develop a 'robust and credible' FT application in what is referred to as the 'SHA/ trust development phase'. This involves (inter alia) a public consultation process of at least 12 weeks and the development of an integrated business plan and long term financial model. When the SHA is satisfied that the trust is ready a formal application is made to the Secretary of State. This is known as the 'Secretary of State support phase' and involves an applications committee that considers the trust's application and advises the Secretary of State on whether or not the trust should be supported to proceed to Monitor's assessment phase.

Monitor's assessment phase takes approximately 3 months and focuses on 3 key criteria:

- Is the trust well governed?
- Is the trust financially viable?
- Is the trust legally constituted?

The process also involves a 'board to board meeting' which is held midway through the assessment period and is designed to allow the applicant board to 'demonstrate that it is aware of the risks facing the trust and provide details on how these risks can or have been managed and mitigated. It also provides Monitor's board with a key opportunity to question the NEDs of the trust to determine whether they have the skills required to effectively challenge the executive team'.[5]

Applicants meeting the required standards are granted a licence that establishes them as an FT in the legal form of a public benefit entity and Monitor issues its terms of authorisation which sets out the conditions under which the FT must operate.

More information about the application process is available on both Monitor's and the Department of Health's websites.

Regulatory approach – the compliance framework

Monitor has established a risk-based approach to regulation which is set out in its *Compliance Framework* which it reviews (and consults on) each year. This means that assessments of risk in a number of key areas are used to determine the level and depth of monitoring that an FT is subject to. Monitor focuses on two risk areas – finance and governance (including mandatory services).

To make its assessment, Monitor relies primarily on the information it receives directly from FTs (including annual plans and in-year monitoring submissions), but it also considers third party reports on a variety of specific issues, in particular those of other regulatory bodies. Details of

---

[5] *Becoming an NHS Foundation Trust*, Monitor.

Monitor's *Compliance Framework*, its approach to risk ratings and FTs' current scores are available on its website.

Finance risk rating

A financial scorecard is used to generate a finance risk rating (FRR). This scorecard looks at four criteria – for each criterion a score of one to five is awarded with one indicating a high risk of a significant breach of the authorisation and five a low risk with no financial regulatory concerns. The four areas are:

- Achievement of plan
- Underlying performance
- Financial efficiency
- Liquidity.

In practice, FTs are scored across five metrics, with financial efficiency being aggregated from two separate metrics. The five metrics are:

- Achievement of plan – EBITDA (earnings before interest, taxes, depreciation and amortisation) achieved (expressed as a % of plan)
- Underlying performance – EBITDA margin (i.e. EBITDA as a % of total income to measure the extent to which operating expenses use up revenue)
- Financial efficiency (1) – return on assets (expressed as a %)[6]
- Financial efficiency (2) – income and expenditure surplus margin net of dividend (expressed as a %)
- Liquidity – defined as cash plus trade debtors (including accrued income) plus unused working capital facility (up to a maximum of 30 days) minus (trade creditors plus other creditors plus accruals) and expressed as the number of days operating expenses (excluding depreciation) that could be covered.

Each FT is rated from one to five in each of these metrics and then, using weightings, an overall aggregate FRR is produced. This is also a whole number from one to five. A series of over-riding rules are then applied. For instance, an FT that scores a one against one financial criterion, can only achieve a maximum risk rating of two. Similarly if an FT has an unplanned breach of its PBL it automatically receives a maximum rating of two regardless of its FRR.

The weightings that have been used to derive the aggregate FRR since April 2007 are:

- Achievement of plan – 10%
- Underlying performance – 25%
- Financial efficiency – 40% (20% for each of the two metrics)
- Liquidity – 25%.

---

[6] From 2011/12, this metric is likely to exclude dividends and include finance lease but the situation will not be clarified until the results of Monitor's *Consultation on amendments to the Compliance Framework 2011/12* are known and the final Framework published.

As stated, one purpose of the FRR is to assist the regulator in determining the frequency with which it needs to monitor the organisation or intervene as appropriate. Another is to grant autonomy to high performing organisations in order that they may maximise the financial freedoms (including borrowing) and responsibilities available to FTs while at the same time ensuring proper risk management. For example, FTs will set their own level of capital expenditure and in so doing must decide on the best method of financing such expenditure.

Governance risk rating

The governance risk rating focuses on the degree to which FTs are complying with their terms of authorisation. Monitor looks at eight criteria:

- Legality of constitution
- Growing a representative membership
- Appropriate board roles and structures
- Service performance
- Clinical quality and patient safety
- Effective risk and performance management
- Co-operation with NHS bodies and local authorities
- Provision of mandatory services (an FT is required to certify that it is able to continue to provide those services that are specified as being mandatory in its application for FT status and the terms of its authorisation. If an FT identifies a risk to this continued provision, the implications for overall governance are considered by Monitor).

A scoring system is used to assess governance risk levels and a graduated 'traffic light' rating is linked to those scores. For example, if an FT achieves a green rating it indicates that there are 'no material concerns' (i.e. a low risk) while a red rating signifies that there is 'likely or actual significant breach of authorisation' (i.e. a high risk). The scores and their related 'traffic light' ratings that are likely to apply from 2011/12 are shown below:[7]

Green	A score of less than 1.0
Amber–green	A score greater than 1.0 but less than 2.0
Amber–red	A score greater than 2.0 but less than 4.0
Red	A score of 4.0 or more

The scoring system also takes into consideration the need for all healthcare providers to comply with the registration requirements of the Care Quality Commission (CQC). If the CQC attaches conditions to an FT's registration, the governance risk rating is adversely affected.

Financial Duties

As part of the NHS, FTs are required to demonstrate high standards of financial stewardship in relation to their use of public funds. As with NHS trusts, PCTs and other commissioning bodies continue to provide the majority of an FT's income.

---

[7] Note that these scores are as set out in Monitor's *Consultation on amendments to the Compliance Framework 2011/12* (they will not be confirmed until the final framework is published).

However, significant differences between NHS trusts and FTs arise when comparing financial duties. For example, FTs are not required to fulfil the current set of financial duties applicable to NHS trusts. In particular:

- There is no statutory duty to break-even – FTs can generate and retain a surplus each year and re-invest; they can also incur a deficit, although the regulatory framework requires FTs to demonstrate financial viability over the medium term
- There is no requirement to remain within an external financing limit target, to achieve a defined capital absorption rate as set by the Treasury or to remain within a capital resource limit. However, any public dividend capital (PDC) dividends must still be paid to the Treasury at 3.5%
- FTs do not have access to financial support from the SHA or Department of Health. However, the Department has established the FT Financing Facility (FTFF) which operates at 'arm's length' from the Department (see later in this chapter)
- FTs can decide locally the capital investment they need to improve their services and increase capacity and are able to borrow in order to support this investment, subject to their terms of authorisation and Monitor's guidance as set out in *Risk Evaluation for Investment Decisions by NHS Foundation Trusts* and in the *Prudential Borrowing Code for NHS Foundation Trusts*.[8]

Monitor sets the financial framework within which FTs operate and issues guidance including the *NHS Foundation Trust Annual Reporting Manual*.

Service Line Reporting and Management

Service line reporting (SLR) involves looking in detail at the revenue and costs of an FT's services in much the same way as a private sector company analyses its business units. In practice, this means that FTs look at profitability information by specialty. Monitor has issued guidance on SLR[9] which lists the characteristics of a typical service line as being:

- Able to operate as an autonomous business unit
- Having clear decision-making and accountability lines
- Having clinicians in prominent leadership roles.

The information gleaned from SLR is used to 'manage' each service line and develop the FT's business plans with the FT overall effectively managed as 'a portfolio of autonomous and accountable business units'.

In its guide *Getting the most out of Managing Service Lines: Organisational Change and Incentive-based Performance*, Monitor states that 'successful SLM requires the fully integrated ownership of clinical, operational and financial objectives and outcomes at sub-board level'. The guide acknowledges that SLM is a developing area that will not achieve its full potential unless FTs

---

[8] Since 2007/08 the capital regime for non-foundation trusts has been bought into line with the FT approach – see chapters 7 and 16.
[9] *Service Line Management: an overview*, Monitor, 2009.

have in place:

- Well defined organisational structures and processes
- Coherent operational strategies
- Comprehensive annual planning processes
- Information systems
- Performance improvement policies.

SLR and SLM are regarded as best practice for FTs and Monitor's guidance is designed to help FTs develop their approaches.

Annual Accounts

All FTs have a statutory duty to produce annual accounts as set out in the *NHS Act 2006*. The form and content of the accounts is currently prescribed by Monitor (with the approval of the Treasury) and must comply with international financial reporting standards (IFRS) unless otherwise directed. The production of the statutory annual accounts is the principal means by which FTs discharge their accountability to taxpayers and users of services for their stewardship of public money.

FTs fall within the authority of the Financial Reporting Advisory Board (FRAB). This body provides independent accounting advice regarding the public sector to HM Treasury. The Treasury has developed a *Financial Reporting Manual*, incorporating the advice of FRAB, which sets out how accounting standards should be implemented in the public sector. For FTs, Monitor produces the *NHS Foundation Trust Annual Reporting Manual* which is broadly consistent with the Treasury's manual – any divergences are approved by the Treasury. The manual includes a summary of extant accounting standards and gives details of their applicability to FTs.

Annual Report

FTs are required to produce an annual report which must be published with the full set of audited accounts. The annual report is primarily a narrative document which includes the directors' and remuneration reports described in the *Companies Act,* with additional information reflecting the FT's position in the community. The report gives an account of activities, performance and achievements over the last financial year.

Provided it complies with IFRS, the layout of the annual report is at each FT's discretion – however, there are mandatory items that must be included – these are set out in the *NHS Foundation Trust Annual Reporting Manual.*

The annual report and accounts must be approved by the Board of Directors prior to submission to Monitor. FTs must lay their report and accounts (the full accounts – not summary financial statements) before Parliament themselves before the summer recess.

The annual report and accounts must also be presented to a meeting of the Board of Governors. This meeting should be convened within a reasonable timescale after the end of the financial year, but must not be before the FT has laid the annual report and accounts before Parliament.

Quality Reports

Along with other provider trusts, FTs must produce an annual quality report (previously known as a quality account) in line with the statutory requirement set out in the *Health Act 2009*. The aim is that these reports will 'enhance accountability to the public and engage the leaders of an organisation in their quality improvement agenda' by reporting the continuous improvement in the quality of the services provided. FTs have prepared quality reports since 2008/09 and a number of examples are available on Monitor's website.

Audit Arrangements

All FTs must have their accounts audited by independent external auditors who are appointed by the FT's Board of Governors. As mentioned above, these audited annual accounts must be laid before Parliament. The Chief Executive, as accounting officer, may be required to appear before the Public Accounts Committee to answer questions.

The *Audit Code for NHS Foundation Trusts*, published by Monitor, prescribes the way in which external auditors carry out their functions.

FTs are also required to have an internal audit function.

Capital Funding and the Prudential Borrowing Code

The most significant challenge posed by the financial freedoms available to FTs is the management of cash (whether for revenue or capital expenditure) and any associated borrowing. Monitor has published a *Prudential Borrowing Code* that FTs must adhere to when applying for new borrowing. The Code itself takes account of generally accepted principles followed by financial institutions and focuses heavily on liquidity, meaning the strength of cash flow available to meet both dividend payments on opening and new PDC and to service interest and principal repayments on new loans. The measures are largely based around 'free cash flow' (FCF) or more specifically, 'revenue available for debt service' (RAfDS), which is defined as the operating surplus before depreciation and interest.

Without ensuring adequate levels of FCF, FTs could find themselves in financial difficulties. For example, the situation might arise where new borrowing is entered into for an expansion in services but, because of a fall in demand (either through a lack of partnership working or due to a failure to assess the risk properly) insufficient patient-related income is generated. FTs must therefore ensure that their financial performance is monitored closely. Monitor has powers to intervene if an FT fails financially.

The *Prudential Borrowing Code* sets out a number of financial ratios that help ensure that all borrowing remains affordable. Since 2009/10 there has been a two tier system for determining borrowing limits. A tier one limit is set for all FTs based on their annual plans and in accordance with the four ratios set out below:

- **Minimum dividend cover** (>1×) -- this ratio effectively requires that an FT has sufficient FCF to meet its annual dividend payment to the Department of Health (at least once) calculated as 3.5% of the value of its assets. The formula is: RAfDS less interest divided by annual dividend payable
- **Minimum interest cover** (>3×) – this financial constraint is the interest coverage ratio measured by the number of times that RAfDS covers interest repayments in any one year. The formula is: RAfDS divided by maximum annual interest
- **Minimum debt service cover** (>2×) – this ratio requires that RAfDS is sufficient to meet all interest and principal payments on long term borrowing, measured as RAfDS divided by maximum annual debt service
- **Maximum debt service to revenue** (<2.5%) – this ratio seeks to ensure that the cost of servicing debt and loans is no more than 2.5% of an FT's total revenue. It is measured by calculating maximum annual debt service as a percentage of revenue.

A tier two limit is available if an FT has a major investment (for example, a PFI scheme) and can be requested on a case-by-case basis from Monitor. The tier two limit applies the same ratios as for tier one but with different thresholds as shown below:

- **Minimum dividend cover** (>1×)
- **Minimum interest cover** (>2×)
- **Minimum debt service cover** (>1.5×)
- **Maximum debt service to revenue** (<10%).

Affordability

The amount an FT can borrow (the prudential borrowing limit or PBL) is initially determined from the service development strategy submitted as part of the application to become an FT, and is reviewed at least annually as part of the annual plan submission. Borrowing includes loans from the FT financing facility, commercial borrowing and finance leases including PFI schemes. It excludes PDC which is classed as equity in this instance.

The PBL is calculated using the plan figures and is set so as to ensure that the financial ratios described above continue to be met. It is important to understand that the FRR is a key factor in determining the PBL, since any significant reduction in this figure during the year could lead to an in-year reduction in PBL.

Sources of borrowing

The main source of operational capital funding is from internally generated resources – retained depreciation, fixed asset sales and surpluses. Larger schemes will require an FT to borrow within its PBL.

Although some FTs have already sought funding from the commercial sector, it was envisaged initially that the market would be too immature to attract significant interest from commercial lenders and that – in the absence of an agreed insolvency regime and asset security – it may prove expensive. For this reason the Department of Health formed the FT financing facility (FTFF) – this operates at arm's length from the Department and makes loan decisions based on the ability of the FT 'to pay back the money, not on the basis of a policy judgement'.[10] Loans are made available at a preferential rate (equivalent to the national loans fund rate) for core business (i.e. 'to fund development to essential protected services'), and at a market rate for commercial developments or 'non-protected activity'.

Another source of funding for capital projects involves working in partnership with the private sector – most commonly using the private finance initiative or PFI. The Department of Health and Monitor have issued guidance as to the relative roles in the assessment of the affordability of PFI projects – *Roles and Responsibilities in the Approval of NHS Foundation Trust PFI Schemes*.

PDC funding

Whereas the primary source of funding for an FT is likely to be borrowing, it is still possible that schemes in existence at authorisation, and some central initiatives will continue to be funded via public dividend capital (PDC) from the Department of Health.

If an FT has agreed PDC funding with the Department, then a 'PDC Limit' is set (by the Department). This is similar to a 'cash based capital resource limit (CRL)',[11] in that an FT may only access the PDC once it has fully utilised its own internal cash generated through retained depreciation (as calculated in the annual capital charges exercise) and sale proceeds from the disposal of fixed assets.

The coalition government intends to replace the FTFF with an 'operationally independent banking function'[12] to manage new lending to FTs. The new banking function will also monitor the 'financial security' of FTs to protect taxpayers' investment.

Corporation Tax

The Treasury announced in October 2009 that the planned implementation of corporation tax legislation had been deferred. This was to allow further consideration about how to introduce the arrangements, the definitions to be used and how they would be applied to all public healthcare providers. As things stand in 2011/12, there is no corporate taxation of hospitals.

What the future holds for Foundation Trusts

Subject to any amendments agreed to the *Health and Social Care Bill 2011*, the coalition government has stated that it expects all remaining non foundation NHS trusts to achieve foundation status over the next three years – so by 2014 all provider trusts in the NHS will operate on the same footing and under the same legislative and regulatory regime. A new

[10] *NHS Foundation Trusts Information Guide – Financial Freedoms*, Department of Health, 2004.
[11] A CRL is an expenditure limit determined by the Department of Health to limit the amount that may be expended by an NHS organisation on capital purchases, as assessed on an accruals basis (i.e. after adjusting for debtors and creditors).
[12] *Liberating the NHS: Legislative Framework and Next Steps*.

special health authority set up within the Department of Health – the Provider Development Authority – will drive progress in the FT pipeline and oversee strategic health authorities' responsibilities for providers. It will have a limited life span, being abolished by 1 April 2014 at which point an 'all FT' sector should have been achieved. The NHS trust legislative model will then be repealed during 2014.

Over the same period of time, the coalition government is expecting FT directors and governors to become more directly accountable for decisions and performance by:

- Placing a duty on governors to hold the Board of Directors to account
- Giving governors powers to require FT directors to attend meetings
- Extending company law duties to FT directors (for example, the requirement to promote the organisation's success)
- Requiring FTs to hold AGMs for their members.

FTs will also have greater freedom in relation to:

- Income generation – in particular, the government plans to remove the private patient income cap (although FTs will produce separate accounts for their NHS and private services)
- Borrowing – the current regime including statutory controls on borrowing will end and a new operationally independent banking function will be set up to manage new public lending
- Mergers – the Office of Fair Trading and the Competition Commission will be in charge of regulating mergers and acquisitions between FTs and with such transactions becoming easier
- Governance arrangements – which will be tailored more closely to local needs and place more emphasis on the responsibilities of governors rather than oversight by the regulator.

Over a similar timescale, it is proposed that Monitor will expand into a wider economic regulator for the health and social care sectors with an overarching duty to 'protect the interests of patients … in the provision of health and adult social care by promoting competition where appropriate and through regulation where necessary'. To be able to fulfil this new role, Monitor will be responsible for licensing all providers of NHS-funded care in England, including existing FTs, private and voluntary sector providers. This will allow Monitor to gather the information it needs to promote competition, set prices and safeguard the continuity of services (see below). The licensing regime will replace the existing system for authorising FTs and the issuing of terms of authorisation. If license conditions are breached, Monitor will be able to order the situation to be rectified and fine the provider if necessary. In carrying out its licensing role, Monitor will be required to co-operate with the Care Quality Commission which will continue to be responsible for registering providers against 'essential levels of safety and quality'. Monitor and the CQC are to establish a single integrated process of licensing and registration.

Monitor will levy fees on those it registers to support the cost of its licensing related activities but its other regulatory activities will be funded by the Treasury.

Monitor's three core functions will be:

- **Promoting competition.** This will involve taking on powers such as those exercised by OFCOM and OFGEM to apply competition law to prevent anti-competitive behaviour, initially only for healthcare providers (public and private) but eventually to include providers of adult social care. To enable it carry out this role, Monitor will have 'concurrent powers' with the Office of Fair Trading to apply the Competition Act 1998 – this will allow it to investigate provider practices that might restrict competition. It will also be able to set specific license conditions if it can demonstrate that this will protect competition. The Secretary of State will have powers to issue regulations to govern commissioners' procurement activities and 'parties with a legitimate interest' can complain to Monitor if they believe commissioners have broken these rules. Commissioners and providers will be able to seek judicial review if they are dissatisfied with Monitor's decisions. Monitor will also be able to conduct market reviews where competition is not functioning properly, and refer markets to the Competition Commission for investigation
- **Setting and regulating prices for NHS-funded services.** The new regime will involve Monitor and the NHS Commissioning Board assuming joint responsibility for setting prices, with Monitor focusing on designing the pricing methodology and using it to set prices and the Commissioning Board developing the pricing structure. GP commissioners and providers will be consulted on the underlying methodology and will be able to raise objections. Monitor will be able to alter tariffs but only in relation to a new category of service – namely those services that are 'designated as subject to additional regulation' which will be identified in providers' licences. These are services which, if lost would result in 'material damage to patients' – essential services for which there is no immediate alternative or re-provision if they cease (this effectively builds on mandatory services in the current system). However, if the tariff is altered, the regulator would have to pay heed to a number of duties – to protect patients and the public through competition where appropriate and regulation where necessary, to promote efficiency and to adhere to European Union rules (ensuring providers do not gain an unfair competitive advantage or the tariff change does not constitute unlawful state aid)
- **Supporting the continuity of services.** Monitor will have a number of levers to ensure essential services are maintained. These will include powers to protect assets, authorising special funding arrangements for essential services that would otherwise be unviable, powers to levy providers for contributions to a risk pool and the ability to intervene in the event of failure (including powers to trigger a special administration regime). However, there will be an overarching principle enshrined in legislation that additional regulation will not apply unless 'commissioners can demonstrate that the loss of a particular service ... would result in material damage to patients ...'

Once the new regime is up and running, Monitor will no longer be responsible for the following activities:

- Protecting taxpayers' investment in FTs – this will be assumed by the new banking function that will be set up by the Department of Health. As mentioned above, this unit will also be responsible for managing new public lending to FTs (a role currently carried out by the FTFF)

- Amendments to FT constitutions – although FTs will need to inform Monitor of any changes to their constitutions, FTs will in future confirm for themselves that they remain compatible with legislation
- The Secretary of State will take over the power to define accounting and reporting requirements for FTs
- The Department of Health will collect information from FTs about their forecast spending.

References and Further Reading

Health and Social Care (Community Health and Standards) Act 2003: www.opsi.gov.uk/Acts/acts2003/ukpga_20030043_en_1

NHS Act 2006: www.opsi.gov.uk/Acts/acts2006/ukpga_20060041_en_1

The NHS Plan: a plan for investment, a plan for reform, Department of Health, 2000: www.dh.gov.uk/en/Publicationsandstatistics/Publications/PublicationsPolicyAndGuidance/DH_4002960

Monitor – all publications and guidance referred to in this chapter are available via Monitor's website: www.monitor-nhsft.gov.uk/publications.php

Foundation Trust Financing Facility – Department of Health archived web pages: http://webarchive.nationalarchives.gov.uk/+/www.dh.gov.uk/en/Healthcare/Secondarycare/NHSfoundationtrust/DH_4131784

Government Financial Reporting Manual: www.financial-reporting.gov.uk/

9. Partnerships between the NHS and Local Authorities

Introduction

NHS organisations are expected to engage with their local community to improve health and well-being and reduce health inequalities. In practice, this means that NHS organisations need to work in partnership with local authorities to manage and deliver services in which both parties have an interest and to plan ahead for the local area. Examples of issues where local partnerships can be productive include:

- Supporting the local economy
- Responding to the needs of the rapidly increasing proportion of older people
- Reducing the number of young people not in education, employment or training
- Addressing shortages in affordable housing
- Improving environmental sustainability
- Reducing crime
- Preventing violent extremism
- Tackling the causes of poor health.

Partnership working operates at a number of different levels and can take a variety of forms. This chapter looks at the key arrangements that health organisations are involved with under the current regime (2011/12), namely:

- Local strategic partnerships (LSPs)
- Joint strategic needs assessments (JSNAs)
- Care trusts
- Pooled budgets
- Aligned budgets
- Lead commissioning
- Integrated provision
- Government grants
- Grants from the NHS to local authorities
- Grants from local authorities to the NHS.

We will also look briefly at the legal, governance and financial framework that enables partnership arrangements to work effectively; common partnership models and other areas where NHS organisations and local authorities come into close contact.

Local Strategic Partnerships

Section 82 of the *NHS Act 2006* requires NHS bodies and local authorities to co-operate with each other 'to secure and advance the health and welfare of the people of England and Wales'. In England local strategic partnerships (LSPs) help achieve this aim.

As the name suggests, LSPs operate at a strategic level. They are led by local authorities and were first introduced in 2001. LSPs are non-statutory, non-executive, multi-agency bodies that are designed to 'bring together at local level the different parts of the public sector as well as the private, business, community and voluntary sectors so that different initiatives and services support each other and work together'.

Local NHS bodies are expected to work within the relevant LSP to help further the partnership's aims and ensure co-ordination in planning and service delivery.

Joint Strategic Needs Assessments

The 2006 White Paper, *Our health, Our care, Our say: a New Direction for Community Services,* identified a need for there to be regular assessments of the health and well-being status of local populations so that meaningful objectives for local services could be established – these assessments are known as 'joint strategic needs assessments' (JSNAs).

JSNAs are designed to 'identify the current and future health and well-being needs of a local population'[13] and are a statutory requirement as set down in section 116 of *the Local Government and Public Involvement in Health Act 2007*. At present, this duty applies to PCTs and upper tier local authorities. In practice they are undertaken jointly by the Director of Public Health, Director of Adult Social Services and Director of Children's Services, working closely with the Directors of Commissioning and Finance.

Under the current regime, JSNAs feed into PCTs own planning processes. In particular, they help PCTs develop and refine their:

- Strategic direction
- Priorities and targets for improving health and social care outcomes and reducing health inequalities
- Operational plans
- Service and financial plans.

Care Trusts

Care trusts were announced in 2000 in the *NHS Plan* and section 45 of the *Health and Social Care Act 2001* (now sections 75 and 77 of the *NHS Act 2006*) legislated for their introduction. A care trust is a statutory NHS body to which local authorities can delegate health-related functions with the aim of providing integrated health and social care to the local community. Care trusts are established on a voluntary partnership basis where there is a joint agreement at local level that this model will offer the best way to deliver better health and social care services. The idea is that by combining NHS and local authority health responsibilities under a single management, care trusts can improve continuity of care and simplify administration.

Care trusts can be formed from an existing NHS trust or a PCT. It is important to note that local authority services are delegated to care trusts, not transferred.

At present (2011) there are 10 care trusts in England.

---

[13] *Guidance on Joint Strategic Needs Assessment,* Departments of Health and Communities and Local Government, 2007.

Pooled Budgets

The Department of Health's website defines pooled funds as 'the ability for partners each to contribute agreed funds to a single pot, to be spent on agreed projects for designated services'. It also states that 'the advantage of pooled budgets is that they remove the barriers between health and social care and allow for innovation in the use of funds for new services without the need to revisit traditional debates over what is a health or what is a social care responsibility'.

In practice, this means that pooled budgets exist where a local authority and an NHS body combine resources and jointly commission or manage an integrated service. Legislation that allows for this was first introduced under section 31 of the *Health Act 1999* (now section 75 of the *NHS Act 2006*) and the concept was given further backing in the *NHS Plan*. The idea is that, once a pooled budget is introduced the public will experience a seamless service with a single point of access for their health and social care needs. There are some services that are particularly well suited to pooled budgets – for example, services for people with a learning disability.

Where a pooled budget exists, regulations for England and Wales require that the partners have written agreements setting out:

- The functions covered
- The aims agreed
- The funds that each partner will contribute
- Which partner will act as the 'host' (i.e. which organisation will manage the budget and take responsibility for the accounts and auditing).

Since 2010/11 the new standard national contract for mental health services has allowed for pooled budget services to be incorporated into that contract.

Aligned Budgets

Aligned budgets can be either an informal or formal (using section 75 flexibilities) arrangement whereby partners align resources to meet agreed aims but have separate accountability for the respective funding streams. The management arrangements can be separate, joint or led by one partner but with joint performance monitoring arrangements against the objectives.

Lead Commissioning

Under a lead commissioning arrangement, partners agree to delegate commissioning of a service to one lead organisation. As with pooled budgets, lead commissioning was made possible by section 31 of the *1999 Act* (now section 75 of the *NHS Act 2006*).

Integrated Provision

Integrated provision involves partners joining together their staff, resources, and management structures so that the service is fully combined (or integrated) from managerial level to the front line. One partner acts as the host for the service to be provided. Again this way of working was made possible by section 31 of the *1999 Act* (now section 75 of the *NHS Act 2006*).

Government Grants

Government grants are available to the NHS for community-based projects run in conjunction with local authorities. Typically these grants are linked to regeneration and renewal programmes in deprived communities where a partnership board with representation from many elements of the local community, including NHS bodies, has successfully bid for and then managed the distribution of the grant. Examples of these types of grant include:

- Sure Start projects aimed at developing services for children
- New Deal for Community projects aimed at developing services in an urban setting at a neighbourhood level.

In terms of the financial framework for these projects, the structure is fairly straightforward – the grant is paid directly to the participating NHS body to cover the costs incurred.

Grants from the NHS to Local Authorities

NHS bodies have for many years been able to make grants to local authorities for the provision of health services. For example, a local authority operating a unit for people with learning difficulties may receive a grant from the NHS body to cover the provision of healthcare to the clients in the unit. Such grants must pay only for medical care and must not contribute towards the provision of social care. They must not involve the transfer of health functions to a local authority.

These grants are now made under sections 256/257 of the *NHS Act 2006* (previously section 28 A and section 28 BB of the *NHS Act 1977*) – this legislation empowers a PCT to make payments to a local authority or a registered social landlord. This is broadly permissive and allows the transfer of capital or revenue resources for most health related functions (but not emergency ambulance services, surgery and other similar invasive treatments) and for most social services and housing functions.

Grants from Local Authorities to the NHS

Section 76 of the *NHS Act 2006* (which replaces section 28 BB of the *NHS Act 1977*) is a parallel provision to section 256 and allows the local authority to make payments to PCTs for the performance of prescribed functions. Again, this includes most hospital and community health services but not surgery, emergency ambulance services, etc.

Practical Considerations

When organisations from different sectors and with different statutory and regulatory regimes work together there are a number of practical issues that need to be thought through to ensure that the partnership is a success. From a financial and stewardship viewpoint it is important that organisations think about:

- Corporate governance
- Risk sharing and control
- Financial framework
- Legal framework
- Human resources/workforce framework
- Benefits of the partnership and how performance will be measured and assessed.

Corporate governance

Local authorities and the NHS are subject to different governance regimes: although each receives significant levels of public funding, local authorities have a democratic mandate and are accountable to the local electorate whereas NHS bodies are ultimately accountable through their boards and the Secretary of State for Health (or Monitor in the case of NHS foundation trusts) to Parliament. See chapter 15 for more about NHS governance arrangements.

Risk sharing and control

Partnerships need to decide how they will share financial and other risks – for example if the partnership overspends there will need to be agreement around how the overspend is financed and reported. Risk sharing agreements are often difficult to negotiate and require a degree of compromise from both partners. Partnerships also imply a loss of control over the service, as partners can no longer make unilateral changes to the service itself or to the level of funding.

Financial framework

The NHS and local government operate under different financial regimes. There are two key areas where this has an impact:

- VAT: local authorities are able to recover VAT on most items of expenditure whereas the NHS may not. HM Revenue and Customs will not allow the creation of partnerships to be used as a mechanism for avoiding VAT – as a result, it may be necessary for the partnership to account for tax as if it were still two bodies
- Charges: local authorities have the power to charge clients for the services provided, whereas the NHS does not. The partnership agreement has to be devised so that there is no loss of revenue.

Legal framework

Greater integration and joint working between the NHS and local government was first made possible by the *Health Act 1999* – before then there were legal limitations on the powers of NHS bodies to enter into partnership agreements with local authorities. Section 31 of the 1999 Act provided the necessary legal framework for greater partnership working and these powers were extended by the *Health and Social Care Act 2001*. Section 31 has now been repealed and replaced (in England) by section 75 of the *NHS Act 2006* which has consolidated NHS legislation. This new provision is in exactly the same terms as section 31 and pre-existing arrangements continue as if made under the new powers.

Human resources/workforce framework

Where staff from different organisations are brought together in integrated arrangements it is essential that employment arrangements, human resources policies and procedures are formalised.

Secondments from one partner organisation into another need to be treated with particular care as difficulties can arise. For example, if the secondment extends beyond two years the employee has rights of tenure within the partnership. Secondment also implies separate employing authorities and separate terms and conditions for staff working alongside each other. The introduction of *Agenda for Change* within the NHS made this a more prominent issue.

Where staff transfer to a partnership the *Transfer of Undertakings (Protection of Employment)* (TUPE) regulations may come into effect – again this can lead to difficulties in relation to staff working side by side.

Benefits of the partnership

Partners need to consider not simply the service and financial benefits of joint working but also the intangible gains – for example, skills transfer, improved trust and understanding, financial transparency, opportunities for future developments, and reduced contractual disputes.

Developing a set of key outcome measures and performance metrics in collaboration allows the partners to consider a broader framework than if they each do it independently.

Partnership Models

As we have seen, partnerships can take a variety of forms – two common models are outlined below.

The quasi partnership

Some organisations decide not to establish a pooled budget and instead set up shared management arrangements with NHS and local authority funding and expenditure kept as two separate streams. A variation is that the budgets for the management of the shared services covered by the agreement are pooled but the budgets for the provision of services are not. In this way decisions relating to the service can be taken in partnership and the services themselves can appear seamless to their users. However, accountability for income and expenditure is still divided.

The diagram below shows a situation where there is joint management and decision-making for the shared service but there is no budget pooling: accountability for the funding side remains with each partner.

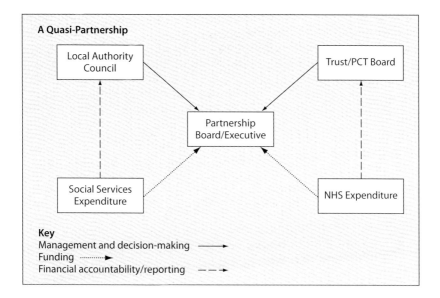

A Quasi-Partnership

Local Authority Council

Trust/PCT Board

Partnership Board/Executive

Social Services Expenditure

NHS Expenditure

Key
Management and decision-making ⟶
Funding ⋯⋯▶
Financial accountability/reporting – – ⟶

The host partner

In a partnership where pooling of budgets takes place one partner will become the host. All financial transactions will go through the host's accounts and be subject to the host's financial regime. The other partner will make payments to the host at the agreed level of funding. The partnership agreement may call for a degree of ring fencing of the cost of the pooled service within the host's books so that the partnership board and executive can see and protect the income and expenditure that relates to the pool.

The diagram overleaf shows the situation where a trust or PCT board acts as the host partner and is accountable for the ring-fenced budget. The local authority provides an agreed budget and participates in the partnership board:

Other Issues

There are a number of other areas where NHS organisations and local authorities currently come into close contact. These include:

- Local authority overview and scrutiny
- Delayed discharges
- Local improvement finance trusts (LIFTs).

Overview and scrutiny

Since January 2003, local authorities with social services responsibilities have been able to establish committees of councillors to provide overview and scrutiny of local NHS bodies by virtue of powers set out in section 38 of the *Local Government Act 2000*. The ultimate aim is

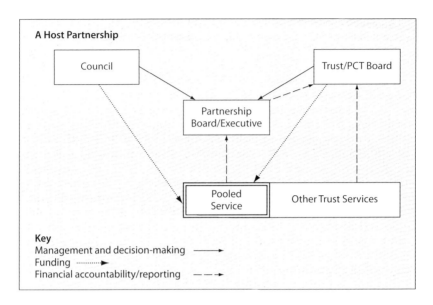

to secure health improvement for local communities by encouraging authorities to look beyond their own service responsibilities to issues of wider concern to local people. This is achieved by giving democratically elected representatives the right to scrutinise how local health services are provided and developed for their constituents. Health organisations are often invited to attend formal meetings of local authorities to answer question on key issues including financial health and operational plans or to undertake formal consultation with elected members.

Delayed discharges

Delayed discharges from hospitals (often referred to as patients who are 'bed blocking') remains a problem for the NHS and the government is keen to see the NHS, local authorities and other local organisations (including housing organisations, primary care and the independent and voluntary sectors) working together to minimise the impact of this. To encourage local authorities to do all they can to make swift discharges possible, a system was introduced whereby if a patient is delayed in being discharged from acute services solely because supporting community care arrangements are lacking, the relevant local authority must financially reimburse the trust concerned. As part of this arrangement, trusts have to notify social services departments of patients who may require community care. For more see the *Community Care (Delayed Discharges) Act, 2003.*

Local improvement finance trusts

The local improvement finance trust (LIFT) initiative was launched in 2001 and is a form of public-private partnership designed to help develop and improve primary care premises. This may include the co-location of related services, including local authority social services. See chapter 10 for more details.

What the future holds for Partnership Working with Local Authorities

One of the stated aims of the coalition government's plans for the NHS is to 'increase local democratic legitimacy in health'. The proposals outlined in *Local Democratic Legitimacy in Health*, a joint Department of Health and Department for Communities consultation paper aimed to achieve this by:

- Giving local authorities 'a stronger role in supporting patient choice and ensuring effective local voice'
- Requiring local authorities to take on local public health improvement functions
- Establishing 'more effective NHS, social care and public health commissioning arrangements'.

In particular, the government wants to strengthen the role of local authorities and build on their existing power to promote local well-being. Subject to any amendments agreed to the *Health and Social Care Bill 2011*, this will involve local authorities having greater responsibility in four areas:

- Leading joint strategic needs assessments (JSNAs) to ensure coherent and co-coordinated commissioning strategies (a role currently carried out jointly with PCTs)
- Supporting local voice, and the exercise of patient choice
- Promoting joined up commissioning of local NHS services, social care and health improvement
- Leading on local health improvement and prevention activity.

The government's proposals will achieve these aims by:

- Requiring every upper tier local authority to establish a 'health and wellbeing board' that will provide a forum for public accountability and join up commissioning across the NHS, social care, public health and other services relating to health and well-being. Core membership of each board will include GP consortia, the Director of Adult Social Services, the Director of Children's Services, the Director of Public Health, local HealthWatch and at least one democratically elected councillor. Health and wellbeing boards will also be able to require the attendance of the Commissioning Board when relevant. Boards will be established in shadow form in 2012/13 and will assume their powers and duties as statutory committees of local authorities in April 2013
- Requiring local authorities and GP consortia to undertake the JSNA through the health and wellbeing board. In addition every health and wellbeing board will develop a high level 'joint health and wellbeing strategy' (JHWS) that sets out how the board plans to address the needs of their population and reduce inequalities. NHS and local authority commissioners will then have to 'have regard to' both the JSNA and JHWS when exercising their functions
- Introducing new statutory arrangements for local authority leadership for health improvement, complemented by the creation of a national public health service – Public Health England (PHE) – with local Directors of Public Health being appointed jointly by local authorities and PHE. Local Directors will have a ring-fenced health improvement budget to deliver national and local priorities (the budget will be allocated by PHE). There will be direct accountability to both the local authority, and (through PHE) to the Secretary of State. As they will be employed by the local authority, local Directors of

Public Health will advise councillors and be part of the senior management team of the local authority

- Developing existing Local Involvement Networks (LINks) into 'local HealthWatch'. Like LINks, HealthWatch services will be contracted by local authorities with the aim of promoting patient and public involvement and seeking views on local health and social care services. However, local HealthWatch powers will be wider with them becoming 'more like a "citizen's advice bureau" for health and social care'. At national level there will be 'HealthWatch England' (described as a 'powerful new consumer champion') which will be established as a committee of the Care Quality Commission. The Chair of HealthWatch England will be appointed by the Secretary of State and have a seat on the CQC's board
- Allowing local authorities to discharge their health scrutiny functions in 'the way they deem most suitable', taking account of the role of local HealthWatch
- Extending the scrutiny role of local authorities to cover any provider of NHS funded services
- Allowing existing pooling etc arrangements to continue and placing a duty on GP consortia and local authorities (through the health and wellbeing board) to consider how to make best use of the flexibilities when drawing up the JSNA and JHWS. To reinforce this duty the Commissioning Board will have a duty to promote the use of flexibilities by consortia.

The idea is that, through the involvement of elected councillors, local authorities will bring greater local democratic legitimacy to these activities and have more influence over NHS commissioning, particularly in relation to public health and social care. It should also make it easier to 'further integrate health with adult social care, children's services (including education) and wider services, including disability services, housing, and tackling crime and disorder'.

References and Further Reading

Our health, Our care, Our say: a new Direction for Community Services, Department of Health, 2006 – archived web pages: http://webarchive.nationalarchives.gov.uk/+/www.dh.gov.uk/en/Healthcare/Ourhealthourcareoursay/index.htm

Local Government and Public Involvement in Health Act 2007: www.opsi.gov.uk/acts/acts2007/ukpga_20070028_en_1

Health Act 2006: www.opsi.gov.uk/acts/acts2006/60041-af.htm

Joint Strategic Needs Assessment guidance, Departments of Health and Communities and Local Government, 2007: www.dh.gov.uk/en/Publicationsandstatistics/Publications/PublicationsPolicyAndGuidance/DH_081097

Care trusts – links to existing trusts: www.nhs.uk/ServiceDirectories/Pages/CareTrustListing.aspx

The NHS Plan: a plan for investment, a plan for reform, Department of Health, 2000: www.dh.gov.uk/en/Publicationsandstatistics/Publications/PublicationsPolicyAndGuidance/DH_4002960

NHS Act 2006 Partnership Arrangements – Department of Health archived web pages: http://webarchive.nationalarchives.gov.uk/+/www.dh.gov.uk/en/Healthcare/IntegratedCare/Healthact1999partnershiparrangements/index.htm

HM Revenue and Customs: www.hmrc.gov.uk

Agenda for Change – Department of Health archived web pages: http://
webarchive.nationalarchives.gov.uk/+/www.dh.gov.uk/en/Managingyourorganisation/
Workforce/Paypensionsandbenefits/Agendaforchange/index.htm

Local Government Act 2000: www.opsi.gov.uk/acts/acts2000/ukpga_20000022_en_1

For more on local authority functions see the Local Government Association's website:
www.lga.gov.uk

10. Public Private Partnerships

Introduction

Partnership working with other organisations is common in the NHS and takes a variety of forms. The overall objective is the same for all approaches – to develop a comprehensive healthcare infrastructure and modern, responsive patient care environment. Although there has been a fall off in the use of public private partnerships as a result of the economic downturn, public private partnerships are still a procurement option. This chapter looks at the two main approaches that are available to NHS organisations – the private finance initiative (PFI) and local improvement finance trusts (NHS LIFT).

Private Finance Initiative

Background

The PFI is a mechanism for funding major capital investments without immediate recourse to public money. Instead private companies are contracted to design and build the assets needed. These are then leased back to the NHS, usually over a period of around 30 years.

The PFI was launched in the Chancellor of the Exchequer's November 1992 autumn statement. Although there had already been a number of high profile transport related private sector infrastructure projects (for example, the Channel Tunnel and the Queen Elizabeth II Bridge for the Dartford Crossing), the 1992 announcement indicated the government's intention to apply PFI principles more widely.

The original aim of the PFI was to involve the private sector more directly in the provision of public sector services and make use of its commercial, entrepreneurial and managerial expertise. As a result, the public sector focus changed from procuring and managing infrastructure projects to enabling service delivery and safeguarding the interests of the users and customers of public services.

Although the PFI has evolved since 1992, it continues to play a role in public sector infrastructure investment and has been used to deliver a range of new facilities in the NHS – for example, hospitals, staff accommodation, information management and technology (IM&T) systems, energy schemes and laboratory services.

Under the PFI, responsibility for the design, construction, maintenance, operation and financing of capital assets rests with the private sector. The public sector focus is on defining the standards of service required – the private sector partner then decides how it can best deliver a service to meet those standards. The public sector client pays for the service only when it becomes operational. The payment itself (which is of a revenue nature), takes the form of an ongoing 'unitary charge' paid to the PFI provider once the services have commenced in a satisfactory manner. The financing of the construction of the asset is the responsibility of the PFI provider through a range of funding mechanisms, which may involve a loan, equity or bonds.

Following the introduction of international financial reporting standards (IFRS) to the NHS in 2009, the way in which a PFI service is accounted for has changed. Under the previous approach, an asset provided under a PFI service contract was not deemed to be owned by the public sector organisation and did not therefore appear on its balance sheet. Instead the asset was owned by the PFI provider who was responsible for ensuring that the asset remained fit for purpose throughout the life of the contract. This reduced the need for public sector capital and the public sector borrowing requirement.

With the application of IFRS, PFI and LIFT schemes now appear on public sector organisations' balance sheets (or 'statements of financial position' as they are now known). As a finance lease, the scheme must be accounted for as an asset with depreciation charges as if the asset were owned by the NHS organisation and a liability recorded for the amount of the lease outstanding. Therefore depreciation charges are incurred with immediate effect. In addition, although the cash leaving the organisation to the private sector partner is unchanged, the unitary payment is now split into its component parts, each of which is accounted for separately – these are:

- Interest payment on the finance lease
- The operating expense
- The capital repayment element
- Life cycle costs.

See 'accounting for PFI transactions' later on in this chapter and chapter 14 for more details.

Reference should also be made to the Treasury's guidance *Consolidated Budgeting Guidance from 2009/10 (IFRS updated)* which sets out the objectives of PFI, an overview of the accounting for such schemes and information on refinancing and terminating contracts.

Benefits of PFI

Supporters of the PFI argue that it helps achieve service improvements and increased value for money through:

- Better allocation of risk – risk is allocated to those best placed to manage it
- Incentives to perform – the provision of a service over a long-term contract with in-built performance clauses concentrates management attention on service quality
- Close integration of service needs with design and construction – traditionally this has not been the case with one party building a facility and another operating it
- A clearer focus on roles and responsibilities – the public sector can concentrate on what services are required and the private sector can determine how best to meet those pre-set requirements
- A continuing commercial incentive for efficiency – the private sector provider will want to achieve efficiency in the delivery of services over the entire period of the contract.

Disadvantages of PFI

PFI critics identify the following disadvantages:

- It involves an overly bureaucratic and lengthy process to gain approvals

- There can be significant revenue costs for advisory assistance – for example on the legal and financial side
- There is a potential for private sector partners to earn excessive profits
- Staff side trade associations can be resistant at both an ideological and practical level
- There are concerns about the affordability of new PFI schemes
- Insufficient risk is transferred to the private sector and risk that is transferred is overpriced.

PFI in the NHS

As PFI schemes involve creating partnerships between the public and private sectors, they allow the NHS to focus on the provision of high quality clinical care to patients while the private sector provides investment to facilitate its delivery.

Major PFI schemes are typically 'design, build, finance and operate' (DBFO) schemes, which mean that the private sector partner is responsible for:

- Designing the facilities (based on the requirements specified by the NHS and in line with technical guidance, regulations and standards)
- Building the facilities to time and at a fixed cost
- Financing the capital costs
- Operating the facilities (providing facilities management and other support services).

In essence a PFI project involves the agreement of a contract between an NHS body and a private sector organisation for the provision of services over an agreed contract period. The private sector organisation will normally be in the form of a special purpose vehicle (SPV) or special purpose company (SPC) established specifically for the project. The SPC may consist of a construction company, a facilities management company and a financing organisation. The exact composition will depend on the project and the prevailing circumstances. Similarly the length of the contract depends on the nature of the service to be provided – a new hospital may have a contract period of 30–35 years.

The contract will set out in detail the obligations of each party. The development of a PFI project must follow a prescribed process in the NHS and comply with EU procurement guidance. This is discussed in more detail below.

Key principles – value for money and risk

There are two fundamental requirements for a PFI project:

- Value for money (VFM) must be demonstrated for public sector expenditure
- The private sector must genuinely assume risk.

Value for money

VFM is assessed by looking at 'whole life' costs and benefits (i.e. over the period of the project). This involves a financial review of the benefits, risks and associated cash flows of public sector and PFI options. Discounted cash flow investment appraisal techniques are used to determine the relative net present values – i.e. the total value in today's terms of all benefits and costs associated with a project or option. The costs are subtracted from the benefits to give a net value.

The Treasury's document *Value for Money Assessment Guidance* sets out a framework that organisations should use to consider whether the PFI procurement route will deliver VFM. This guide emphasises that 'procuring authorities should begin detailed assessments of the VFM of PFI projects at the earliest stage possible'. In 2008, the Department of Health published its own guidance based on the Treasury's guide: *Treasury's Value for Money Assessment for PFI – Guidance for NHS build schemes.*

Risk

A risk matrix is used to determine those risks to be taken by the public sector, those assumed by the private sector and those that are shared. The key principle is to allocate risk to the party that is best able to manage it. In particular, there needs to be an assessment in VFM terms of whether a risk should be transferred, retained, managed or insured against. It is also important to remember that every risk transferred has a price. The key risks that need to be considered when assessing a project include:

- Design and construction risk – failure to meet requirements; time and cost overruns
- Commissioning and operating risks – operating costs, availability and performance
- Demand, volume or usage risks
- Risk associated with the asset's residual value at the end of the PFI arrangement
- Technology or obsolescence risk
- Regulatory risk – for example, taxation and planning permission
- Project financing risk.

How a PFI scheme works

The development of a PFI project can be a lengthy and time-consuming process and there is a wealth of detailed practical guidance available to NHS organisations contemplating going down this route. The best place to start is the Department of Health's website which also provides links to other key sources, including the Treasury whose *Green Book* sets out the approach that the public sector should take to investment appraisal generally, including in relation to PFI transactions. Organisations also need to think about appointing technical, financial and legal advisers to help support and guide them through the process.

A PFI scheme in the NHS follows the same principles and procedures that have been established to ensure that all investment in the NHS is soundly based whether it is publicly or privately funded. This means the development of robust business cases using the Office of Government Commerce's (OGC) *Five Case Model* which is designed to ensure that schemes:

- Are supported by a robust case for change that provides strategic synergy – the strategic case
- Optimise value for money – the economic case

- Are commercially viable – the commercial case
- Are financially affordable – the financial case
- Are achievable – the management case.

The HFMA has published a toolkit designed to help organisations implement the *Five Case Model*.

For a PFI scheme the process will include the following stages:

- Establish the strategic context, assess the options and, for major schemes, make the case for change in a strategic outline case (SOC), and get approval
- Identify and develop a preferred option through an investment appraisal, make the case in an outline business case (OBC), and get approval
- Prepare for procurement by turning the approved option into a detailed specification of outputs, outcomes and desired allocation of risks
- Advertise the project in the Official Journal of the European Union (OJEU), identify potential providers and the best privately financed solution
- Select a preferred bidder with whom negotiations can be completed involving stakeholders in the assessment of the proposals
- Complete the definitive investment appraisal and full business case (FBC) to obtain approval
- Finalise, award and implement the contract
- Evaluate and monitor the project.

The steps described above are affected to a certain degree by the 'competitive dialogue' process introduced by EU Directive 2004/18/EC. This came into effect for OJEU notices placed after January 2006 and is designed to identify far more detail of what is required to deliver the project (for example, design, shape, size, functionality) at the point of submitting tenders.

In the early stages of potential PFI schemes (for example at SOC or OBC stage), it may be difficult to achieve a consensus view within an organisation about what exactly is required, what the timescales should be and what resources are needed to ensure success. It is important that agreement is reached through a robust process that tests and challenges current and projected levels of service provision and service configuration – otherwise there is a danger that the organisation's requirements will be over- or under-estimated. The business case process should drive a consideration of changing circumstances, future requirements and opportunities and lead to an agreed corporate view on the best way forward backed up by sound and reasoned assumptions and projections.

Potential PFI providers need to have a sound grasp of an organisation's requirements as articulated in invitations to negotiate (ITN). The documentation of assumptions from an early stage of a project supports the development of output specifications and the ITN. For example, in the case of health sector schemes the use of activity data and performance indicators will assist in the sizing of projects. Changes in inpatient to day case ratios, shorter lengths of stay for inpatients and improved occupancy levels need to be modelled to determine the optimum size of new or upgraded facilities. These factors will clearly have an impact on the demand for services. Similarly, there is often an opportunity to provide services in a more efficient and effective way in a new setting. Improved design of facilities coupled with investment in technology may allow new models of service to be developed. Organisations should use the early stages of PFI projects to consider these opportunities and develop robust assumptions.

Delegated limits

The capital value of a project determines what approvals are required – current requirements as set out in the Department of Health's 2010 guidance *Delegated Limits for Capital Investment* are:

- Business cases for projects with a capital value over £35m require approval from both HM Treasury and the Department of Health
- SHAs can approve business cases up to £35m.

Individual trust approval limits no longer depend on turnover and performance ratings. NHS trusts now have a delegated limit for all business cases up to a value of £3m – above this limit, SHA approval is required. The Department of Health has introduced two exceptions to this rule and if either applies, the limit for approval may be reduced to £1m at the discretion of the SHA Director of Finance:

- If the project is deemed to be 'complicated and contentious' by the SHA director of finance
- If the trust reported a financial deficit at the previous year end, is forecasting a full year deficit in the current financial year or has an unplanned year to date deficit.

With the coalition government's 2010 White Paper, *Equity and Excellence: Liberating the NHS* and the *Health and Social Care Bill 2011* signalling the dissolution of PCTs, all capital contracts entered into by PCTs prior to their abolition in 2013 must be approved by the appropriate SHA. Consequently, PCTs have a delegated limit of zero.

NHS foundation trusts are not subject to delegated limits for capital investment set by the Department of Health.

Accounting for PFI transactions

As mentioned earlier, the accounting treatment of agreed PFI deals changed with the introduction of IFRS and must be in line with latest Treasury and Department of Health guidance. The key documents are *Accounting for PFI under IFRS* and *Accounting for NHS LIFT under IFRS* (both published in October 2009). Under this guidance, PFI and LIFT schemes must be broken down and accounted for in terms of their component parts. The guidance available is very detailed and includes the accounting entries for each element. It can be found on the NHS finance manual website and via the links at the end of this chapter.

Although it is important to refer to the detailed guidance, the key components in accounting for PFI and LIFT schemes can be summarised as follows:

- Organisations must consider whether their scheme represents a service concession under IFRIC12 (*Service Concessions Arrangements*) for which a number of specific 'tests' exist, and if not, whether the scheme is a finance lease or an operating lease under IAS17 (*Accounting for Leases*)

- They must also review their schemes within the context of the European System of Accounts (ESA) 95 to be able to mitigate the impact of a scheme coming onto their statement of financial position. In January 2010, the Department of Health produced a guidance note – *PFI and NHS LIFT budgeting and ESA95 opinions* – which is currently being revised
- The asset is recognised in the organisation's accounts at 'fair value' which is the capital cost of the asset at the inception of the scheme. This is most likely to be the capital cost elements of the full business case at the point of financial close of the contract for the development of the scheme
- Where there is an annual unitary payment made to the private partner, a finance lease liability is shown equal to the fair value of the asset
- The unitary payment itself is then allocated between:
  - payment for services
  - payment for the property in terms of repayment of the liability; the interest charge relating to the lease and the contingent rent (a contingent rent is one where the value is not fixed at the start of the lease and varies over time by an external factor such as the retail price index)
  - life cycle costs which is the part of the unitary payment relating to future capital expenditure (i.e. keeping the asset maintained to a certain specification throughout the duration of the contract such that when it passes to the public sector body at the end of the contract, it is in the same condition as it was when it was brought into operation)
- Accounting for the asset as if the organisation owns it means that a corresponding depreciation charge must also be recognised within its non-operating expenses; this can be a significant non-cash charge, depending on the value of the scheme. There will also be changes in value to be accounted for as with any other asset owned by the organisation.

Management of PFI projects

The operational phase of a PFI scheme is often taken for granted even though it tends to involve organisational change and new ways of doing things. Although standard guidance is available from the Department of Health for many aspects of the PFI process, each scheme is unique in terms of its detailed content. For example, there will be differences between contracts in the services covered, availability and performance regimes, payment method and timing, how changes will be dealt with, indexation agreements (i.e. the rate at which payments rise) and monitoring regimes.

The onus for the delivery of services, in accordance with output specifications, lies with the SPC. However, it is incumbent on the purchaser of the services to determine how it is going to manage the contract. For example, the performance and availability regimes will operate on an on-going basis throughout the contract period and purchasers need to have processes in place to highlight performance failure and the 'unavailability' of facilities from day-to-day or even hour-to-hour. Indexation is likely to occur on an annual basis, while benchmarking and market testing to ensure that the service remains competitive may be on a seven-year cycle. Dealing with changes will be driven by strategic and operational need. The purchaser of services needs to manage this wide range of adjustments to the unitary charge.

The complexity of the agreed elements of the unitary charge payments mechanism will also have an impact on the level of effort needed to manage the contract successfully. For example, an extremely detailed performance and availability regime coupled with a quarterly in-advance payment of the unitary charge will require a lot more effort than a monthly-in-arrears payment on account process with a reconciled balancing payment within an agreed period.

Key issues that need to be considered in the management of PFI schemes include:

- Contract awareness – performance and availability regimes, services, change control
- Organisational arrangements – purchaser representative, SPC interface, roles and responsibilities
- Monitoring
- Payments mechanism and process
- Systems and procedures.

Contract awareness

In many organisations the development of the PFI scheme and the negotiation of the PFI project agreement will be undertaken by a relatively small number of key staff supported by external financial, legal and technical advisers. Many of the organisation's staff, who will be involved in day-to-day contact with the SPC's service providers, will be unaware of the detailed content of the PFI project agreement. In particular, the output specifications for services and the availability and performance regimes will be critical to ensuring that services are delivered to the required quality standards. If staff are unaware of the agreed standards, they will be unable to judge the quality of the services delivered and the extent to which the output specification standards are being achieved.

Similarly, the advent of a PFI project may have a significant impact on the way in which services are delivered within an organisation. Innovative solutions or the transfer of duties will require change within the organisation and a full understanding of the implications. Processes for ordering specific outputs, with a potential impact on the unitary charge, may not be readily understood by those who have not been involved in the contract development and negotiations. For example, the undertaking of minor alterations such as the addition of a shelf to an office which may have been carried out by the estates department prior to a PFI arrangement is likely to be added to the value of the PFI contract and maintained to the required standard with an accompanying life cycle charge. The manager requesting the alteration may be unaware of the on-going costs that will now be incurred.

There is therefore a need to raise contract awareness throughout the organisation via a good communication process that informs staff of the implications of the PFI contract and the impact it will have on how they and the organisation operate.

Organisational arrangements

Organisational arrangements will differ depending upon the type and scale of scheme. However, for all PFI projects it is essential that:

- There is clarity over the detail of the payment mechanism. What services does it cover, what are the financial penalties and what are the time limits on corrective action? At what point are additional costs incurred?
- Roles, responsibilities and accountabilities for contract management (including how the organisation works with the provider of services at a strategic and operational level) are clear. For example, who is the senior purchaser representative for the contract? What are the key interfaces with the provider at an operational level?
- The roles and functions of staff in checking and authorising payments to the provider of services are set out and understood
- There is clarity over the detail of what is covered in any 'soft' arrangements – for example, maintenance or light bulb replacement.

Monitoring

Responsibility for delivering services to the prescribed standards and the monitoring of services lies with the SPC which is expected to produce monthly reports setting out information on compliance and identifying failures. This forms a key element in the calculation of the monthly unitary charge. To ensure robustness and compliance with output specifications, the purchaser of services needs to consider how to monitor the SPC's processes and the extent of any random test checking of service delivery.

Payments mechanism and process

The unitary payment changes regularly in response to a range of general, annual and monthly adjustments. The payments process also needs to be in line with the timings set out in the PFI contract. Depending on the nature of the payment mechanism, the timescales may be relatively tight so both purchaser and provider need to have systems in place that can cope. In developing these systems, it is essential that organisations think about payments that may exceed normal standing order and standing financial instruction levels and require special authorisation procedures.

Systems and procedures

In keeping with good practice, organisations should document the systems and procedures associated with the management of PFI contracts in order to ensure clarity, continuity, accountability and 'auditability' of processes. This may seem self-evident but can be overlooked, particularly in the short term. A failure to document processes can lead to a lack of effective control of the contract.

The implications of payment by results

Under the payment by results regime, payments are made by commissioners to providers of NHS healthcare for individual spells of patient care charged at a nationally set tariff for each healthcare resource group (HRG). This means that provider trusts have to meet contractual payments relating to any PFI schemes out of the income they receive from the activities undertaken at national tariff values. Clearly this income also has to cover the costs associated with providing the patient related activity. Organisations embarking on PFI schemes need to ensure that projects remain affordable under PbR – in practice, this may be difficult to guarantee and PFI schemes may be less attractive and prevalent as a result.

NHS LIFT

Background and objectives

NHS LIFT aims to improve and develop front line primary and community care facilities. It was developed to try and tackle the problem of sub-standard premises whose condition and functionality meant that quality and access were below an acceptable standard, with a knock on effect on the potential for service development and improvement. Initially, the focus of NHS LIFT was to deliver primary care centres and new, refurbished or upgraded GP premises. However, the approach has also been used to deliver much larger and more complex facilities such as community hospital developments.

To develop this new market for investment, the Department of Health entered into a national joint venture with Partnerships UK and established Partnerships for Health (PfH). PfH completed waves 1–3 of the programme, delivering 42 local NHS LIFT companies, plus another 8 approvals from wave 4. In 2006, the Department of Health purchased Partnerships UK's 20% stake in PfH, making PfH 100% owned by the Department. PfH was renamed Community Health Partnerships (CHP) in autumn 2007.

CHP delivers NHS LIFT on behalf of the Department in partnership with the local health economy through the establishment of a LIFT company. This is a limited company with the local NHS, CHP and the private sector partner as shareholders. This limited company – the LIFTco – owns and maintains the building and leases the premises to PCTs, GPs, local authority social services, dentists and pharmacists, often creating a 'super health centre'. At present, local PCTs are shareholders in the LIFTco to protect the public interest. A management board comprising private sector partners, local NHS nominees and CHP works together to deliver the PCT's investment programmes.

How NHS LIFT works

In terms of assessing the case for investment, all new LIFT schemes must follow a process set down by the Department of Health in its guidance document *NHS LIFT Business Case Approval Guidance*. This emphasises that the work involved in developing a business case should be proportionate to the scheme in question. As with PFI schemes, NHS LIFT proposals must demonstrate that they will achieve VFM and provide improved services, in line with:

- National targets and objectives
- Commissioning objectives
- Transforming Community Services objectives
- The quality, innovation, productivity and prevention (QIPP) agenda.

Current state of play

Some 50 projects, in four waves, have been approved. The Department of Health website includes a progress report on specific schemes containing such information as the financial-close date and capital values.

'Express LIFT'

In March 2009, the Department of Health and CHP launched 'Express LIFT' as a way of reducing the time and cost of procuring a LIFTco compared to the traditional procurement process. The Department of Health established a framework of seven pre-approved LIFT partners from which PCTs and local authorities could select. The initiative was aimed at those PCTs that had not got a LIFTco so that they could conduct a local procurement process within three or four months as opposed to two years with the traditional method.

Local Partnerships

It is possible to construct local partnership arrangements with private sector developers for schemes such as residential accommodation. Under the current regime, business cases are developed as in PFI schemes and approved by the SHA, which also gives the authority to proceed. There are no unitary payments as the partner receives income from tenants. However, the trust may have to give some guarantees on occupancy levels.

What the future holds for Public Private Partnerships

The coalition government's proposals for the NHS do not contain anything specific about PFI or LIFT. However, the abolition of PCTs and SHAs would clearly have an impact on how current and future capital projects are handled. The reduction in capital monies announced in the 2010 spending review will also have an impact – although total spending on the NHS is set to rise from £104bn in 2010/11 to £114bn in 2013/14, the 0.4% increase includes a 1.3% rise in current (revenue) spending and a 17% cut in the capital budget. However, the government has confirmed that it will 'support a number of new-build hospitals, including St Helier, Royal Oldham and West Cumberland'. It is assumed that the new NHS Commissioning Board would have a role in allocating any capital funding to GP consortia but there are no details yet available.

References and Further Reading

Department of Health Guidance on PFI: www.dh.gov.uk/en/Managingyourorganisation/NHSprocurement/Publicprivatepartnership/Privatefinanceinitiative/index.htm

Consolidated Budgeting Guidance, HM Treasury: www.hm-treasury.gov.uk/psr_bc_consolidated_budgeting.htm

Value for Money Assessment Guidance, HM Treasury, 2006: www.hm-treasury.gov.uk/d/vfm_assessmentguidance061006opt.pdf

Treasury's Value for Money Assessment for PFI – Guidance for NHS Build Schemes, Department of Health, 2008: www.dh.gov.uk/en/Publicationsandstatistics/Publications/PublicationsPolicyAndGuidance/DH_091229

Public Private Partnerships guidance, HM Treasury: www.hm-treasury.gov.uk/ppp_index.htm

The Green Book, HM Treasury: www.hm-treasury.gov.uk/data_greenbook_index.htm

Office of Government Commerce: www.ogc.gov.uk

Public Sector Business Cases using the Five Case Model: a toolkit: www.hfma.org.uk

EU Public Procurement Directive on Competitive Dialogue: www.dh.gov.uk/en/
Managingyourorganisation/NHSprocurement/Publicprivatepartnership/Privatefinanceinitiative/
DH_4132174

Delegated Limits for Capital Investment, Department of Health, 2010: www.dh.gov.uk/en/
Publicationsandstatistics/Publications/PublicationsPolicyAndGuidance/DH_122791

Manual for Accounts, Department of Health (FINMAN website): www.info.doh.gov.uk/doh/
finman.nsf/

IFRIC 12: Service Concession Arrangements: www.iasb.org/Current+Projects/IFRIC+Projects/
IFRIC+12+Service+Concession+Arrangements/IFRIC+12+Service+Concession+Arrangements.htm

IAS 17, International Accounting Standards Board: www.iasb.org/Home.htm

Department of Health Guidance on LIFT (and 'express LIFT'): www.dh.gov.uk/en/
Managingyourorganisation/NHSprocurement/Publicprivatepartnership/NHSLIFT/index.htm

Community Health Partnerships: www.communityhealthpartnerships.co.uk/

Transforming Community Services, Department of Health: www.dh.gov.uk/en/Healthcare/
Primarycare/TCS/index.htm

QIPP: www.institute.nhs.uk/cost_and_quality/qipp/cost_and_quality_homepage.html

11. Commissioning

Introduction

The Department of Health has described commissioning in the NHS as 'the process of ensuring that the health and care services provided effectively meet the needs of the population. It is a complex process with responsibilities ranging from assessing population needs, prioritising health outcomes, procuring products and services, and managing service providers'. In practical terms this means that commissioners negotiate agreements with service providers (in the NHS, private and voluntary sectors) to meet the health needs of a particular population.

Although commissioning has existed since the start of the NHS, reforms introduced by the labour government to the financial regime and in particular the introduction of payment by results (PbR), practice based commissioning (PBC) and world class commissioning (WCC) made it more prominent. Indeed, the Department of Health's 2007 document *World Class Commissioning: vision* placed significant emphasis on getting commissioning right and saw it as being at the heart of delivering an NHS that is 'fair, personalised, effective and safe, and which is focused relentlessly on improving the quality of care'.

Although the coalition government halted the world class commissioning approach when it came to power, it has recognised the importance of getting commissioning right with plans to introduce a new NHS Commissioning Board to support and guide commissioning across the NHS.

This chapter focuses on what commissioning involves but first looks at the policy background to give an insight into how commissioning has developed over recent years.

Policy Background and Context

The internal market

Between 1991 and 1999, the NHS operated an internal market that separated the function of service provision from commissioning. Health authorities received funding allocations for their populations and commissioned services from providers to meet the needs of their population. Service providers received payment for services usually in the form of block monthly payments for a range of services provided under a service agreement or contract.

Although, the internal market focussed attention on issues such as price, performance and deliverables, it also fragmented the NHS and hardened the demarcations between purchasers and service providers. From 1999 the labour government developed the role of primary care in commissioning with the result that PCTs currently have the lead role, managing over 80% of the service's budget, the bulk of which they use to commission services from other NHS bodies, the private sector, voluntary and 'third sector' providers. At present (2011/12), PCTs are also responsible for commissioning primary care services including GP, ophthalmic, pharmacy, dental and community health services (see chapter 6 for more details).

Commissioning at GP practice and locality (i.e. groups of practices) level was also introduced as a means of encouraging and ensuring that front line primary care professionals were engaged in the commissioning of services.

The labour government's reform agenda

The labour government's reform agenda – first articulated in the *NHS Plan* – involved a number of strands all designed to deliver an improved NHS that was more 'locally driven, looking outwards not upwards'.[14] Effective commissioning was central to this agenda but was also affected by other key elements. In particular, the introduction of PbR shifted the focus of commissioning away from price negotiations to specifying quantity, quality and delivery of service targets.

PbR was developed initially to increase efficiency and cost-effectiveness within the NHS and to encourage investment in new capacity to help meet access targets. Under PbR, activity has in the main been paid for at full rather than marginal cost – as a result, effective demand management is essential. However, the downturn in the national economic climate and reduced growth funding for PCTs mean that the way NHS and foundation trusts are rewarded for performance under PbR has changed and will continue to change over the coming years (see chapter 13 for more about PbR).

Patient choice and plurality of provision also had a significant impact on commissioning. For example, since December 2005, patients have had a choice of four or five providers at the point of referral and from April 2008, choice was extended still further with patients effectively having a 'free choice' in relation to hospital-based services. This is now backed by Directions[15] that came into force on 1st April 2009 and which mean that PCTs have a statutory duty to ensure that patients get the choice set out in the *Free Choice* (or *'Hospital Choice'*) guidance.

Commissioning decisions are affected by a range of other influences such as the need to adhere to condition specific 'national service frameworks', covering a wide range of areas – for example, diabetes and coronary heart disease.

World class commissioning

As mentioned earlier, the key policy development in the commissioning arena in recent years was world class commissioning (WCC). This followed on from the Department of Health's 2006 publication *Health Reform in England: Update and Commissioning Framework* which set out a framework of key changes designed to strengthen commissioning and ensure that it could drive health reform, improved health and healthcare and improved financial health for the NHS. This *Commissioning Framework* set out an over-arching vision for the commissioning role of PCTs, working in partnership with general practices to promote PBC.

WCC was launched in 2007 by the Department of Health and comprised four main elements:

- A vision – that WCC would deliver better health and well-being for all; better care for all and better value for all
- A set of organisational competencies

---

[14] *World Class Commissioning*, Department of Health, 2007.
[15] *The Primary Care Trusts (Choice of Secondary Care Provider) Directions*, 2009.

- An annual assurance system that reviewed PCTs' 'progress towards achieving better health outcomes for their populations' and provided 'a common basis for agreeing further development'. This assurance process assessed three elements – outcomes (the rate of improvement); competencies (using a rating of one to four) and governance (using a red, amber, green traffic light score)
- A support and development framework that gave PCTs access to the tools they needed to 'become world class commissioners, either by sharing services and good practice, developing internal resources, or buying in external expertise, for example through the *Framework for Securing External Support for Commissioners* (FESC)'.

The WCC framework was dispensed with when the coalition government came to power in 2010.

What is Commissioning?

Commissioning involves making 'the best use of allocated resources to achieve the following goals:

- Improve health and well-being and reduce health inequalities and social exclusion
- Secure access to a comprehensive range of services
- Improve the quality, effectiveness and efficiency of services
- Increase choice for patients and ensure a better experience of care through greater responsiveness to people's needs'.[16]

The focus for commissioning is therefore on achieving the best possible health outcomes (including reduced health inequalities) and the best possible healthcare within the resources made available by the taxpayer.

As it is inevitable that demand for healthcare will exceed the level of funds available, there will always be an element of 'prioritising' within commissioning. This involves a focus on local needs, targets and desired outcomes together with reviewing services in the search for greater effectiveness, economy and efficiency.

The labour government's *NHS Plan* placed particular emphasis on key government targets, as well as on the planning and commissioning process to deliver these targets. More recently, national priorities have been set out in annual operating frameworks issued by the Department of Health.

Also of interest to commissioning is *High Quality Care for all* which was published following a wide ranging review carried out during 2007 and 2008 by the then health minister Lord Darzi. This report recommended a change of focus for the NHS to a service that 'gives patients and the public more information and choice, works in partnership and has quality of care at its heart'. The themes and focus of the Darzi review were re-iterated in the *Operating Framework 2010/11* which emphasised that quality should be the 'organising principle' that underlies all that the NHS does and identified the goals for commissioning as being:

---

[16] *Health Reform in England: Update and Commissioning Framework,* 2006, Department of Health.

- Improved health outcomes
- Reduced health inequalities
- Improved provider quality
- Increased productivity.

The Commissioning Cycle and Commissioning Competencies

Commissioning is not a one off activity but rather a continuous cycle that involves:

- Assessing health needs
- Reviewing service provision and identifying gaps or areas where change is needed
- Deciding priorities
- Designing services
- Shaping the structure of supply
- Managing demand while ensuring appropriate access to care
- Ensuring effective clinical decision-making
- Managing performance
- Undertaking patient and public feedback.

This cycle is shown below in diagrammatic form as taken from the Department of Health's 2006 guidance *Health Reform in England: update and commissioning framework*:

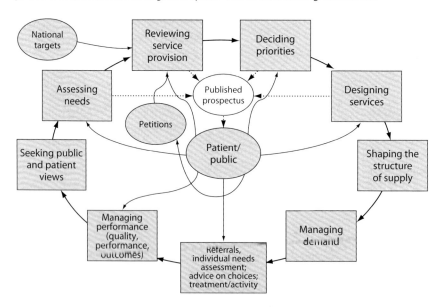

To be effective commissioners need to:

- Have access to information and skills that will support their decisions (for example, population risk assessments)
- Engage with a broad range of clinicians

- Improve community engagement
- Use incentives and contracts
- Ensure choice for patients.

The WCC guidance identified eleven organisational competencies that set out what PCTs as commissioners should do, many of which remain relevant and can be linked to the commissioning cycle. These were that PCTs should:

- Locally lead the NHS
- Work with community partners
- Engage with public and patients
- Collaborate with clinicians
- Manage knowledge and assess needs
- Prioritise investment
- Stimulate the market
- Promote improvement and innovation
- Secure procurement skills
- Manage the local health system
- Make sound financial investments.

Commissioning Approaches

Under the arrangements that exist in 2011/12, there are a number of different approaches to commissioning including:

- Individual PCTs commissioning on their own
- Co-ordinating commissioners ('lead' consortia arrangements) where groups of PCTs work together formally. In this approach, a single contract is negotiated by the lead commissioner with the local service provider and it is 'performance managed' across all member PCTs
- Specialist commissioning groups (SCGs) – there are ten SCGs that commission specialist high cost, low volume treatments (for example, transplant surgery) for their regional populations, which range in size from 2.8 million people to 7.5 million people. Following the 2006 *Carter Review* SCGs are at present co-located within SHA boundaries (i.e. there are currently 10 SCG 'hubs')
- Network arrangements (for example, for cancer services) have undertaken some commissioning functions on behalf of their constituent PCTs
- Practice based commissioning (i.e. by primary care clinicians – see below)
- Partnership working with local authorities (see below).

Practice Based Commissioning

Practice based commissioning (PBC) was first introduced in 2005/06 through the document *Practice Based Commissioning: achieving universal coverage* and is concerned with 'engaging practices and other primary care professionals in the commissioning of services'. Through PBC, front line clinicians are provided with the resources and support to become more involved in commissioning decisions. By enabling primary care clinicians to take commissioning decisions themselves, patients receive higher quality services that better suit their needs and circumstances. The underlying presumption is that primary care professionals are in the best position to decide what services their patients need and to redesign them accordingly.

Under PBC, responsibility for commissioning along with an associated budget from the PCT is allocated to primary care clinicians. This is designed to align clinical and financial responsibilities. However, because the PCT remains legally responsible for managing the money and negotiating and managing all contracts with providers, the budget allocated to primary care practitioners is notional or 'indicative'. In practice this means that although primary care clinicians determine the range of services to be provided for their population, the PCT acts as their agent to undertake any required procurements and to carry out the administrative tasks that underpin these processes.

As well as involving clinicians more closely in commissioning decisions, PBC was designed to incentivise improvements in services including the development and provision of services outside of hospitals. A proportion of any resources freed up through changes in commissioning practice can be used for the benefit of the practice's patients. There are also incentive payments for practices that sign up to PBC and for achieving their PBC plans.

Under the current regime, the PCT remains responsible for the overall commissioning strategy and for ensuring that PBC is implemented. This was emphasised in the Department of Health's 2006 guidance *Practice Based Commissioning: practical implementation*, which stated that PCTs 'are charged with ensuring that PBC continues to flourish'. It also set out a number of 'key expectations' placed on PCTs which included the need for there to be:

- A locally agreed incentive scheme offered to all practices
- Timely activity and financial information relating to practices that meet practice preferences
- Tools and support provided to practices so that they can discharge their commissioning responsibilities, either directly or through agreed alternative arrangements.

In December 2007, the Department issued *Practice Based Commissioning – budget setting refinements and clarification of health funding flexibilities, incentive schemes and governance*. This built on earlier guidance and encouraged practice based commissioners to use NHS funds more flexibly to secure alternatives to traditional NHS provision. In particular, the guidance stated that 'PCTs should agree with practice based commissioners a menu of local flexibilities, to support their achievement of local and national priorities'. A possible menu of flexibilities was included in the document along with guidance on setting practice budgets.

The WCC programme also emphasised the pivotal role that practice based commissioners play with the publication of *Clinical Commissioning: our vision for practice-based commissioning*. As well as setting out the overall aims for clinical commissioning, this identified the:

- Hallmarks of successful clinical commissioning – for example, clinical engagement at all stages of the commissioning cycle (including assessing needs; reviewing how resources are used and services delivered; identifying changes; working to deliver continuous quality improvement); developing proposals for new services and shaping investment with the PCT; reviewing patient pathways and shifting care into more local settings; strong patient and public engagement; integrated working across traditional boundaries

- Support and entitlements that practice based commissioners could expect (for example, management and financial information and swift budget setting and decision-making)
- Principles that should underpin productive partnerships between PCTs and PBCs (for example, a clear and transparent system of governance).

PBC budget setting

Under the current regime (2011/12), PCTs are responsible for ensuring that practices receive an indicative budget that reflects the needs of the population as accurately as possible. This allows a practice to access a 'fair share' of the resources available to the whole of the PCT for its patients. Budget guidance and a toolkit issued by the Department set out the approach that PCTs should follow and explain any changes to the methodology used – these tend to reflect changes to the PCT allocation formula.

Over time, the expectation was that practice budgets would move away from historic spending towards a 'fair shares' approach. For example, for 2010/11 the budget guidance suggested that 'if "fair share" budgets or historic activity differ by more than a locally determined threshold, the difference should be reduced'.

Partnership Working with Local Authorities

As many PCTs are coterminous with district or unitary council boundaries, joint commissioning between the NHS and local authorities for particular services and client groups is increasingly common. This follows changes originally introduced by the *Health Act 1999* facilitating the movement of funds between the NHS and local authorities, including the option of pooling budgets where this is considered advantageous. The focus on integrated care pathways has also given impetus to greater partnership working with local authorities. This allows services to be pulled together on a 'whole systems' basis from the perspective of the service user rather than the organisation delivering the service. In this context, lead responsibility for commissioning may now sit with the local authority and not the health organisation (see chapter 9 for more about partnership working with local authorities).

Planning and Contracting

Service planning

At present, PCTs are required to produce operational plans outlining how they intend to meet national targets and local priorities within their financial allocations. The 2011/12 *Operating Framework* emphasises the importance of ensuring that these operational plans 'support wider local arrangements' and makes clear that PCTs will be performance managed against a set of indicators and milestones grouped under three domains – quality, resources and reform.

Performance management

Commissioning activity within PCTs entails managing performance against contracts and service agreements (see below). Under the current regime, PCTs are performance managed by

SHAs in terms of the agreed operational plan. Performance information is aggregated at SHA level as part of monitoring government targets and delivery of each SHA's own area plan.

Information

Accurate information is essential to effective commissioning. Key information includes:

- Historical referral patterns
- Historical spend and how this compares with other practices
- Real time information to monitor actual activity against plans and expenditure against budgets.

A national information system developed by NHS Connecting for Health and known as the 'secondary uses service' (SUS) is designed to collect patient level activity information from providers and make it available to commissioners. This system then applies the tariff to providers' activity information, calculates the payment due and notifies each commissioner.

At present, information on how PCTs spend their resources across 23 different programmes of care is also collected as part of the programme budgeting initiative. This information enables PCTs to benchmark their own spend in a particular area with that of a similar organisation covering a similar population. PCTs can then challenge their historical spending patterns and ensure that they are commissioning the right level and mix of services.

Contracts

Service agreements

The traditional approach to commissioning in the NHS used service agreements between commissioners and providers. These agreements set down the expectations of each party and were analogous to contracts. They included as much detail as was felt necessary – in particular, service agreements specified the activity volume, financial value and tolerances.

Service agreements are still used for some non-acute activities where PbR does not yet apply and tend to take the form of 'block contracts' specifying activity levels and payment amounts – in other words, a fixed sum is paid for access to a defined range and volume of service. Cost and volume contracts are also used – here a fixed sum is paid for access to a defined range and volume of services but if there is a variation from the intended level of activity, there is a variation in payment levels according to a variation, or threshold agreement clause. This determines the marginal rate of payment for higher or lower than target performance. The threshold agreement represents a mechanism for sharing the risk of unforeseen events between commissioner and service provider. In most contracts of this kind, the variation agreement is not enforced within a narrow range of target activity. This band of activity is called the threshold or tolerance.

Cost per case contracts identify for each episode or unit of care a payment to the service provider. Cost per case contracts are commonplace where waiting list activity is placed with private sector providers, and for individual, expensive, and bespoke care package agreements (for example, the placement of patients in medium secure mental health facilities). Cost per case contracts suit procedures that are infrequent, unpredictable, or can have significant cost variations. They are also used for treatments under the patient choice regime, where patients may choose a provider that the commissioner does not have an established contract with.

The standard/'new NHS contract'

Service agreements have now largely been superseded by standard contracts which are in place for mental health and learning disability services, ambulance services, acute hospital and community services. Contracts have also been developed for 2011/12 for acute and mental health service organisations that are integrating with local PCT provider arms and for care homes.

The Department of Health produces contract documentation and guidance to support each year's *Operating Framework*. The contracts cover agreements between PCTs and all types of provider and must be signed before the start of the financial year. Any disputes must be resolved swiftly with any outstanding problems dealt with via mediation and formal adjudication.

The contracts should be read in conjunction with the *Principles and Rules for Co-operation and Competition* and the *PCT Procurement Guide*.

Contracts usually run for three years with prices 'refreshed' annually – however, the 2011/12 *Operating Framework* emphasises that for this contracting round, PCTs should be 'mindful that the contracts with providers of NHS funded services must smoothly transition to GP consortia'.

Commissioning for quality and innovation payment framework

Following a recommendation in *High Quality Care for all*, an additional element has been introduced into contractual arrangements between PCTs and providers. This is known as the commissioning for quality and innovation (CQUIN) payment framework and is designed to ensure that a proportion of providers' income is conditional on quality and innovation.

As the Department of Health's website states, the aim of CQUIN is to enable 'commissioners to reward excellence by linking a proportion of providers' income to the achievement of local quality improvement goals'.

Guidance on CQUIN is available on the Department's website which explains the rationale for the approach and sets out in broad terms what a CQUIN scheme should look like. In particular, the guidance emphasises that although the detailed content of a scheme is 'for local discretion and discussion between the commissioner and provider' they must cover:

- Safety
- Effectiveness (including clinical outcomes and 'patient reported outcomes')
- User experience (including timeliness of provision)
- Innovation.

The CQUIN guidance must be read in conjunction with the *Operating Framework* and the national standard contracts for acute, ambulance, community, mental health and learning disability services. For example, in 2011/12 for all standard contracts, providers can earn 1.5% 'on top of actual outturn value'. For acute providers, two national goals must also be included in CQUIN schemes, namely:

- Reducing the impact of venous thromboembolism
- Improving responsiveness to the personal needs of patients.

Never events

One other aspect of the contractual arrangements that is worth highlighting is the national set of 'never events' that PCTs must use as part of their contract agreements with providers. Any such events must be reported publicly and notified to the National Patient Safety Agency. The full list is included within the standard contract documentation on the Department's website but examples include:

- Wrong site surgery
- Retained instrument post operation
- Wrong route of administration of chemotherapy
- Misplaced naso- or orgogastric tube not detected prior to use
- Inpatient suicide by non collapsible rails
- In-hospital maternal death from post-partum haemorrhage after elective caesarean section
- Intravenous administration of mis-selected concentrated potassium chloride.

Working with Foundation Trusts

Foundation trusts (FTs) follow a different financial regime to other provider trusts but commissioning from FTs follows the same principles as with NHS trusts – good commissioning is the same whatever organisation is providing services. Agreements between PCTs and FTs are in the form of legally binding contracts which tend to focus more attention on information flows.

At present, if a PCT has a contractual dispute with an NHS trust, the SHA arbitrates. If there is a dispute between a PCT and an FT, the initial approach is for the SHA and Monitor (the independent regulator of FTs) to mediate. The option exists to invite the Centre for Effective Dispute Resolution (CEDR) to mediate in place of the SHA and Monitor although the costs will be borne by the parties to the dispute.

What the future holds for Commissioning

The coalition government's plans for the NHS (as set out in the *Health and Social Care Bill 2011*) involve significant structural change with the abolition of PCTs and SHAs and the introduction of a new NHS Commissioning Board and GP consortia. However, although the key players in the commissioning field are set to change, the function itself will continue with the same overall objectives.

GP consortia

In terms of roles in the future (subject to any amendments agreed to the *Health and Social Care Bill 2011*), GP consortia will commission the majority of NHS services for their patients with money allocated to them by the NHS Commissioning Board. Specifically, consortia will be responsible for commissioning:

- Planned hospital care
- Rehabilitative care
- Urgent and emergency services including out-of-hours services
- Community health services
- Mental health services
- Maternity services
- Learning disabilities services.

To be able to do this, consortia will need to agree what care the patients registered with their constituent practices require, negotiate contracts with healthcare providers and monitor their implementation. These contracts will set out the level and quality of the services required and their cost and will follow the new NHS Commissioning Board's model contract (the existing suite of contracts is to be reviewed between 2011 and 2013 in preparation). These healthcare services may be provided by foundation trusts or other public or private sector providers (i.e. 'any willing provider'). To ensure that commissioning decisions fully reflect the healthcare needs of patients each practice will nominate a clinician to represent it on the consortium.

Each consortium will be under a duty to prepare commissioning plans before the start of each year that show how it intends to use its budget and improve outcomes for patients. These plans will need to be discussed with the relevant local health and wellbeing board(s) to ensure that they reflect the joint strategic needs assessments and joint health and wellbeing strategies (see chapter 9). Consortia (and the Commissioning Board) will also be under a duty to ensure that people who receive services 'are involved in its planning and development, and to promote and extend public and patient involvement and choice'.

GP consortia will receive their funding from the NHS Commissioning Board with budgets including a maximum allowance to cover management costs. Consortia will be free to decide how best to use this allowance to carry out commissioning activities. Although consortia may choose to undertake some or all of these roles themselves, they will also have the flexibility to use the money to buy in the services needed including data analysis and contract monitoring, roles which are currently undertaken by PCTs.

As far as governance arrangements are concerned, the coalition government is proposing that each consortium will be a statutory body with an Accountable Officer (AO) with an accountability line to the NHS Commissioning Board. Consortia will also have a Chief Financial Officer although he or she could fulfil this role for more than one consortium. Under the current arrangements, the PCT Chief Executive is the AO and it is expected that in the new structure it will be the 'senior official' within each consortium.

In terms of timing, the *Health and Social Care Bill 2011* proposes that consortia will be in place in shadow form during 2011/12, taking on responsibility for commissioning in 2012/13 and assuming financial responsibility from April 2013.

NHS Commissioning Board

Subject to any amendments agreed to the *Health and Social Care Bill 2011*, the new NHS Commissioning Board will commission the primary medical services provided by GPs, dentists, community pharmacists, primary ophthalmic practitioners and national and regional specialised services. There will also be special arrangements made for high security psychiatric facilities.

Other responsibilities that the Commissioning Board will take on include:

- Setting commissioning guidelines
- Establishing model contracts for consortia to use when commissioning services
- Remaining within the 'NHS commissioning revenue limit' for which the Board's Chief Executive (the Accounting Officer) will be held to account by the Department of Health
- Holding GP consortia to account for their stewardship of resources and outcomes achieved. In particular, each consortium will have a duty to achieve financial balance
- Reporting the consolidated financial position of consortia to feed into the Department of Health's overall resource account
- Specifying the form and content of accounting information that consortia must provide and a timetable for submission
- Intervening where there is financial or systemic failure, or a significant risk of this happening
- Determining the structure of future payment/pricing systems
- Promoting and extending choice and championing patient and carer involvement.

The NHS Commissioning Board is due to be 'live' from April 2012.

References and Further Reading

Commissioning – Department of Health archived web pages: http://webarchive.nationalarchives.gov.uk/+/www.dh.gov.uk/en/Managingyourorganisation/Commissioning/index.htm

Payment by Results, Department of Health: www.dh.gov.uk/en/Managingyourorganisation/NHSFinancialReforms/index.htm

World Class Commissioning – Department of Health archived web pages: http://webarchive.nationalarchives.gov.uk/+/www.dh.gov.uk/en/Managingyourorganisation/Commissioning/Worldclasscommissioning/index.htm

Patient Choice – Department of Health archived web pages: http://webarchive.nationalarchives.gov.uk/+/www.dh.gov.uk/en/Healthcare/PatientChoice/index.htm

The Primary Care Trusts (Choice of Secondary Care Provider) Directions 2009: www.dh.gov.uk/en/Publicationsandstatistics/Publications/PublicationsLegislation/DH_093004

Health Reform in England: Update and Commissioning Framework, Department of Health, 2006: www.dh.gov.uk/prod_consum_dh/groups/dh_digitalassets/@dh/@en/documents/digitalasset/dh_4137230.pdf

The Framework for Procuring External Support for Commissioners, Department of Health, 2007: www.dh.gov.uk/en/Publicationsandstatistics/Publications/PublicationsPolicyAndGuidance/DH_065818

Next Stage Review Final report, Department of Health, 2008: www.dh.gov.uk/en/ Publicationsandstatistics/Publications/PublicationsPolicyAndGuidance/DH_085825

High Quality Care for all, Department of Health, 2008: www.dh.gov.uk/en/Healthcare/ Highqualitycareforall/index.htm

Specialised Services Commissioning: www.specialisedservices.nhs.uk/

Practice Based Commissioning – Department of Health archived web pages: http:// webarchive.nationalarchives.gov.uk/+/www.dh.gov.uk/en/Managingyourorganisation/ Commissioning/Practice-basedcommissioning/index.htm

Standard NHS Contracts, Department of Health: www.dh.gov.uk/en/Publicationsandstatistics/ Publications/PublicationsPolicyAndGuidance/DH_111203

Principles and Rules of Cooperation and Competition, Department of Health, 2010: www.dh.gov.uk/en/Publicationsandstatistics/Publications/PublicationsPolicyAndGuidance/ DH_113746

Primary Care Trust Procurement Guide for Health Services, Department of Health, 2010: www.dh.gov.uk/en/Publicationsandstatistics/Publications/PublicationsPolicyAndGuidance/ DH_113745

Commissioning for Quality and Innovation (CQUIN), Department of Health: www.dh.gov.uk/en/ Publicationsandstatistics/Publications/PublicationsPolicyAndGuidance/DH_091443

Centre for Effective Dispute Resolution: www.cedr.co.uk/

Secondary Uses Service: www.connectingforhealth.nhs.uk/systemsandservices/sus

Programme Budgeting: www.dh.gov.uk/en/Managingyourorganisation/Financeandplanning/ Programmebudgeting/DH_075743

12. Costing

Introduction

This chapter looks at an activity that is increasingly prominent in today's NHS. Although costing has always been important, the use of payment by results (PbR) means that the production of accurate cost information by NHS organisations is critical as it informs the development of the national tariff. NHS organisations also need to have a detailed understanding of their own cost base so that they can manage their activities effectively.

What is Costing?

Costing is the quantification, in financial terms, of the value of resources consumed in carrying out a particular activity or producing a certain unit of output. Costing therefore involves:

- Being clear about the activity whose costs you are seeking to identify – it must be defined clearly and unambiguously
- Making sure that the correct costs of everything and everyone involved in carrying out that activity are included in the costing calculation.

It is also important to analyse the costs themselves –the classification most often used involves a distinction between:

- Direct costs – those costs that can readily and easily be identified with a particular activity
- Indirect costs – those costs that contribute to the cost of an activity but in a less clear cut way
- Overheads – costs that contribute to the general running of an organisation rather than to specific activities.

Costs also behave differently – some are fixed (i.e. they do not change with activity levels); others are variable (i.e. they increase or decrease in line with changes in activity) and some are 'semi fixed' (i.e. they stay the same until activity increases above a certain amount – often referred to as 'step' changes).

We will look in more detail at the cost classifications used in the NHS later on in this chapter.

What is Costing Information used for?

In the NHS, costing involves looking closely at healthcare services and identifying how much they cost. This can be at a variety of levels – for example, the total annual cost of the orthopaedic department in a hospital; the cost of a particular activity or group of procedures within that department (for instance, hip replacements) or the cost of an individual patient undergoing that hip replacement.

It is important to recognise that costing is not an end in itself – it is only worth doing if the information generated is used in a meaningful way to deliver improvements in healthcare services. In the NHS, costing information is used both within organisations and at a national level.

NHS organisations need costing information for a variety of reasons – for example to:

- Help run their businesses effectively and efficiently
- Help decision makers, managers and budget holders decide how services should develop in the future
- Manage 'services lines' (see later in this chapter)
- Understand how the costs of providing a particular activity compare with the income received for undertaking that activity
- Identify the costs of different activities at different levels (for example, for a particular specialty/department or for an individual patient)
- Support the development of commissioning strategies
- Compare potential investment opportunities
- Build up realistic budgets and plans
- Monitor performance and benchmark services
- Support negotiations for funding.

At a national level, the Department of Health currently uses costing information provided by NHS bodies to develop:

- Reference cost comparisons
- The tariff for activities covered by PbR
- National service frameworks
- Programme budgeting data and comparisons
- Comparative data/benchmarking
- Efficiency targets
- Healthcare resource groups (HRGs).

What does Costing involve?

An important element of any approach to costing is identifying the activities that are to be evaluated. Rather than record every single cost incurred separately (which would be unmanageable) costs are grouped and categorised into a number of distinct headings referred to as 'cost centres'. The cost centres used by organisations will vary according to their type, size, structure and range of activities but – as a general rule – tend to be in line with budget headings in the general ledger.

Costing in the NHS in England must be carried out in accordance with the Department of Health's *Costing Manual*. This is revised and updated on a regular basis and is designed to ensure consistency of approach across all organisations that provide healthcare services.

The *Costing Manual* states that costs and income have to be:

- 'Calculated on a full absorption basis to identify the full cost of services delivered' – in other words, all income and costs must be attributed to an activity or cost centre. This means that the full cost of each activity is identified and all costs are allocated somewhere

- 'Allocated and apportioned accurately by maximising direct charging and where this is not possible using standard methods of apportionment'. This means that costs should be charged directly to the activity that incurs them wherever possible – for example a general surgeon's costs will be charged to a cost centre for general surgery. Where direct charging is not possible the manual sets out standard methods of apportionment/ allocation that must be used. Generally apportionments tend to be used when dealing with indirect costs that relate to a range of activities – for example, ward costs that need to be spread across a range of specialties in proportion to the bed days used by each. Allocations are used most commonly for overheads (for example, finance or human resources) that relate to the overall running of the organisation. These costs must still be absorbed by activities but are charged out on a more general basis
- 'Matched to the services that generate them to avoid cross subsidisation' – in other words, the costs of a particular service or activity should not be lowered artificially by loading costs that relate to it to another service or activity.

The *Manual* also states that the costing process should 'be transparent with a clear audit trail' and includes detailed appendices that list those costs that must be charged directly and those that may be indirect or an overhead.

Although the *Costing Manual* is mandatory in terms of the costing approach that must be followed, it does not prescribe cost centres or activities – these will vary (and be grouped) according to the structure and nature of an organisation. For example, a large acute trust may have a surgical cost centre or budget head with multiple sub departments or wards dealing with a single specialty. A small district hospital may have a single ward that deals with a range of patients including some who have had surgical procedures. The *Manual* does emphasise that whatever cost centres an organisation chooses it is important that they can 'clearly map to the treatment/function/programme/service definitions required in the current reference costs collection guidance' (see later in this chapter).

Cost classifications

All NHS costs are classified as direct, indirect or overhead costs within each specialty and care programme. A minimum standard categorisation of costs has been identified to achieve a consistent approach to the costing of services for all providers. The *Costing Manual* sets out these minimum standards of classification and makes clear that costs identified as 'direct' should 'in no circumstances' be allocated indirectly or apportioned as overheads, although 'reducing levels of overheads and a move to indirect or even direct cost classification is actively encouraged'.

Direct costs

Direct costs are those costs that can be directly attributed to the particular patient, activity or output being measured. For example, within a hospital ward the cost of drugs supplied and consumed can be directly attributed to that ward by the pharmacy system. Hence, drugs would be a direct cost of the ward cost centre.

Indirect costs

Indirect costs cannot be directly attributed to a particular patient or cost centre but can be associated with a number of them. Such costs need to be allocated to individual cost centres, and generally this is achieved through apportioning the costs using a unit of activity or work measure appropriate to the area concerned. For example, where linen costs cannot be directly attributed to wards these may be allocated using occupied bed days.

Overheads

Overhead costs are those costs that contribute to the general running of the organisation but cannot be related directly to an activity or service. For example, the total heating costs of a hospital may be apportioned to individual departments using floor area or cubic capacity; the costs of finance or human resources may be spread across all cost centres in proportion to those cost centres' total direct and indirect costs. The key here is that overheads are apportioned on a logical and consistent basis.

Cost pools

For indirect and overhead costs that relate to identifiable activities, 'cost pools' tend to be used to collect the costs (examples are theatres and diagnostic services). The costs are then apportioned (or attributed) to the cost centres/patients/activities that they have provided a service or resources to.

The *Manual* defines cost pooling as: 'the aggregation of costs from more than one cost centre separately identified in the general ledger'. For example, the employee services cost pool may aggregate the costs of personnel, crèche, staff restaurant and welfare services and these may then be apportioned to a clinical cost centre. Again the *Costing Manual* sets out guidance on the pooling of costs, but each organisation decides which cost pools it needs depending on its structure and range of activities.

Cost analysis

All NHS costs must be analysed into their fixed, semi-fixed and variable components. As mentioned earlier, this relates to the manner in which costs respond within a given period to the changes in level of activity. The descriptions from the *Costing Manual* are:

- 'Fixed. Where they are not affected by in-year changes in activity. For example, costs such as rent and rates
- Semi-fixed. Where costs are fixed for a given level of activity but change in steps, when activity levels exceed or fall below these given levels. For example, costs such as nursing staff
- Variable. Where costs vary directly with changes in activity. For example, costs such as drugs'.

Total cost approach

The *Costing Manual* states that NHS providers must identify three key elements as part of the compilation of overall cost:

- 'a "high level control total" based on actual costs by services identifying direct, indirect and overhead costs in line with the national minimum standards. The national high level control totals should be able to be mapped to the national classification found in the current reference costs guidance
- a continuous reconciliation process at all stages of the costing process is required to ensure all costs are recovered, and that costs can be matched to relevant services and final accounts
- a "resource profile" analysis of the key conditions which represent a minimum of 80% of the high level control total in both activity and cost terms. Specific reference should be made to clinicians' and nurses' knowledge of the:
  - conditions they treat
  - frequency with which they are performed
  - resources used to perform them'.

See the *NHS Costing Manual* for more details.

Healthcare Resource Groups

As mentioned earlier in this chapter, costing information is used to develop the tariffs for PbR. However, because there is such a vast range of specific interventions, procedures and diagnoses (around 23,000 patient treatment codes exist), it is not possible to have a separate tariff for each. Instead, a 'currency' is used to collate them into common groupings to which tariffs can be applied. In England the chosen currency is healthcare resource groups or HRGs. HRGs place patient procedures and/or diagnoses into bands, which are 'resource homogenous', that is, clinically similar and consuming similar levels of resources.

HRGs 'sit' between top-level specialities and individual patient procedures and treatments, thus reducing the number of individual care profiles that need to be costed. One of the key aims of HRGs is to provide a practical currency to enable sensible discussions between clinicians and managers about the costs of delivering healthcare – it is therefore essential that HRGs are clinically meaningful.

Since 2006/07 HRG version 4 has been used for costing purposes in the reference cost collection. HRG 4 was designed and endorsed by clinicians and developed with the involvement of 33 expert working groups and four expert reference panels. It was developed 'to accurately capture clinical activity in the NHS, irrespective of setting (the place of treatment)'.

HRG 4 comprises more than 1400 groupings arranged into 22 'chapters' each covering a clinical specialty area such as the nervous system or cardiac surgery. The groupings take account of recent developments in healthcare and new interventions, as well as adding a number of previously uncovered areas such as chemotherapy, rehabilitation and critical care.

The HFMA has produced a detailed briefing on HRG 4 (in conjunction with the NHS Information Centre for Health and Social Care) which looks at each HRG chapter in turn and is available via the HFMA's website: www.hfma.org.uk

Procedure/HRG Costing

Although costing of activities is not specifically required at procedure level, trusts may still calculate them as it helps in service planning and in targeting productivity and efficiency initiatives. It is also of particular relevance to negotiations with commissioners about single patient services and specialised services.

In terms of the actual costing process, procedure/HRG costing involves looking at costing from the HRG perspective and uses a mixture of 'top down'[17] and 'bottom up'[18] costing to derive the cost.

Specialty Costing

Specialty costing breaks down the overall cost of providing healthcare into the costs for delivering care within the different healthcare specialties provided. Some costs can be assigned directly to a specialty or cost centre. For instance the cost of an orthopaedic surgeon can be assigned directly to the orthopaedic cost centre. Other costs have to be pooled and then apportioned to the orthopaedic cost centre using an appropriate method. For example, theatre costs could be apportioned on the basis of the time spent in theatre or the sessions used by orthopaedics. Ward costs could be apportioned on the basis of bed days consumed by orthopaedic patients. Overheads and support costs are also apportioned.

At this point a trust has established its specialty cost totals and also knows the various cost pools within that specialty – for example, the theatre costs. The next stage of the process attempts to break down these specialty costs among all the HRGs within that specialty. For instance within orthopaedics, a trust might typically undertake more than 40 different orthopaedic HRGs.

Reference Costs

Reference costs were originally intended for management information purposes, but now also form the basis of the PbR tariff. They record activity levels, unit cost data and average length of stay for a range of specified activities and are collected each year from all providers of health services (acute, community and paramedic) to NHS patients using NHS resources. This includes any activity that has been commissioned from or sub-contracted to non-NHS providers (including independent sector providers). HRG 4 is used as the currency for the reference cost collection and admitted patient care is recorded at both finished consultant episode (FCE) and 'spell' level (a spell is the time from entry to discharge – it is used as the basic denominator for PbR as a patient can pass from one consultant to another during a hospital stay).

Increasingly, NHS organisations are using more detailed 'patient level information and costing systems' (PLICS) that go beyond FCE and spell costing. The Department of Health guidance for

---

[17] Top down costing is where cost pool costs are allocated to HRGs using the total cost of that cost pool weighted for each HRG/procedure based upon the best available data/clinical estimates.

[18] Bottom up costing builds up the costs of that HRG using actual known costs – for example, prosthesis costs in hip replacement HRGs.

the 20010/11 reference cost collection acknowledges this trend but notes that PLICS systems should 'be fully compatible with HRG 4' (for reference costs) resource groupings. See later in this chapter for more on PLICS.

National schedule of reference costs

The submission of reference costs is mandatory for all NHS providers of services and for the commissioning of services for NHS patients who receive care from non NHS providers. The information submitted is collated by the Department of Health and published annually as the national schedule of reference costs (NSRC). The NSRC shows the national average cost for a range of treatments and procedures and can be used by organisations for comparative purposes.

National reference cost index

In addition to the NSRC, a national reference cost index (RCI or NRCI) is published. The RCI gives a single figure (effectively a ranking) for each NHS provider organisation enabling comparisons of their activity with similar providers (for example, district general hospitals) and with providers in their local health economy. In most cases activity is measured in HRGs.

In the index there are a range of scores. For example an organisation with costs equal to the national average for its casemix will score 100; if it scores 125 it shows that costs are 25% above the national average and a score of 75 shows that its costs are 25% below the national average.

A market forces factor (MFF) is also published to recognise the differences in costs in different geographical areas that are outside NHS control. Index scores are published pre and post application of the MFF. The post MFF index is the one generally used.

On the whole, with all other factors being equal, an organisation with a reference cost score (MFF adjusted) of less than 100 can expect to gain financially under PbR as their costs are lower than the tariff (see chapter 13 for more on PbR).

Costing for reference costs

As mentioned above, reference costs is a mandatory annual exercise which captures the total cost to an organisation of the patient contacts that it has had in the previous financial year. Financial costs are allocated and apportioned to the HRGs that the organisation has performed in line with the prescribed classification as set out in guidance issued by the Department of Health each year. Clinical staff feed into the process by identifying the key drivers of costs and the weights which need to be applied to HRGs to reflect the cost of these drivers.

To ensure that all NHS providers' costs are compared on a consistent basis, details of the definitions to be used and refinements to the standard costing approach are set out in reference costs collection guidance and the *NHS Costing Manual*.

Reference costs are based on full costs and all relevant costs are included. The main emphasis is on the cost of delivering a service and not the funding streams that are used to recover the costs.

Cost variations

The most recent reference costs available are for 2009/10 and show that the organisation wide RCI (adjusted for MFF) for NHS trusts and PCTs ranged from 157 to 69. The huge variation can be attributed to a number of factors. Some of the variation will be a result of differences in efficiency and effectiveness leading to real cost differences between providers. However, some of the variation (particularly in relation to outliers) will be the result of poor data quality, inconsistency in the costing and recording of activity between different organisations and because HRGs do not adequately reflect some specialist services.

In the 2009/10 reference costs, there was also substantial variation in the different procedure costs included in the national schedule of reference costs (NSRC) – for example, the national average unit cost of elective inpatient cochlea implants (without complications or co-morbidities) was £17,324, but the inter-quartile range (i.e. the costs of the middle 50% of trusts) stretched from £3,671 to £23,041.

Data quality is a particular cause for concern – in its reference costs guidance for 2010/11 the Department of Health stated that 'there are still a number of organisations where data quality issues are unresolved (for example, levels of unclassified data, erroneous clinical coding, etc). The onus on the production of sound, accurate and timely data rests with each NHS organisation … The implications of poor quality activity and cost data are now far-reaching and will influence the financial position of each NHS organisation under the PbR programme. The need for high quality data cannot be overestimated'.

Service Line Reporting and Management

Another level of costing that is becoming more common in the NHS involves focussing on 'service lines' – in other words looking in detail at the income and costs of an organisation's services in much the same way as a private sector company analyses its business units. In practice, this means that the focus is on profitability information (or the contribution made) by specialty. Service line reporting (SLR) is considered best practice in the FT sector and is also used in other non-foundation trusts. Monitor has issued guidance on SLR which lists the characteristics of a typical service line as being:

• Able to operate as an autonomous business unit
• Having clear decision-making and accountability lines
• Having clinicians in prominent leadership roles.

The information gleaned from SLR is used to 'manage' each service line and develop the FT's business plans with the FT overall effectively managed as 'a portfolio of autonomous and accountable business units'. Costing information gathered at this level is then used to 'manage' each service line (hence 'service line management' or SLM) and develop business plans.

For more about SLR and SLM see chapter 8 and Monitor's website.

Patient Level Information and Costing Systems (PLICS)

As mentioned earlier, systems have been developed at a more detailed level that identify and record the cost of individual patients. This can provide organisations with an extremely rich source of data on which to base their activity and business plans. Patient level costing involves attributing the costs 'consumed' by an individual patient on a basis that is meaningful in clinical terms – in other words it is an approach that recognises that it is the clinical activity that leads to (or 'drives') the associated costs.

The Department of Health's website states that PLICS 'represent a change in the costing methodology in the NHS from a predominantly top down allocation approach, based on averages and apportionments, to a more direct and sophisticated approach based on the actual interactions and events related to individual patients and the associated costs'. Once costs have been identified at individual patient level, they can still be aggregated to HRG-level for wider comparison and to inform the national tariff.

PLICS systems are becoming increasingly common and are encouraged by the Department which identifies the following as key benefits:

- An ability for an organisation to truly understand their economic and financial drivers. PLICS can provide transparency to an organisation of their income and costs at a service and sub service level on a monthly basis. It provides the capability to benchmark, analyse, investigate and evaluate the makeup of the organisation's service costs. There is a further ability to benchmark individual cost elements (for example, nursing costs, drugs, theatre cost) and patient cost profiles against other providers
- Dramatically improved clinical ownership of operating information. Dialogue can be had about resources consumed by individual patients with similar diagnoses and comparisons can be made against peer groups, teams, individuals as well as care pathways
- Provides crucial information to inform any future change in the grouping and classification of patients. A detailed knowledge of the cost distribution of individual patients rather than the average cost is a necessary precondition for best in class classification
- Provides necessary and crucial information to inform funding policy for payment of high and low outliers for each HRG. Distribution of patient cost is again a prerequisite to ensure the calculation and payment of a long term sustainable price to an efficient provider – a critical goal of PbR
- Provides valuable data in discussions with commissioners.

More information about PLICS is available on the Department's website.

Clinical Costing Standards

Another key development in the costing arena is the development of clinical costing standards for acute and mental healthcare. These standards are designed to support a bottom-up approach to costing, setting out recommended best practice in producing patient level costs. A more granular approach to costing still supports the analysis of costs at higher levels such as HRG level, but crucially enables organisations to drill down into this data to understand exactly how costs have been incurred. This provides opportunities to improve pathways for patients and identify potential areas for cost improvement. The standards were initially drawn up by the Department of Health, but their development has subsequently been taken on by the HFMA.

Cost Return and Programme Budgeting

NHS organisations are required to submit a costing return to the Department of Health each year that analyses costs by cost type – for example medical staff and drugs. Since 2004/05 there have also been 'programme budgeting' requirements.

The aim of programme budgeting is to provide a source of information about how the money invested in the NHS is spent. To achieve this, commissioners (currently PCTs) submit data about their spending patterns each year split across 23 broad healthcare headings or 'programmes' (for example, infectious diseases; cancer and tumours). This data is published by the Department and provides a 'benchmarking tool' that commissioners can use to identify how:

- They spend their allocation
- Their spending pattern compares with other commissioners nationally, locally or with similar characteristics
- Their spending pattern has changed over time.

See chapter 3 for the latest programme budgeting data.

What the future holds for Costing

The coalition government's proposals for the NHS do not contain anything specific about costing and it is assumed that the current approach will continue largely unchanged. However, the abolition of PCTs would mean that responsibility for data collection and submission would move to GP consortia.

References and Further Reading

Payment by Results: www.dh.gov.uk/en/Managingyourorganisation/NHSFinancialReforms/index.htm

Costing and cost collection (including the Costing Manual, reference costs, PLICS and clinical costing standards), Department of Health: www.dh.gov.uk/en/Managingyourorganisation/NHScostingmanual/index.htm

Healthcare Resource Groups Version 4: www.ic.nhs.uk/services/the-casemix-service

HFMA Briefing on HRG4, March 2008 www.hfma.org.uk/TrainingAndDevelopment/InformationServices/

The Information Centre for Health and Social Care: www.ic.nhs.uk

Monitor (for guidance on service line reporting and management): www.monitor-nhsft.gov.uk

Programme budgeting: www.dh.gov.uk/en/Managingyourorganisation/Financeandplanning/Programmebudgeting/DH_075743

13. Payment by Results

Introduction

Payment by results (PbR) is a system of financial flows that was introduced to 'reward efficiency, support patient choice and diversity and encourage activity for sustainable waiting time reductions'.[19] Under PbR, payments made to providers of care for NHS patients, be they from the NHS, private or independent sector, are linked to the activity and services actually provided. Payment is based on a national tariff that recognises the type, mix and severity of the treatment. It is intended to be a fair and consistent basis for financing providers, rather than one based on historical budgets and negotiating skills.

PbR does not in itself affect the way funding is allocated to commissioners (currently PCTs) – they still receive allocations from the Department of Health based on a weighted capitation formula (see chapter 3). However, PbR does require commissioners to develop a stronger focus on service quality and demand management.

Why was PbR introduced?

In the 2002 budget a large and sustained increase in NHS funding was announced and the then labour government wanted to be sure that these resources were used to develop and deliver more and better services. This in turn required a system of financial flows that contained the right balance of reward, incentive and equity – hence the introduction of PbR.

Before PbR was introduced, PCTs had 'block contracts' with the hospitals that their patients used. Many of these were not based on activity, work done and/or achievement of plans – the hospital effectively received a block of funding irrespective of the number of patients treated or the type of treatment provided. Providers were not rewarded for achieving budgets or increasing activity. Management of demand was variable and costs and benefits of different patterns of activity were not always clear.

Block contracts were generally based on historical patterns of care and reflected local costs irrespective of relative cost efficiency when compared to the rest of the NHS. Because service level agreements (SLAs) were set at local prices, PCTs' real purchasing power was affected as much by the relative costs of their principal providers as by the resource allocation formula. Block contracts were also very limited in their ability to respond to changes in patterns of service provision or patient casemix.

The flow of funds under the 'old' system is shown below. In this example, trust A has high costs and trust B low costs – as a result, PCT 1 was commissioning at high local prices and PCT 2 at low local prices:

---

[19] Department of Health's website.

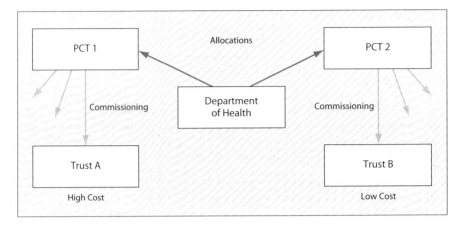

PbR was designed to overcome these limitations by:

- Reimbursing providers fairly and transparently for the services they deliver
- Encouraging PCTs to plan and manage demand for services more effectively
- Rewarding efficiency and quality in service provision
- Enabling patients to be treated at the provider of their choice as payment is at a fixed price and follows the patient
- Applying to all providers of healthcare to NHS patients irrespective of their organisational or legal status, be they public or private providers.

PbR was therefore a key tool in the delivery of the labour government's reform agenda and changed the way funds flow through the NHS, as shown in the diagram that follows – again, trust A is high cost and trust B low cost:

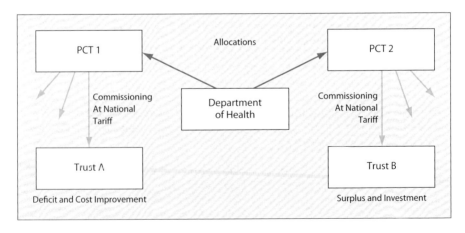

What is Payment by Results?

PbR is based around the use of a prospective tariff that links a preset price to a defined measure of output or activity. The two key issues are therefore:

- How is the activity measure defined?
- How is the tariff determined?

Activity measurement is not uncommon or new in the NHS but is more advanced in acute services, where models of defining and measuring casemix have been developed over the past 35 years. These have generally used, as a starting point, the methods and methodologies developed by Fetter and colleagues in the USA in the 1970s, which led to the development of diagnostic related groups (DRGs). English variants, known as healthcare resource groups or HRGs were developed by the NHS Information Authority (now the NHS Information Centre for Health and Social Care). PbR uses the HRG classification of casemix as the basis for making payments as they are the most developed and comprehensive tools in England for classifying the outputs of the health system. At present, HRGs mainly cover the acute sector, with significant gaps in other areas – for example, in mental health and ambulance services. The latest version – HRG 4 – has been designed to be setting independent (i.e. the HRG applies for a procedure regardless of where it takes place) and to support the provision of components of healthcare outside of hospitals through the use of unbundled tariffs (i.e. the payment can be split between providers).

HRGs group services that are clinically similar and require similar resources for treatment and care. They are often referred to as the 'currency' that is used for commissioning. They have been developed by clinicians in order to provide clinically meaningful groups of patients who require similar levels of resources. There are some 1400 HRGs in HRG 4. If you want to know more, the HFMA has produced a detailed briefing in conjunction with the NHS Information Centre for Health and Social Care.

A tariff for reimbursement – effectively a national set of prices – is published annually by the Department of Health based on the average reference costs for HRGs as reported by the NHS (see chapter 12 for more about reference costs).

How the Tariff is set

As mentioned above, the tariff is based on information provided by NHS organisations. There is effectively a four stage process:

- Stage 1 – activity is coded. Clinical coders assign a diagnosis or procedure code to activity based on the patient notes or discharge summary
- Stage 2 – HRG is assigned. Activity is automatically assigned to an HRG (via software called the HRG grouper) based on the diagnosis or procedure codes – as logged by the clinical coder
- Stage 3 – local costs are submitted to the Department of Health. In the summer each year, all providers are required to submit details of their activity, costed locally, to the Department for all their provided services. Costs and activity are based on the previous financial year – for example, for the June 2010 submission, costs and activity were based on the 2009/10 financial year
- Stage 4 – the Department of Health calculates the prospective national tariff. This involves working out the national average local cost for each HRG/service within the scope of PbR. From 2010/11 (i.e. when reference costs are submitted in July 2011), these

costs will be based on 'spells' (rather than 'finished consultant episodes'). These costs are then uplifted to create a prospective tariff for the coming financial year. For example, reference costs submitted to the Department of Health in July 2011 for the financial year 2010/11 will form the basis of the 2013/14 national tariff. The tariff is calculated annually based on the reference cost submission. Each year, tariff prices are adjusted (or 'uplifted') to reflect inflation, generic cost pressures, changes in technology and practice (for example, the cost of recommendations made by the National Institute for Health and Clinical Excellence – NICE) and assumptions on efficiency improvements. For 2011/12 the tariff has been reduced by 1.5% – i.e. the amount of the required efficiency improvement is greater than the increase to reflect cost pressures and inflation. The Department may also make a number of 'normative' changes to individual tariffs to correct known problems or to provide an incentive to drive a specific behaviour.

The table that follows shows some examples of the combined day case/elective tariff for 2010/11 and 2011/12. In both years the tariff uses HRG 4 (introduced as the basis for the tariff from 2009/10). The structure of the tariff under HRG 4 means that the treatment of patients with complications or co-morbidities (i.e. the presence of one or more condition/disorder/disease in addition to a primary disease) is recognised in the tariff payment (this is shown as 'with or without cc' in the description). The differences in prices between the two years are a result of three influencing factors:

- The efficiency included within the tariff for 2011/12 through setting the price below the average (as described above)
- The uplift for cost increases (as mentioned above)
- The use of a more recent set of reference costs. (In theory, as costing practices improve, reference costs should become more accurate leading to more accurate tariffs. This practice of refreshing the reference costs can lead to significant changes in tariff rates, both up and down).

HRG	HRG Name	Tariff (£) 2010/11	Tariff (£) 2011/12
CZ01Y	Minor mouth or throat procedures19 years and over without cc	436	476
HA11C	Major hip procedures category 2 for trauma without cc	9,038	6,292
HA26B	Minor knee procedures category 1 for trauma with cc	1,620	1,253
LA07A	Acute kidney injury with major cc	3,554	5,009

Cost Differences

As the tariff is based on the average cost of each HRG, providers receive either more or less than they need to cover their costs. There can be a number of reasons why costs vary including casemix (for example, a hospital that undertakes more of the higher cost procedures within a particular HRG may not cover its higher costs from a tariff set on average costs), clinical practice, local initiatives and market forces.

The area that generates most debate is the impact of market forces on an organisation's costs – it is simply a matter of fact that organisations in some parts of the country have higher costs purely because of their location and because labour, land, buildings and even equipment cost more. These differences are unavoidable and to ensure equity, a compensating adjustment is made. This adjustment is called the market forces factor or MFF. The most obvious area affected is London and the South East.

Until 2009/10, the MFF relating to activity covered by PbR was paid by the Department of Health directly to providers as a separate sum rather than making an adjustment to the tariff. This was designed to avoid price based competition and discourage PCTs from directing patients to services provided by trusts in a lower MFF zone. However, since April 2009 the MFF for PbR activity is included within each PCT's allocation. It is not yet clear how the MFF will operate under the coalition government's new regime.

How PbR has Developed

PbR was a fundamental change to the way money moved around the NHS. To allow time for organisations to prepare and manage transitional issues, a five-year programme was set for its introduction (from 2003 to 2008) with the original aim that by 2008 all commissioning would be within the framework of PbR. However, this objective was not achieved and a number of activities remain outside the scope of PbR – most notably community, mental health and ambulance services, although steps are being taken to introduce tariff prices to these areas in the future.

At a practical level, the Department issues guidance on how PbR should work in practice. The key publication here is the *Code of Conduct for Payment by Results*, which (as the Department's website states) aims to:

* 'establish core principles, with some ground rules for organisational behaviour, and expectations as to how the system should operate
* minimise disputes, as well as guide the resolution of them'.

A major consultation on the future development of PbR took place during 2007/08 with the publication of *Options for the Future of Payment by Results: 2008/09 to 20010/11*. This set out three basic principles:

* PbR must make clinical sense
* NHS organisations require stability and predictability as PbR continues to grow
* Local innovation should be encouraged in pursuit of national objectives.

One key proposal in the consultation was for PbR to mean more than simply a national tariff. It was proposed that depending on the services covered, three models were possible:

* National currency and price
* National currency, local price
* Local currency and price.

The consultation also raised the possibility of using costs from a sample of providers to set the tariff, rather than using national averages, and expanding the use of normative pricing (i.e.

setting a tariff price based on a judgement about what efficiencies can be achieved or to encourage the take-up or dropping of particular treatments/activities).

The Department of Health response to the consultation in January 2008 outlined a number of key themes for future work in PbR. These were to:

- Get the building blocks right – ensuring that the PbR infrastructure (i.e. classifications, coding, casemix, costing and currencies) was as robust as possible
- Ensure that future work was in line with the findings of Lord Darzi's review (*Our NHS, Our Future*). This meant developing a tariff that 'supports the localising of care where possible and the centralising of treatment where necessary'. This also involved examining 'the effect on casemix of shifting care out of hospitals' and looking at 'how PbR can better support the functioning of clinical networks and co-operation between providers'
- Expand the scope – the five priority areas identified were mental health, community services, critical care, urgent and emergency care and long term conditions
- Encourage local involvement in the development of PbR (i.e. so that it is locally driven)
- Involve clinicians at all levels so that PbR is 'clinically led'.

Quality

Another key development affecting PbR was the renewed focus on quality which led to the introduction of four best practice tariffs in 2010/11 for two elective and two emergency high volume areas of service, namely:

- Cataracts
- Cholecystectomy (gall bladder removal)
- Fragility hip fracture
- Stroke.

Best practice tariffs aim to bring together quality and efficiency by rewarding high quality care. Rather than being set at the national average cost of delivering the procedures concerned, they reflect the costs of delivering best practice, for example by undertaking cholecystectomies as a day case procedure or admitting stroke patients directly to a dedicated stroke unit. The standard tariff (i.e. *not* best practice) is set lower than the normal tariff price. An addition to this is then applied to give the best practice tariff. As a result, there is a financial incentive for providers to adopt best practice patient pathways and treatments as those providers failing to deliver best practice will attract a lower payment for their activity. As this is applied across the NHS in England, national improvements in the quality of care in these areas should be achieved.

This approach has been extended for 2011/12 with the number of best practice tariffs increased to include:

- Interventional radiology
- Primary hip and knee replacements
- Transient ischaemic attacks (mini-strokes)
- Paediatric diabetes
- Adult renal dialysis.

In addition, changes in tariff prices will support the overall policy of increasing the number of patients treated in a day case setting rather than being admitted to hospital. To that end, best practice tariffs in 2011/12 also include twelve specific day case procedures across the following specialties:

- Breast surgery
- General surgery – for the treatment of hernias
- Gynaecology/urology
- Orthopaedic surgery
- Urology.

The *Operating Framework 2011/12* makes clear that the expansion of best practice tariffs 'will accelerate in 2012/13 and beyond'.

The introduction of best practice tariffs came at a time when the reward available to healthcare providers under commissioning for quality and innovation (CQUIN) schemes was increased to 1.5% of contract income in 2010/11 and 2011/12 with an expectation that this percentage may rise in future years.

Scope

Although community, mental health and ambulance services currently remain outside the scope of PbR, significant steps are being taken to pave the way for the introduction of a tariff to these services. A new currency (a unit of healthcare for which payment is made) for adult mental health services will be available for use in shadow form in 2011/12 in order to establish local prices for these services. In addition, the collection of ambulance service reference cost data based on the outcome of calls made to the service will facilitate the introduction of a national tariff in 2013/14.

Currencies will be introduced for a number of other services during 2011/12 to increase coverage, although prices will still be agreed via local negotiations between commissioners and providers. This model of national currency, local price covers three areas:

- Adult and neonatal critical care
- Cystic fibrosis
- Smoking cessation.

Following the publication of the coalition government's plans for the NHS in 2010, it is expected that the speed with which new currencies are developed will increase, with the scope of PbR widening as a result.

Influence

Increasingly, the tariff is used to influence the behaviour of those commissioning and providing services to patients and to support the overall strategic aims of the NHS. For example, in 2010/11 a change to the way in which accident and emergency activity was paid for was introduced to:

- Facilitate closer working between PCTs and provider organisations
- Minimise the number of emergency admissions to hospital
- Support the movement of care out of hospitals into the community.

This change (which continues in 2011/12), involves providers of accident and emergency services being paid at full tariff for the number of patients attending emergency departments up to the value of the activity recorded for the baseline financial year 2008/09 (costed at 2010/11 tariff). However, attendances over and above this baseline are paid only at a marginal rate of 30% of tariff. Therefore, health economies where the accident and emergency admissions consistently exceed the contracted level have an incentive to redesign services and manage patient demand for those services. The money which the PCT would have spent on paying for 'over performance' at full tariff in previous years is managed by strategic health authorities in order to change the way these services are provided.

In a similar vein, the *Operating Framework 2011/12* confirms the announcement made by the coalition government soon after it came to power in 2010 that from 2011/12, service providers will no longer receive any further payment for a patient admitted within 30 days of their discharge following an elective admission (in other words, hospitals are now responsible for patients' care for 30 days after they are discharged). This comes into effect from April 2011 although there will be a number of exclusions (for example, maternity patients). To support the drive to reduce readmission rates, commissioners will not make a payment for patients readmitted to hospital following an emergency admission within 30 days, over and above an agreed threshold. Any savings made by commissioners as a result of these changes will need to be disclosed and will be used to support patients following discharge from hospital.

What the future holds for PbR

As can be seen from the changes introduced for 2011/12, the coalition government plans to retain PbR but with an increased focus on the quality of service delivery and structured around outcomes. In particular the government wants to use the tariff to deliver four priorities as outlined by David Flory (NHS Deputy Chief Executive) in his letter to the NHS in December 2010. This set out four key principles underpinning the tariff:

- Incentivising quality and better patient outcomes
- Embedding efficiency within the tariff
- Integration and patient responsiveness
- Expanding the scope of PbR.

The government has also indicated that in certain circumstances, the tariff will represent the maximum price payable by a commissioner for patient activity.

As far as the mechanics of PbR are concerned the Department of Health will no longer be responsible for setting the PbR tariff. Instead, under the new regime (subject to any amendments agreed to the *Health and Social Care Bill 2011*), Monitor and the NHS Commissioning Board will assume joint responsibility for setting prices with Monitor focusing on designing the pricing methodology and using it to set prices and the Commissioning Board developing the pricing structure.

Monitor will be able to alter tariffs but only in relation to a new category of service – namely those services that are 'designated as subject to additional regulation' which will be identified in providers' licences. These are services which, if lost would result in 'material damage to patients' – in other words, essential services for which there is no immediate alternative or re-provision if they cease (this effectively builds on mandatory services in the current system). However, if the tariff is altered, the regulator would have to pay heed to a number of duties – to protect patients and the public through competition where appropriate and regulation where necessary, to promote efficiency and to adhere to European Union rules (ensuring providers do not gain an unfair competitive advantage or the tariff change does not constitute unlawful state aid).

References and Further Reading

The Department of Health publications referred to in this chapter are available on the Payment by Results pages of its website: www.dh.gov.uk/en/Managingyourorganisation/ NHSFinancialReforms/index.htm

Fetter R.B: DRGs, their design and development, Health, Administration Press, Ann Arbor, Michigan 1991

DRGs and Healthcare, Bardsley, Coles, Jenkins (eds) Kings Fund, London 1987

For information about the latest version of HRGs, go to the NHS Information Centre for Health and Social Care: www.ic.nhs.uk/casemix

HFMA Briefing on HRG4, March 2008: www.hfma.org.uk/TrainingAndDevelopment/ InformationServices/

Reference Costs, Department of Health: www.dh.gov.uk/en/Managingyourorganisation/ NHScostingmanual/index.htm

Code of Conduct for Payment by Results, Department of Health, 2011: www.dh.gov.uk/en/ Publicationsandstatistics/Publications/PublicationsPolicyAndGuidance/DH_124426

Options for the Future of PbR – 2008/09 to 2010/11 (consultation paper and response) – Department of Health archived web pages: http://webarchive.nationalarchives.gov.uk/+/ www.dh.gov.uk/en/Consultations/Responsestoconsultations/DH_082424

Our NHS, Our Future: NHS Next Stage Review Interim Report, Department of Health, 2007: www.dh.gov.uk/en/Publicationsandstatistics/Publications/PublicationsPolicyAndGuidance/ DH_079077

Commissioning for Quality and Innovation (CQUIN), Department of Health: www.dh.gov.uk/en/ Publicationsandstatistics/Publications/PublicationsPolicyAndGuidance/DH_091443

Operating Frameworks for the NHS in England, Department of Health: www.dh.gov.uk/en/ Managingyourorganisation/Financeandplanning/Planningframework/index.htm

14. Financial and Performance Reporting

Introduction

Every NHS organisation needs to provide timely, accurate and balanced information about its stewardship, use of resources and non-financial performance to its stakeholders. This information should be presented in a form that is tailored to user needs, is easy to understand and highlights key issues. Also, to run organisations effectively, management needs to receive up-to-date financial and non-financial performance information on a timely basis.

This chapter considers the nature of financial and performance reporting in the NHS by considering in turn:

- External reporting
- Internal reporting
- Financial performance targets
- Financial performance management
- Non-financial performance standards and targets
- Performance assessment.

External Reporting

Statutory requirements

All NHS bodies have a statutory duty to produce annual accounts. For NHS trusts, primary care trusts (PCTs) and strategic health authorities (SHAs) the relevant legislation at present is section 232 and paragraph 3(1) of schedule 15 of the *NHS Act 2006*; for NHS foundation trusts (FTs) the relevant legislation is section 30 and paragraph 25(1) of schedule 7 of the *NHS Act 2006*. The form and content of the accounts is prescribed by the Secretary of State for Health – or the independent regulator for FTs (Monitor). The production of the statutory annual accounts is the principal means by which NHS bodies discharge their accountability to taxpayers and users of services for their stewardship of public money.

NHS accounting framework

Since 2009/10, international financial reporting standards (IFRS) have been followed for the preparation of accounts. These standards are intended to provide a framework for good practice and the common disclosure of information and a benchmark against which an organisation's audited accounts are judged. Implementation of IFRS resulted in significant changes to the treatment of PFI funded assets and leases, holiday accruals and non-current assets. There were also a number of changes in disclosure requirements.

Although NHS bodies now adhere to the accounting standards issued or endorsed by the International Accounting Standards Board (IASB), the government has the final say on how these standards are applied to the public sector, including NHS bodies. The Treasury has developed a *Financial Reporting Manual* setting out how the accounting standards should be implemented in the public sector. At present, the Department of Health also produces a *Manual for Accounts* for SHAs, PCTs and NHS trusts that is consistent with the requirements of the *Financial Reporting Manual* and which NHS bodies are required to follow. Monitor produces a similar manual for FTs, called the *NHS Foundation Trust Annual Reporting Manual*. These manuals are updated each year and include a summary of the relevant accounting standards. However, if an organisation needs a more detailed understanding of a particular aspect it should refer to the relevant standard in full.

A list of current standards issued as international accounting standards (IAS), international financial reporting standards (IFRS), and their interpretations (IFRIC and SIC) and their applicability to the NHS is shown in the table that follows.

Number	Subject	Applicable?
IAS 1	Presentation of Financial Statements	Yes
IAS 2	Inventories	Yes
IAS 7	Cash Flow Statements	Yes
IAS 8	Accounting Policies, Changes in Accounting Estimates and Errors	Yes
IAS 10	Events after the Balance Sheet Date	Yes
IAS 11	Construction Contracts	No
IAS 12	Income Taxes	No
IAS 16	Property, Plant and Equipment	Yes
IAS 17	Leases	Yes
IAS 18	Revenue	Yes
IAS 19	Employee Benefits	Yes
IAS 20	Accounting for Government Grants and Disclosure of Government Assistance	Yes
IAS 21	The Effects of Changes in Foreign Exchange Rates	Yes
IAS 23	Borrowing Costs	Yes – but cost of capital is not a borrowing cost and therefore does not fall under IAS 23
IAS 24	Related Party Disclosures	Yes
IAS 26	Accounting and Reporting by Retirement Benefit Plans	No
IAS 27	Consolidated and Separate Financial Statements	Yes
IAS 28	Investments in Associates	Applies to NHS trusts only

Number	Subject	Applicable?
IAS 29	Financial Reporting in Hyperinflationary Economies	No
IAS 31	Interests in Joint Ventures	Yes
IAS 32	Financial Instruments: Presentation	Yes
IAS 33	Earnings per Share	No
IAS 34	Interim Financial Reporting	Only applicable if bodies elect to publish interim financial reports
IAS 36	Impairment of Assets	Yes
IAS 37	Provisions, Contingent Liabilities and Contingent Assets	Yes
IAS 38	Intangible Assets	Yes
IAS 39	Financial Instruments: Recognition and Measurement	Yes
IAS 40	Investment Properties	No
IAS 41	Agriculture	No
IFRS 1	First-time Adoption of International Financial Reporting Standards	Yes
IFRS 2	Share-based Payment	No
IFRS 3	Business Combinations	Yes
IFRS 4	Insurance Contracts	No
IFRS 5	Non-current Assets Held for Sale and Discontinued Operations	Yes
IFRS 6	Exploration for and Evaluation of Mineral Resources	No
IFRS 7	Financial Instruments: Disclosures	Yes, but not relevant currently
IFRS 8	Operating Segments	Yes
SIC 7	Introduction of the Euro	Yes
SIC 10	Government Assistance – No Specific Relation to Operating Activities	Yes
SIC 12	Consolidation – Special Purpose Entities	Yes

Number	Subject	Applicable?
SIC 13	Jointly Controlled Entities – Non-Monetary Contributions by Venturers	Applies to NHS trusts only
SIC 15	Operating Leases – Incentives	Yes
SIC 21	Income Taxes – Recovery of Revalued Non-depreciable Assets	No
SIC 25	Income Taxes – Changes in the Tax Status of an Entity or its Shareholders	No
SIC 27	Evaluating the Substance of Transactions Involving the Legal Form of a Lease	Yes
SIC 29	Service Concession Arrangements: Disclosures	Yes
SIC 31	Revenue – Barter Transactions Involving Advertising Services	Yes
SIC 32	Intangible Assets – Web Site Costs	Yes
IFRIC 1	Changes in Existing Decommissioning, Restoration and Similar Liabilities	Yes, but circumstances unlikely to arise
IFRIC 2	Members' Shares in Co-operative Entities and Similar Instruments	No
IFRIC 4	Determining whether an Arrangement contains a Lease	Yes
IFRIC 5	Rights to Interests arising from Decommissioning, Restoration and Environmental Rehabilitation Funds	No
IFRIC 6	Liabilities arising from Participating in a Specific Market – Waste Electrical and Electronic Equipment	No
IFRIC 7	Applying the Restatement Approach under IAS 29 *Financial Reporting in Hyperinflationary Economies*	No
IFRIC 8	Scope of IFRS 2	No
IFRIC 9	Reassessment of Embedded Derivatives	Yes
IFRIC 10	Interim Financial Reporting and Impairment	Applies if bodies elect to publish interim financial reports
IFRIC 11	Group and Treasury Share Transactions	No
IFRIC 12	Service Concession Arrangements	Yes

Number	Subject	Applicable?
IFRIC 13	Customer Loyalty Programmes	No
IFRIC 14	IAS 19 – The Limit on a Defined Benefit Asset, Minimum Funding Requirements and their Interaction	Relevant where NHS bodies have pension assets and liabilities for staff still in a Local Government Pension Scheme
IFRIC 15	Agreements for the Construction of Real Estate	No
IFRIC 16	Hedges of a Net Investment in a Foreign Operation	No
IFRIC 17	Distributions of non-cash assets to owners	No
IFRIC 18	Transfer of assets from customers	Yes, but circumstances unlikely to arise

Annual accounts

The Department's *Manuals for Accounts* and the *NHS Foundation Trust Annual Reporting Manual* specify the format and timing of the annual accounts. The format of the accounts differs slightly depending upon the type of NHS body concerned, but consist of:

- The foreword to the accounts
- The four primary statements:
  - Statement of comprehensive income (formerly the income and expenditure statement) or operating cost statement
  - Statement of financial position (formerly the balance sheet)
  - Statement of changes in taxpayers' equity (formerly the statement of total recognised gains and losses)
  - Statement of cash flows (formerly the cash flow statement)
- Notes to the accounts
- Statements and certificates: directors' statement of responsibilities (for FTs – the accounting officer's statement of responsibilities); the statement on internal control (SIC); and the auditors' report.

To help non-executive directors and others to understand the accounts of PCTs, NHS trusts and FTs, the HFMA and the Audit Commission have produced a series of practical guides – see their websites for details.

Once the NHS body has prepared the annual accounts they must be audited. After the accounts have been audited and any necessary amendments made, the board is required to formally adopt the accounts. The certificates will be signed at the same time. The auditor then signs the audit report.

NHS bodies must publish an annual report and audited accounts as one document and present it at a public meeting. NHS bodies can also prepare and distribute an annual report and summary financial statements – however, this is additional to the annual report and accounts, which must be available if requested by a member of the public. The auditors must be given a copy of the annual report along with the accounts and working papers at the start of the audit so that they have sufficient time to carry out the required work before the completion of the auditor's opinion. Other quantitative aspects of the annual report are reviewed by auditors to ensure consistency with the annual accounts. To find out more about the work of auditors see chapter 15.

As well as preparing the statutory annual accounts, NHS trusts, PCTs and SHAs are required to submit financial monitoring and accounts (FMA) forms to the Department of Health. The FMA forms are consistent with the annual accounts, but contain slightly different information and are used by the Department to prepare the summarised accounts for each type of NHS body and the Department's own resource account. Similarly FTs have to complete consolidation schedules which are used by Monitor to produce a summary of FT accounts. The use of FMA forms and consolidation schedules also facilitates the preparation of whole of government accounts (WGA).

The *Manuals for Accounts/FT Annual Reporting Manual* set out the timetable for completion of the accounts and audit. The timetable for accounts production has been brought forward over recent years and for 2010/11, draft accounts must be submitted for audit by 21 April 2011 with an audit deadline of 10 June 2011. FTs currently work to a slightly quicker timetable – they must submit audited accounts by 7th June 2011.

Annual report

As mentioned above, all NHS bodies are required to produce an annual report which must be published with the full set of audited accounts. The annual report is primarily a narrative document similar to the directors' report described in the *Companies Act*, but with additional information reflecting the NHS body's position in the community. The report gives an account of the body's activities and performance over the last financial year.

Although the layout of the annual report is not prescribed, the *Manuals for Accounts* specify the areas that should be covered – these are *Companies Act* requirements which apply to NHS bodies.

It is also best practice for the public sector to produce an 'operating and financial review' (OFR). A reporting statement by the ASB makes it clear that the detailed content of the OFR must be decided by the board. It is therefore the responsibility of the directors of each NHS body to ensure that the OFR includes reference to current performance and policy targets. The OFR should include details of performance that are not reported in the annual accounts including useful non-financial and financial information. The HFMA has produced guidance on preparing OFRs which is available on its website.

The annual report must be approved by the NHS body's Board of Directors before presentation at a public meeting. This meeting must be held before 30 September following the end of the relevant financial year. For FTs, the annual report and accounts must be presented to a meeting of the Board of Governors. This meeting should be convened within a reasonable timescale after the end of the financial year, but must not be before the FT has laid its annual report and accounts before Parliament (see chapter 8 for more about FTs).

Internal Reporting

Reporting to budget holders

The reporting of performance against the budget and any corrective action taken as a result is an essential element of financial management in the NHS. Budget reporting to budget holders must therefore be sufficiently detailed to ensure that all significant variances are identified and issues that need to be corrected are highlighted.

Budget monitoring information is produced at a range of levels, allowing managers to see not only summary performance, but also the performance of individual departments and teams. The exact nature of this reporting depends on the organisation's management structure but in each case it is essential that the information is timely, accurate and fit for purpose. To ensure accuracy, financial commitments should be recognised as soon as possible and be reflected in the monthly financial reports. Without accurate budget reporting at budget holder level, costs cannot be controlled properly. These reports on income and expenditure are often referred to as the 'management accounts'.

Over recent years a development in the management accounting field has introduced the concepts of service line reporting (SLR) and patient level costing. A service line is a distinct clinical operating unit, with clearly definable income and costs. SLR is made possible through the payment by results (PbR) system and allows a trust to see the profitability of each of its service lines, not just the overall position. This approach allows clinicians and managers to better understand cost drivers and the financial effect of clinical decisions. It also provides the evidence to support strategic decisions such as investment and expansion of particular service lines.

Patient level costing is the natural extension of service line reporting. Whereas SLR analyses costs and revenues at departmental level, patient level costing assigns costs and revenues to individual patient spells. This is more complex and requires detailed recording of all activity relating to a patient spell – for example, operating theatre time; the time spent by individual clinicians and the amount of drugs and other medical supplies used. However, the benefit is increased accuracy both in terms of reporting and in relation to reference cost returns, on which the PbR tariff is based (see chapter 12 for more about costing and chapter 13 for PbR).

NHS bodies should ensure that budget holders receive continuous training so that they have sufficient skills to undertake the task of budget management.

Reporting to NHS boards

NHS boards need financial information if they are to properly direct the organisation. This information has to be accurate and timely so that the board can take early and corrective action where necessary. The form and content of board financial reports will vary and it is for the board to identify the format, content and frequency of the financial information that it receives. The types of information NHS bodies may report to their boards include:

- Performance against the achievement of statutory and departmental duties and targets (see later in this chapter)
- In-year income and expenditure position and year-end forecasts, including an analysis of financial risks, the likelihood of them arising and how they will be managed
- Activity levels linked to financial data
- Progress on the achievement of any cost improvement programmes and financial recovery plans
- Statement of financial position
- Cash forecast
- Losses
- Performance of outsourced services
- Progress against internal and external audit recommendations
- Progress on major capital schemes
- Staffing and establishment reports.

As well as considering the above on a monthly basis, there is financial information that the board needs to consider every year, including:

- Annual accounts
- Financial plans
- Annual audit letters.

The board should also be updated and advised regularly on the nature and development of new systems and initiatives in the NHS so that they are better able to understand the implications and prepared to manage the impact when implementation takes place.

Information produced for both internal and external purposes should be derived from the same financial system – this will ensure consistency in reports and that decisions throughout the organisation are made on the basis of the same information.

Financial Performance Targets

NHS bodies are subject to a range of statutory and departmental financial targets. The targets and their nature vary according to the type of NHS body – those that apply in 2011/12 are shown below:

NHS trusts

Statutory duties (i.e. that are a formal requirement of trusts as laid down in statute through Parliament)	• Income and expenditure balance (the 'break-even duty'). Every trust has to ensure that its revenue is not less than sufficient, taking one financial year with another, to meet outgoings properly charged to the statement of comprehensive income (formerly the income and expenditure account) • 'Taking one financial year with another' has been interpreted to mean that over a three (or exceptionally a five) year period, trusts are required to achieve break-even position in the statement of comprehensive income. Further details on trusts' financial duties and surpluses and deficits are set out in chapter 7.

Departmental (i.e. an additional rule and regulation set down by the Department of Health that clarifies or specifies how a trust will operate)	• Every trust must break-even each and every year
	• The external financing limit (EFL). The EFL is a control on a trust's net cash flows. It sets a limit on the level of cash that an NHS trust may:
	  – draw from either external sources or its own cash reserves (a positive EFL) **OR**
	  – repay to external sources to increase cash reserves (a negative EFL)
	A target EFL is set at the start of the financial year by the Department of Health and the trust is expected to manage its resources to ensure it achieves the target (see chapters 7 and 16). Trusts must not overshoot their EFL.
	• Capital cost absorption. Trusts are required to achieve a cost of capital absorption equivalent to 3.5% of average relevant net assets. Relevant net assets are calculated as follows:

Total capital and reserves	X
minus donated asset reserve	(−)
minus assets in the course of construction	(−)
minus cash held in paymaster accounts	(−)
Total relevant net assets	Y

	• The capital resource limit (CRL). Measured on an accruals basis, expenditure must remain within CRLs set by the Department of Health for accrued capital expenditure each year. The trust is required to stay within this limit when measuring gross capital expenditure less the book value of assets disposed of during the year • Apply the *Better Payment Practice Code*. Trusts have to achieve a public sector payment standard of valid invoices paid within 30 days of the receipt of the invoice. A target (currently 95%) is set at the start of the year by the Department of Health for the value and volume of invoices that must be paid within 30 days.

PCTs and SHAs

Statutory	• Keep expenditure, measured on an accruals basis, within revenue resource limits (RRLs). The RRL is set by the Department of Health for accrued revenue expenditure. PCTs and SHAs are required to stay within this limit when measuring gross revenue expenditure less miscellaneous income • Keep expenditure, measured on an accruals basis, within CRLs set by the Department of Health each year for accrued capital expenditure. PCTs and SHAs are required to stay within this limit when measuring gross capital expenditure less the book value of assets disposed of during the year • Remain within cash limits. There is a combined cash limit for both revenue and capital.

Departmental	• Apply the *Better Payment Practice Code*. PCTs and SHAs have to achieve a public sector payment standard of valid invoices paid within 30 days of the receipt of the invoice. A target (currently 95%) is set at the start of the year by the Department of Health for the value and volume of invoices that must be paid within 30 days.

NHS foundation trusts

FTs' financial targets differ significantly from NHS trusts. There is no requirement for FTs to break-even, remain within an external financing limit, achieve a predetermined capital cost absorption rate or remain within a capital resource limit. This reflects the different financial regime that FTs operate within. FTs are allowed to incur deficits and operate on a similar basis to commercial organisations. However, under the terms of their authorisation, FTs must 'operate effectively, efficiently and economically and as a going concern' and 'comply with a range of operational and financial requirements'. In effect this means that FTs' main financial target is to remain solvent.

At present, FTs also have to comply with:

• A statutory limit on the increase in income from private patient activity. The proportion of income from private patient activity relative to total income must be no greater than it was for the predecessor NHS trust. This is known as the 'private patient income cap'
• Monitor's *Prudential Borrowing Code*. Each FT is set a prudential borrowing limit (PBL) by Monitor which is reviewed at least annually. FTs must keep the total of all their borrowing from all sources within the set PBL.

More details on FTs, their financial regime and how things are set to change over the coming years (including the removal of the private patient income cap and borrowing controls) are set out in chapter 8.

Financial Performance Management

NHS boards are responsible for ensuring that there are high standards of financial stewardship through effective financial planning, financial control and ensuring value for money. To achieve this, NHS boards require an effective system of financial and performance reporting. It is for the board to decide the form and content of the reports it requires and it should review its information needs regularly. The board should also make use of assessments carried out by external bodies.

The Department of Health requires the financial performance of NHS bodies to be monitored on a regular basis. The first element of the financial performance management process is the financial plan. All NHS organisations are required to undertake medium term financial planning and as part of this process, the organisation must plan to achieve its financial duties. The plan must cover all expected sources of income and expenditure and the full range of responsibilities under the management of the organisation.

At present, SHAs require PCTs and NHS trusts to report regularly on their financial performance against the plan submitted at the start of the financial year to ensure that there is effective financial management of NHS resources. This information is collated by the SHA and reported to the Department of Health. The timing of the reporting to the Department is designed to reflect the information requirements of Parliament. The Parliamentary requirements are:

- Reporting the national revenue and capital financial position
- To inform Parliamentary estimates
- To ensure effective management of the Department of Health vote.

Under the current regime (2011/12), the Department of Health expects the Director of Finance at the SHA to alert it immediately if there are any significant variances against NHS trust or PCT plans and to ensure that appropriate recovery plans are put into place.

Although Monitor does not performance manage FTs in the same way, it does receive information from them on a regular basis with the frequency depending on each FT's risk rating. Monitor compares the information received against the annual plan submitted at the beginning of the year and will take action if there are significant deviations (see chapter 8 for more about FTs and the role of Monitor).

Non-financial Performance Standards and Targets

As well as financial targets, there are a number of other targets that NHS bodies are required to meet. The *Health and Social Care (Community Health and Standards) Act 2003* established the power for the Secretary of State for Health to set standards which are published by the Department of Health. Guidance issued by the National Institute for Health and Clinical Excellence (NICE) and in national service frameworks (NSFs) are also important elements of the standards system.

Since 2008/09 the Department of Health has set out in its *Operating Frameworks* health and service priorities for the year ahead. The 2011/12 *Operating Framework* identified a number of indicators and milestones that will be used to assess how well SHAs and PCTs are delivering their plans. These are grouped into three domains:

- 'Quality – covering safety, effectiveness and experience
- Resources – covering finance, workforce, capacity and activity
- Reform – covering commissioning, provision, partnership building, putting patients first and development of the new public health infrastructure'.

Performance Assessment

The Department of Health

In 2009 the Department of Health introduced *The Performance Framework*. This framework is intended to provide a regular assessment of the performance of NHS providers and commissioners against minimum standards. The framework identifies poor performance on an ongoing basis using a series of indicators from across four domains (finance; operational standards and targets; quality; and safety and user experience) to trigger intervention as required.

The results of the assessment are published each quarter in the Department of Health's *The Quarter* publication. Based on the indicators underpinning the *Performance Framework*, organisations are categorised as either:

- Performing
- Performance under review
- Underperforming
- Challenged.

The *Performance Framework* applies to acute and ambulance trusts, mental health trusts and PCTs.

The Care Quality Commission

As well as establishing the power for the Secretary of State for Health to set standards, the *Health and Social Care (Community Health and Standards) Act 2003* established the Healthcare Commission and set out its functions. The Healthcare Commission was responsible for (amongst other activities) undertaking an annual review of the provision of healthcare by each NHS body in England, including FTs. In October 2008 (following a review of healthcare regulation), the Healthcare Commission, the Commission for Social Care Inspection and the Mental Health Act Commission were replaced by the Care Quality Commission (CQC). The CQC took over the regulation of health and social care from April 2009.

Assessments of quality of health organisations

The CQC introduced three types of review:

- Periodic reviews of commissioners, which assess how well services are commissioned
- Periodic reviews of providers, which assess the performance of providers
- Special reviews and studies, which look in depth at different aspects of health and social care to assess and drive improvement.

Registration standards

The CQC is also responsible for operating a registration system which came into force on 1 April 2010 for NHS trusts and on 1 October 2010 for adult social care and independent healthcare providers. The registration process is designed to ensure that people receive services that meet essential standards of quality and safety that respect their dignity and protect their rights. The system is focused on outcomes rather than systems and processes and places the views and experiences of people who use services at its centre.

There are 28 outcomes, each reflecting a specific regulation. Of these 28 regulations and outcomes, there are 16 that relate most directly to the quality and safety of care and which apply to all types of provider. The other 12 regulations may apply differently to different types of provider.

These 28 outcomes are grouped into six areas:

- Involvement and information

- Personalised care, treatment and support
- Safeguarding and safety
- Suitability of staffing
- Quality and management
- Suitability of management.

The CQC uses a 'judgement framework' when making decisions about compliance and assessing each provider's compliance with registration standards. Compliance will be monitored continuously by analysing and inspecting services, by asking providers to assess themselves and by collecting information from other sources.

If providers do not meet the standards, or if the CQC believes people's basic rights or safety are at risk, they will take action. CQC has a wide range of enforcement powers, such as fines and public warnings, and wide ranging flexibility about how and when these are used. Specific conditions can be applied in response to serious risks. For example, the CQC can demand that a ward or service is closed until the provider meets safety requirements or suspend or take a service off the register.

The Audit Commission

Until 2009/10 the Audit Commission's 'Auditors' Local Evaluation (ALE)' was used to assess how well NHS trusts managed and used their financial resources. ALE was developed to enable auditors to make scored judgements on five key themes:

- Financial reporting
- Financial management
- Financial standing
- Internal control
- Value for money.

In each of the five themes there were a number of key lines of enquiry (KLOEs).

The scores were published each year until 2009/10 and the overall ALE score was used by the CQC in its periodic reviews of providers.

For PCTs the Audit Commission used an approach known as 'Use of Resources' (UoR) which covered three themes on which scored judgments were made:

- Managing finances
- Governing the business
- Managing resources.

In each of the three themes there were a number of key lines of enquiry (KLOEs).

The ALE and UoR are no longer carried out. Auditors continue to focus on reviewing the annual accounts and organisations' arrangements for securing economy, efficiency and effectiveness in their use of resources but organisations' performance is not scored. See chapter 15 for more about the role of auditors.

What the future holds for Financial and Performance Reporting

The coalition government's *Health and Social Care Bill 2011* does not propose any changes to financial reporting per se. However, the planned abolition of SHAs, PCTs and the Audit Commission means that the players involved in producing and assessing financial information and the relationships between them would change dramatically. In particular, with the proposed change of role for Monitor, the Secretary of State will take over the power to define accounting and reporting requirements for FTs and the Department of Health will collect information from FTs about their forecast spending.

As far as the financial reporting regimes for the new organisations (NHS Commissioning Board and GP consortia) are concerned (subject to any amendments agreed to the Bill), consortia will receive their funding from the NHS Commissioning Board which will be required to remain within an 'NHS commissioning revenue limit' for which the Board's Chief Executive (the Accounting Officer) will be held to account by the Department of Health. The Board will also be required to prepare a consolidated annual account for all consortia which will be a key element in the Department of Health's overall resource account. To be able to fulfil these requirements, the Commissioning Board will itself hold GP consortia to account for their stewardship of resources and outcomes achieved. In particular, each consortium will have a duty to achieve financial balance. The Board will also specify the form and content of accounting information that consortia must provide and a timetable for submission.

Consortia budgets will include a maximum allowance to cover management costs – although consortia may choose to undertake some or all of these roles themselves, they will also have the flexibility to use the money to buy in the services needed including data analysis and contract monitoring, roles which are currently undertaken by PCTs.

References and Further Reading

NHS Act 2006: www.opsi.gov.uk/Acts/acts2006/pdf/ukpga_20060041_en.pdf

International Accounting Standards and International Financial Reporting Standards, International Accounting Standards Board: www.ifrs.org/Home.htm

Government Financial Reporting Manual, HM Treasury: www.hm-treasury.gov.uk/frem_index.htm

NHS Manual for Accounts 2009/10 for SHAs, PCTs and NHS trusts: www.info.doh.gov.uk/doh/finman.nsf

Details about the NHS foundation trust financial regime (including the publications referred to in this chapter) are available on Monitor's website: www.monitor-nhsft.gov.uk

PCT, NHS Trust and FT Accounts: Guides for Non-executives, HFMA and the Audit Commission: www.hfma.org.uk or www.audit-commission.gov.uk

A Guide to Good Practice on the Annual Report/ Review incorporating requirements under Reporting Standard 1 (RS 1) for NHS Organisations including the Operating and Financial Review (OFR) – available from the HFMA: www.hfma.org.uk

Better Payment Practice Code: www.payontime.co.uk

HSC 1999/146 Guidance to Health Authorities and NHS Trusts on Break-Even Duty; Provisions and Accumulated Deficits. Available via the HSC pages of the Department of Health's website: www.dh.gov.uk/PublicationsAndStatistics/LettersAndCirculars/HealthServiceCirculars/fs/en

Health and Social Care (Community Health and Standards) Act 2003: www.opsi.gov.uk/acts/acts2003/ukpga_20030043_en_1

Operating Frameworks for the NHS in England, Department of Health: www.dh.gov.uk/en/Managingyourorganisation/Financeandplanning/Planningframework/index.htm

National Institute for Health and Clinical Excellence (NICE): www.nice.org.uk

National Service Frameworks: www.nhs.uk/nhsengland/NSF/pages/Nationalserviceframeworks.aspx

Care Quality Commission: www.cqc.org.uk/

15. Governance

Introduction

Governance as a topic has received considerable attention over the years following spectacular failings across all sectors of the economy – recent examples include the 2008 banking crisis and Mid Staffordshire NHS Foundation Trust. These (and many other) crises have demonstrated just how important good governance is to the well-being of an organisation and made clear that it encompasses all that an organisation does, not just its administrative and support functions. In the NHS this means that effective governance is as much of a concern to a nurse or consultant as it is to an accountant or manager. The most important message is that achieving the highest standards of governance depends on everyone, both as individuals and as members of any corporate entity within or connected to the NHS.

This chapter explains the concept of governance and looks at the need for and aims of the different elements that are found in the NHS, with a particular focus on finance and financial management.

What is Governance?

A clear understanding of what governance is all about and what makes an effective approach to governance in practice is critical to all organisations across the public, private and voluntary sectors – without this, stakeholders cannot be sure that their interests are being safeguarded, that their organisations are well managed and that their objectives will be met.

The terms governance and corporate governance are now used interchangeably but it was the use of 'corporate governance' as a phrase in the 1992 *Cadbury Committee Report* that initiated widespread debate in this area. Corporate governance was defined in that report as 'the system by which companies are directed and controlled'. In essence it is all about how an organisation is run – how it structures itself, how it is led and how it is held to account. Organisational culture is also a key factor as it is crucial that the principles of good governance permeate to all levels.

What this means in practice is that, on the structural side, governance is concerned with the systems, processes and controls that are in place to provide a sound framework for clear and accountable decision-making by senior managers across an organisation. In terms of leadership, governance is to do with the responsibilities, behaviour and approach of senior managers and with the organisation's underlying culture and values. And in terms of accountability, governance is both to do with how those running the organisation account for their actions to their stakeholders and how stakeholders can hold them to account.

The Cadbury definition is still widely used and has been adapted to suit specific circumstances. Also of interest to the public sector environment is the Organisation for Economic Co-operation and Development's (OECD) interpretation – its 2005 *Glossary* refers to corporate governance as the 'Procedures and processes according to which an organisation is directed and controlled. The corporate governance structure specifies the distribution of rights and responsibilities among the different participants in the organisation – such as the board, managers, shareholders and other stakeholders – and lays down the rules and procedures for decision-making'.

The key point to bear in mind is that governance is not a tick box bureaucratic process that can be carried out periodically and then forgotten about. Instead its aims and principles must underlie all that an organisation does – good governance should be a natural way of life embedded at all levels.

Governance in the NHS

The NHS has been well aware of the importance of governance for many years with a wide range of separate regulatory frameworks and ethical codes in operation for the different professions working in NHS bodies. The NHS has also been swift to learn from and respond to private sector developments – partly because, as the governance structures of NHS bodies are similar to those of listed companies, the principles adopted have a more direct application.

However, the focus on governance has strengthened in recent years, largely as a result of a number of high profile failures which dented public confidence in the health service as a whole. These included:

• The Bristol Royal Infirmary and Royal Liverpool Children's (Alder Hey) inquiries in 2001
• The Shipman crimes in 2003/04
• The Healthcare Commission's reports into Stoke Mandeville hospital (2006), Maidstone and Tunbridge Wells NHS Trust (2007) and Mid-Staffordshire NHS Foundation Trust (2009).

In each case there were governance failings of various kinds. The clear linkages drawn between the clinical scandals and the governance failings that made them possible emphasises that effective governance must cover all that an organisation does. It has also driven home to NHS board members just how wide ranging their responsibilities and accountabilities are. In particular, NHS boards must assure themselves that the organisation:

• Is providing high quality services in a safe environment
• Has staff that have been trained appropriately
• Is meeting its legal and regulatory requirements
• Is meeting its strategic objectives.

Some of the more recent investigations into governance lapses have also underlined the need for governance policies, procedures and structures to be comprehensive, and based on intelligent and rigorous scrutiny of processes which may appear adequate on paper, but do not operate in practice. For example, the Healthcare Commission's 2009 investigation into Mid-Staffordshire NHS Foundation Trust (where multiple management failures led to high mortality rates), found that the Trust appeared to 'have lost sight of its real priorities'.

The Audit Commission's 2009 report *Taking it on Trust – a review of how NHS trusts and foundation trusts get their assurance* suggests that future governance failures are likely unless a systematic approach is taken to identifying and managing key risks, and to evaluating assurances. The report concludes that effective assurance depends on an organisation having in place:

- The right governance framework and risk culture and a clear understanding of strategic objectives and risks
- Good internal controls
- Evidence that internal controls are operating effectively
- Good data quality.

This focus on risk and assurance across all that an organisation does is a key part of an integrated approach to governance which was recognised in the Department of Health's 2006 *Integrated Governance Handbook*. This Handbook encourages organisations to focus on establishing a comprehensive corporate governance framework covering all elements (clinical, financial and organisational) and emphasises that while the presence of well defined structures is important, treating governance issues through functional or compartmentalised processes is unlikely to be effective.

This stance was re-iterated in the HFMA's 2007 publication – *Integrated Governance: Delivering Reform on two and a half days a month*. This guide is aimed primarily at NHS board members and provides practical pointers about developing an integrated approach to governance. It focuses on board behaviours, structures and systems and looks at ways in which boards can put in place supports that will give them the assurances they need. A revised and updated version of this Guide is due for release in 2011.

Governance from a Financial Perspective

As mentioned above, governance underpins all activities and consists of a number of different elements. The HFMA's guide – *Effective Governance in Healthcare* – identifies these as:

- Culture and values (the people issues – for example, leadership style and codes of practice)
- Policies, structures and processes (for example, statutory and regulatory requirements, committee structures)
- Control frameworks (for example, risk management and assurance, audit, clinical governance, counter fraud and corruption).

As this guide's focus is NHS finance, the remainder of this chapter looks at governance from this narrower perspective. In particular it looks at:

- Assurance and risk management
- Healthcare standards
- Registration standards
- Statement on internal control
- The board
- Governors
- The Accountable (or Accounting) Officer
- The Finance Director

- Codes of conduct
- Committees
- Audit – external and internal
- Organisational processes and controls
- Counter fraud and corruption.

Assurance and risk management

The *NHS Audit Committee Handbook* describes the assurance framework as 'the key source of evidence that links strategic objectives to risks, controls and assurances, and the main tool that the board should use in discharging its overall responsibility for internal control'.

To achieve this, each organisation needs to design its own assurance framework based on a sound understanding of the principal risks that could prevent it from achieving its agreed objectives and the potential effect each risk could present to those objectives. To help boards do this, the Department of Health issued *Building an Assurance framework: a Practical Guide* which defines the essential steps as being:

- Establish strategic objectives
- Identify the principal (or strategic) risks that may threaten the achievement of these objectives
- Identify and evaluate the design of key controls intended to manage these principal risks
- Identify the arrangements for obtaining assurance on the effectiveness of these key controls
- Evaluate the reliability of the assurances identified
- Identify positive assurances and areas where there are gaps in controls and/or assurances
- Put in place plans to take corrective action where gaps have been identified in relation to principal risks
- Maintain dynamic risk management arrangements including, crucially, a well-founded risk register.

A key element of an effective assurance framework is a sound approach to the identification, assessment and management of risk. Although a lot of jargon has grown up around risk management it is actually something that happens all the time – it is about being aware of potential problems, thinking through what effect they could have and planning ahead to prevent the worst-case scenario. In this context it is important to recognise that no approach to managing risks can give an absolute guarantee that nothing will ever go wrong. It is also worth remembering that risk is also about opportunities as well as threats. Good risk management encourages organisations to take well-managed risks that allow safe development, growth and change.

It is particularly important that NHS boards establish their 'strategic risks' which are defined by the Audit Commission in its publication *Taking it on Trust* as those risks 'that represent major threats to achieving the trust's strategic objectives or to its continued existence. Strategic risks will include key operational service failures'.

Risk management is now a high profile industry in its own right but the basics are simple – every organisation needs to:

- Identify the strategic objectives and aims of the organisation
- Identify existing and future risks that may affect those aims
- Evaluate the potential impact
- Identify ways of mitigating or reducing risks (for example, in its *Orange Book: Management of Risk – Principles and Concepts*, the Treasury suggests the five Ts – treat, transfer, tolerate, terminate or take)
- Manage risks by putting in place controls and warning mechanisms
- Continuously review the effectiveness of the approach and update as necessary.

Good risk management requires leadership and commitment from the top and ownership throughout the organisation. It is not about putting risks in a register and forgetting about them, it is about identifying and managing those risks, particularly those that present the biggest challenge in management terms.

The application of an appropriate risk management model, the establishment of a process to identify risks, the setting of control standards (such as standing financial instructions) and the use of benchmarking are all risk management techniques that together provide reassurance to board members.

The benefits of an effective approach to assurance and risk management include:

- Reduction in risk exposure through more effective targeting of resources to address key risk areas
- Improvements in economy, efficiency and effectiveness resulting from a reduction in the frequency and/or severity of incidents, complaints, claims, staff absence and other loss
- Demonstrable compliance with applicable laws and regulations
- Enhanced reputation and increased public confidence in the quality of NHS services.

Healthcare standards

A key consideration in the overall risk management and assurance framework for the NHS is the need to achieve pre-set standards designed to underpin the delivery of high quality services. The *Health and Social Care (Community Health and Standards) Act 2003* established the power for the Secretary of State for Health to set standards. Guidance issued by the National Institute for Health and Clinical Excellence (NICE) and in national service frameworks (NSFs) are also important elements of the standards system.

Since 2008/09, the Department of Health has also set out health and service priorities for the year ahead in its operating frameworks. The 2011/12 *Operating Framework* identified a number of indicators and milestones that will be used to assess the how well SHAs and PCTs are delivering their plans. These are grouped into three domains:

- 'Quality – covering safety, effectiveness and experience
- Resources – covering finance, workforce, capacity and activity
- Reform – covering commissioning, provision, partnership building, putting patients first and development of the new public health infrastructure.'

Registration standards

Since April 2010, all NHS providers must register with the Care Quality Commission (CQC). This process is designed to ensure that people receive services that meet essential standards of quality and safety that respect their dignity and protect their rights. The new system is focused on outcomes rather than systems and processes and places the views and experiences of people who use services at its centre. See chapter 14 for more details.

Statement on internal control

The focus on risk management and assurance referred to above finds formal expression in the statement on internal control (SIC). Since 2001/02, NHS bodies have had to submit a SIC as part of their annual financial statements. The SIC requires the following disclosures:

- The scope of the Accountable Officer's responsibility
- The purpose of the system of internal control
- The organisation's capacity to handle risk
- A description of the risk and control framework
- Confirmation that a review of effectiveness has been undertaken
- Any significant internal control issues.

The SIC must be signed off by the Chief Executive (the Accounting or Accountable Officer – see below), on behalf of the board. The Head of Internal Audit provides an annual opinion to the Accountable Officer and the audit committee on the adequacy and effectiveness of the risk management, control and governance processes to support the SIC. The SIC is an extremely important statement that covers the whole of an organisation and is a board responsibility. Chief executives and boards will be held to account if they sign a statement that subsequent events show they did not understand or take seriously.

Detailed guidance on SICs is available on the Department of Health's website.

The board

At present, every NHS organisation (including FTs) must have a board comprising a non-executive Chair, non-executive directors and executive directors. Boards take corporate responsibility for the strategies and actions of their organisations and are accountable to the public, Secretary of State (or Monitor in FTs) and Parliament.

A board's prime duty is to 'add value to the organisation, enabling it to deliver healthcare and health improvement within the law and without causing harm. It does this by providing a framework within which the organisation can thrive and grow'. As the board is the pre-eminent governing body there is a range of responsibilities and decisions that it cannot delegate. These are sometimes referred to as being 'reserved' to the board and include:

- Financial stewardship responsibilities, including adopting the annual report and accounts
- Determining the organisation's strategy and policies and setting its strategic direction
- Appointing senior executives

- Overseeing the delivery of services
- Standards of governance and behaviour.

The board is free to agree other issues that only it will deal with and must also decide which responsibilities it will delegate.

Governors

Unlike other NHS organisations, the foundation trust governance structure includes a Board of Governors to represent local interests and to 'bind a trust to its patients, service users and stakeholders'.[20] These governors consist of both elected and appointed individuals who represent FT members and other stakeholder groups (including the public, patients and staff). See chapter 8 for more details about FT finance and governance.

The Accountable (or Accounting) Officer

The Department of Health has formally given chief executives the status of Accountable Officers for their organisations and they are sent a memorandum setting out their responsibilities. The Accountable Officer must sign a statement confirming that he or she has properly discharged the responsibilities set out in this memorandum. These are that chief executives must ensure that their organisations:

- Operate effectively, economically and with probity
- Make good use of their resources
- Keep proper accounts.

The Chief Executive is accountable to Parliament via the Department of Health Accounting Officer and the Secretary of State for Health.

In FTs the line of accountability is different as the Chief Executive is the Accounting Officer responsible to Parliament via Monitor. Monitor has issued its own Accounting Officer memorandum which emphasises that 'Accounting Officers are responsible to Parliament for the resources under their control'.

The Accountable Officer is responsible and accountable for maintaining a sound system of internal control that supports the achievement of the organisation's strategic objectives. The system of internal control itself must be an ongoing process designed to:

- Identify and prioritise the risks to the achievement of these objectives
- Evaluate the likelihood of those risks being realised and the consequent impact
- Manage the risk efficiently, effectively and economically.

The Audit Commission's guide, *Taking it on Trust* defines internal control as 'the process that provides assurance that an organisation is achieving its objectives and meeting its legal and

---

[20] *Your Statutory Duties: a Reference Guide for NHS Foundation Trust Governors*, Monitor, 2009.

other obligations. It includes the governance framework, risk management, information and communications, monitoring processes and assurance activities. It is the effectiveness of all this that the Accountable Officer is certifying when signing the SIC.'

The Finance Director

Directors of finance of health organisations are automatically executive directors with a seat on the board. Their three key responsibilities as identified in the Finance Staff Development Board's guide to *The Role of the Finance Director in a Patient-led NHS – a Guide for NHS Boards* are:

- To provide financial governance and assurance
- To provide business and commercial advice to the board
- Corporate responsibilities as an executive director of the board.

The HFMA has also issued a policy statement on the *Role of the Finance Director* which recognises that the Finance Director's role is one of the most challenging in the NHS with responsibilities ranging from statutory duties relating to accountability, governance and probity; 'traditional' treasurer activities; corporate strategic management and day-to-day operational management. The Statement identifies four core areas of activity:

- Corporate leadership and management
- Stewardship and accountability
- Financial management
- Professional leadership and management.

If you want to know more about what each of these roles involves, the Statement is available as a free download from the HFMA's website.

Codes of conduct

The NHS Constitution

From January 2010 all providers and commissioners of NHS care have a statutory duty to have regard to the *NHS Constitution* in all their decisions and actions. As the Department of Health's website states: 'This means that the Constitution, its pledges, principles, values and responsibilities need to be fully embedded and ingrained into everything the NHS does.'

Of particular note in governance terms are the principles and values set out in the Constitution as these need to underpin everything that an organisation does. The seven principles are:

- The NHS provides a comprehensive service, available to all
- Access to NHS services is based on clinical need, not an individual's ability to pay
- The NHS aspires to the highest standards of excellence and professionalism
- NHS services must reflect the needs and preferences of patients, their families and carers
- The NHS works across organisational boundaries and in partnership with other organisations in the interests of patients, local communities and the wider population

- The NHS is committed to providing best value for taxpayers' money and the most effective, fair and sustainable use of finite resources
- The NHS is accountable to the public, communities and patients that it serves.

The values are:

- Respect and dignity
- Commitment to quality of care
- Compassion
- Improving lives
- Working together for patients
- Everyone counts.

Code of Conduct: Code of Accountability in the NHS

These codes were originally issued in 1994 and revised in 2004. They define the public service values that must underpin the work of NHS boards, set out accountability regimes and describe the basis on which NHS organisations should fulfil their statutory duties.

Code of Practice on Openness in the NHS

This 2003 code sets out the basic principles underlying public access to information about the NHS. It defines openness in NHS management as a natural part of its accountability to the local population and sets out the minimum documents and matters that are expected to be disclosed publicly and those that must not, such as confidential patient information.

Code of Conduct for NHS Managers

The *Code of Conduct for NHS Managers* was issued in October 2002 following a recommendation in the Kennedy Report (the *Inquiry into the Management of Care of Children Receiving Complex Heart Surgery at the Bristol Royal Infirmary*). It sets out core standards of conduct expected of NHS managers to guide them and employing health bodies in the work they do and the decisions and choices they have to make. It also reassures the public that these important decisions are being taken against a background of professional standards and accountability.

Code of Business Conduct (Standards of Business Conduct for NHS Staff)

This code was developed and issued in 1993 and defines the relationships between NHS officers and third parties, including:

- Declaration of interests – employees must declare if they have an interest/relationship in contracts or other organisations that could affect business
- Awarding contracts – strict rules are laid down about how contracts should be awarded to prevent bias
- Rules on the acceptability of commercial sponsorship.

Committees

To help the board discharge its duties effectively, a number of committees exist in NHS bodies. It is up to each organisation to decide what committee structure best suits its needs. However, within the finance area, there are two mandatory committees:

Audit committee

At present, every NHS organisation (including FTs) must have an audit committee that reports to the board. This committee's distinctive characteristic is that it comprises only non-executive directors (NEDs) – and the Chair of the organisation should not be a member. The Chief Executive and all other executive directors will attend whenever they are invited by the audit committee Chair and, in particular, to provide assurances and explanations to the committee when it is discussing audit reports or other matters within their areas of responsibility.

Detailed guidance about the role of audit committees is set out in the *Audit Committee Handbook* produced by the Department of Health and HFMA.

Remuneration and terms of service committee

The remuneration (and terms of service) committee reports to the board and advises it about the pay, other benefits and terms of employment for the Chief Executive and other senior staff. To ensure that people involved in the day-to-day running of the organisation do not make sensitive decisions, the committee's membership comprises the organisation's Chair and at least two other NEDs. The Chief Executive may attend other than when his or her own position is being considered.

PCT professional executive committee

All PCTs must have a professional executive committee (PEC). The PEC is a committee of the PCT's board and is designed to bring together clinical and managerial perspectives. It is important that the PEC's responsibilities are clearly set out at local level and understood by all board and PEC members. The precise role and structure of PECs varies across PCTs to suit local circumstances but there are a number of guiding principles that are common to all which are set out in *Primary Care Trust Professional Executive Committees – Fit for the Future*, issued by the Department of Health. In particular:

- PECs need to be patient-focussed and promote the health and well-being of communities, as well as addressing health inequalities
- PECs need to be drivers of strong clinical leadership and enablers of clinical empowerment
- PECs need to be decision-making and firmly part of the governance and accountability framework of the PCT
- PECs should reflect a range of clinical professions and the wealth of experience this brings.

Charitable funds committee

NHS organisations with charitable funds will usually have a dedicated charitable funds committee that will review the use of charitable funds and investment performance. Such charitable funds are legally separate from NHS monies and (in most cases) are managed by 'NHS corporate trustees' – in other words, it is the NHS corporate body (i.e. an NHS trust or special health authority) that is the trustee. The board of the trust or authority acts on behalf of the corporate trustee in the administration of the charitable funds – they are not themselves individual trustees. In practice this means that the charitable funds committee is a committee of board directors, but not formally a sub-committee of the organisation itself (see chapter 17 for more on charitable funds).

External audit

The public is entitled to expect that money raised by local or national taxation is properly accounted for. To provide an assurance that this is the case, there is a need (among other things) for a wide-ranging and independent external audit covering both the financial statements and the organisation's arrangements for securing value for money from its use of resources.

At present, external auditors for SHAs, PCTs and NHS trusts must follow the Audit Commission's *Code of Audit Practice* which requires them to review and report on:

- The annual accounts and SIC
- Arrangements for securing economy, efficiency and effectiveness in the use of resources.

The *Audit Commission Act 1998* provides auditors with the power to report where they have specific concerns arising from their audits:

- Section 8 requires auditors to consider whether, in the public interest, they should report on any matter coming to their notice
- Section 19 requires the auditor to refer matters to the Secretary of State for Health if he or she has reason to believe that an NHS organisation has made a decision that involves, or may involve, unlawful expenditure.

The external auditor is required to issue an annual audit letter to board members at the conclusion of each year's audit. The letter acts as a brief for the board and summarises the major issues arising from the audit which the auditor wishes to raise.

The Audit Commission's role is to:

- Appoint external auditors (from its own audit practice or accountancy firms) who audit each body's annual financial statements
- Set the required standards for appointed auditors
- Regulate the quality of audits.

Although the coalition government plans to abolish the Audit Commission, external audits will still take place.

Foundation trusts (FTs) select and appoint their own external auditors who must carry out their role in line with Monitor's own *Audit Code*.

Internal audit

Internal audit is defined in the *NHS Internal Audit Standards* as 'an independent and objective assurance and consulting activity designed to add value and improve an organisation's operations. It helps an organisation accomplish its objectives by bringing a systematic, disciplined approach to evaluate and improve the effectiveness of risk management, control and governance processes'.

At present, all NHS bodies are required to have an internal audit service and the Head of Internal Audit's opinion is a key element of the framework of assurance that the Accountable Officer needs to inform the annual statement on internal control (SIC).

As the definition above indicates, the internal audit service has two aspects – assurance and consultancy. The first of these is to provide an independent and objective opinion to the Accountable Officer, board and audit committee on the extent to which risk management, control and governance arrangements support the aims of the organisation. In this context, risk management, control and governance means the policies, procedures and operations established to ensure:

• The achievement of objectives
• The appropriate assessment of risk
• The reliability of internal and external reporting and accountability processes
• Compliance with applicable laws and regulations
• Compliance with the behavioural and ethical standards set for the organisation.

The second aspect is to provide an independent and objective consultancy service specifically to help line management improve the organisation's risk management, control and governance. When performing consultancy services, the internal auditor must maintain objectivity and not take on management responsibility.

Organisational processes and controls

Board reports

Boards must ensure that they receive regular financial and other information in a succinct and efficient form so they can make informed decisions on spending. It is for the board to decide the form and content of the reports – however, they must have what they need to fulfil their responsibilities.

In particular, they need 'intelligent information' as reflected in *The Intelligent Board*, produced by the independent research and analysis body, Dr Foster, in conjunction with the Appointments Commission. This guidance proposed a number of principles for board reporting and set out a framework for strategic issues and operational performance – it states that 'the key tests of the success of any information resource for the board will be the extent to which it:

• Prompts relevant and constructive challenge
• Supports informed decision-making

- Is effective in providing early warning of potential financial or other problems
- Develops all directors' understanding of the organisation and its performance.'

Annual accounts

All NHS bodies have a statutory duty to produce annual accounts. At present, the relevant legislation for NHS trusts, PCTs and SHAs is section 232 and paragraph 3(1) of schedule 15 of the *NHS Act 2006* and for FTs section 30 and paragraph 25(1) of schedule 7 of the *NHS Act 2006*. The form and content of the accounts is prescribed by the Secretary of State for Health – or the independent regulator Monitor for FTs. The production of the statutory annual accounts is the principal means by which NHS bodies discharge their accountability to taxpayers and users of services for their stewardship of public money. See chapter 14 for more details.

Standing orders (SOs)

Standing orders (SOs) provide a comprehensive framework for carrying out activities within NHS bodies and are therefore a critical element in the governance framework. For SHAs, PCTs and NHS trusts, SOs are the link to an organisation's statutory powers and translate these powers into a series of practical rules designed to protect the interests of both the organisation and its staff. In many ways SOs are similar to the memorandum and articles of association of a company. In FTs SOs form part of their constitution.

The majority of provisions set out within SOs relate to the business of the board and structure of its committees. This includes procedural issues such as:

- The composition of the board and committees
- How meetings are run
- Form, content and frequency of reports submitted to the board
- What constitutes a quorum
- Record of attendance
- Voting procedures.

Other areas covered in SOs include:

- Appointment of committees and sub-committees
- Scheme of delegation
- Decisions reserved to the board
- Standards of business conduct
- Declarations of interest
- Register of interests and hospitality
- Duties and obligations of board members.

One area covered by SOs that often receives particular attention relates to standards of business conduct, declarations of interest and hospitality. The fact that this is deliberately included in SOs rather than delegated to standing financial instructions (SFIs) indicates to managers and staff how important it is to follow the procedures set down and the importance attributed to probity.

Reserved decisions and schemes of delegation

An NHS body's SOs must include a schedule of decisions reserved to the board and a scheme of delegation to other committees or officers. This is a detailed listing of what the board alone can decide on and who the board empowers to take actions or make decisions on its behalf. Examples of decisions reserved to the board include:

- Approving of SOs
- Establishing terms of reference and reporting arrangements for all committees
- Agreeing the schedule of reserved decisions and scheme of delegation
- Approving standing financial instructions
- Appointing the board's vice chair
- Defining the organisation's strategic aims
- Approving business cases for capital investment
- Approving budgets
- Receiving and approving the annual report and annual accounts.

Standing financial instructions (SFIs)

SFIs cover financial aspects in more depth and set out detailed procedures and responsibilities. SFIs are designed to ensure that NHS organisations account fully and openly for all that they do.

Model SFIs for SHAs, PCTs and NHS trusts are available on the Department of Health's website. Many organisations inform their staff of the agreed SOs and SFIs using their intranet sites, supplemented by summarised handbooks and presentations on key points. It is good practice to ensure that new employees are made aware of these documents as part of the induction process.

Although FTs do not have to have SFIs, many do and others have written financial procedures that fulfil the same function.

Counter fraud and corruption

The emphasis on dealing with fraud and corruption in the NHS has increased significantly over recent years. As a result, NHS bodies are now required to have a local counter fraud specialist (LCFS). The LCFS may be a person nominated from within the organisation or an external appointment. The LCFS has a vital role to play in acting as the 'first line of defence' against fraud and corruption. Their responsibilities are outlined in Secretary of State Directions/Minister of Health and Social Services Directions. Although FTs are not bound by these directions they have LCFSs through the terms of their healthcare contracts and Monitor has a 'memorandum of understanding' with the NHS Counter Fraud and Security Management Service (CFSMS).

The role of the LCFS is to take forward work to counter fraud and corruption in the health body for which they are the nominated officer. Activity should take place in seven generic areas:

- Creating an anti fraud culture
- Deterrence

- Prevention
- Detection
- Investigation
- Sanction
- Redress.

Counter fraud work should take place within a clear ethical framework. This describes principles of professionalism, propriety, fairness, objectivity, vision, and expertise. All LCFSs have to undergo training on this ethical framework if they are to receive their professional accreditation as 'accredited counter fraud specialists'.

Every NHS organisation is also required to have a Local Security Management Specialist (LSMS). The LSMS is required to undertake work to reduce the levels of violence and abuse against staff and patients, but is also required to help safeguard NHS resources from damage and theft.

Other policies/procedures

For NHS bodies to run smoothly, many more policies and procedures (both financial and non-financial) are required; and these are usually pulled together in organisational policy and procedure manuals. These cover a wide variety of areas from banking procedures, use of credit cards to health and safety and equal opportunities policies.

What the future holds for Governance

The government's proposals (as set out in the *Health and Social Care Bill 2011*) do not spell out in detail what the governance arrangements for the proposed new organisations (GP consortia and the NHS Commissioning Board) will be as it takes the view that this should be a matter for local determination. However, certain minimum requirements have been set down – in particular (subject to any amendments agreed to the Bill), consortia will be statutory bodies with an Accountable Officer (AO) in each with an accountability line to the NHS Commissioning Board. Under the current arrangements, the PCT Chief Executive is the AO and it is expected that under the new structure it will be the 'senior official' within each consortium. It is also assumed that the inclusion of an AO in the structure means that he or she will need to comply with the Treasury's requirements for all other AOs in the public sector, namely that the AO will have to ensure that the consortium operates efficiently and to a high standard of probity and that governance, decision making and financial management standards (as set out in the Treasury's guide *Managing Public Money*) are met and value for money demonstrated. The proposals also specify that each consortium will have a Chief Financial Officer.

As far as financial governance is concerned, consortia will receive their funding from the NHS Commissioning Board which will be required to remain within an 'NHS commissioning revenue limit' for which the Board's Chief Executive (its AO) will be held to account by the Department of Health. The Board will also be required to prepare a consolidated annual account for all consortia which will be a key element in the Department of Health's overall resource account. To be able to fulfil these requirements, the Commissioning Board will itself hold GP consortia to account for their stewardship of resources and outcomes achieved. In particular, each consortium will have a duty to achieve financial balance. The Board will also specify the form and content of accounting information that consortia must provide and a timetable for submission.

It is not yet clear whether there will be a requirement for consortia to have boards, audit/remuneration committees, assurance frameworks etc, or whether they will be expected to comply with the codes of practice outlined in this chapter. The coalition government has however made clear that it will 'uphold and reinforce the NHS Constitution, which all providers and commissioners will be obliged to have regard to in carrying out their functions'.

References and Further Reading

The Financial Aspects of Corporate Governance (the Cadbury Committee Report, 1992): www.ecgi.org/codes/code.php?code_id=132

OECD: www.oecd.org

Bristol Royal Infirmary Inquiry (The Kennedy Report): www.bristol-inquiry.org.uk/

The Royal Liverpool Children's Inquiry (Alder Hey): www.rlcinquiry.org.uk/

The Shipman Inquiry: www.the-shipman-inquiry.org.uk/

Investigation into Mid Staffordshire NHS Foundation Trust, Healthcare Commission, 2009: www.cqc.org.uk/_db/_documents/
Investigation_into_Mid_Staffordshire_NHS_Foundation_Trust.pdf

Stoke Mandeville Inquiry: www.hse.gov.uk/healthservices/hospitalinfect/stokemandeville.pdf

Maidstone and Tunbridge Wells Inquiry: www.cqc.org.uk/_db/_documents/
Maidstone_and_Tunbridge_Wells_investigation_report_Oct_2007.pdf

Taking it on Trust – a review of how NHS trusts and foundation trusts get their assurance, Audit Commission, 2009: www.audit-commission.gov.uk/health/nationalstudies/
financialmanagement/Pages/takingitontrust29april2009_copy.aspx

Integrated Governance Handbook, Department of Health, 2006: www.dh.gov.uk/en/
Publicationsandstatistics/Publications/PublicationsPolicyAndGuidance/DH_4128739

Integrated Governance: delivering reform on two and a half days a month, HFMA, 2007 (a new updated version will be published in 2011): www.hfma.org.uk

Effective Governance in Healthcare: an Introductory Guide, HFMA, 2006: www.hfma.org.uk

The NHS Audit Committee Handbook, Department of Health and HFMA, 2011: www.hfma.org.uk

Assurance: The Board Agenda, Department of Health, 2002: www.dh.gov.uk/en/
Publicationsandstatistics/Publications/PublicationsPolicyAndGuidance/DH_4006064

Building an Assurance Framework: A Practical Guide, Department of Health 2003: www.dh.gov.uk/en/Publicationsandstatistics/Publications/PublicationsPolicyAndGuidance/
DH_4093992

The Orange Book: Management of Risk – Principles and Concepts, HM Treasury, 2004: www.hm-treasury.gov.uk/orange_book.htm

National Institute for Health and Clinical Excellence (NICE): www.nice.org.uk/

National Service Frameworks: www.nhs.uk/nhsengland/NSF/pages/ Nationalserviceframeworks.aspx

Operating Frameworks, Department of Health: www.dh.gov.uk/en/Managingyourorganisation/ Financeandplanning/Planningframework/index.htm

Care Quality Commission: www.cqc.org.uk/

Statements on Internal Control, 2009/10 – disclosures guidance, Department of Health: www.dh.gov.uk/en/Publicationsandstatistics/Lettersandcirculars/Dearcolleagueletters/ DH_111781

Accountable Officer Memorandum, Department of Health: www.dh.gov.uk/en/ Publicationsandstatistics/Publications/PublicationsPolicyAndGuidance/DH_4066570

The Role of the Finance Director in a Patient Led NHS, Finance Staff Development Network: www.fsdnetwork.com/documents/roleofdf.pdf

The Role of the NHS Finance Director: an HFMA Policy Statement, 2009: www.hfma.org.uk

The NHS Constitution: www.dh.gov.uk/en/Managingyourorganisation/Workforce/ NHSStaffExperience/DH_110432

The Code of Conduct: Code of Accountability in the NHS, Department of Health: www.dh.gov.uk/en/Publicationsandstatistics/Publications/PublicationsPolicyAndGuidance/ DH_4093864

Code of Practice on Openness in the NHS, 2003: www.dh.gov.uk/en/Publicationsandstatistics/ Publications/PublicationsPolicyAndGuidance/DH_4050490

Code of Conduct for NHS Managers: www.dh.gov.uk/en/Publicationsandstatistics/Publications/ PublicationsPolicyAndGuidance/DH_4005410

Standards of Business Conduct for NHS Staff, Department of Health, 1993.

PCT Professional Executive Committees – Fit for the Future, Department of Health, 2007: www.dh.gov.uk/en/Publicationsandstatistics/Publications/PublicationsPolicyAndGuidance/ DH_073508

Code of Audit Practice – details available from the health pages of the Audit Commission's website: www.audit-commission.gov.uk

Monitor (including the Governance and Audit Codes for NHS Foundation Trusts, reference guide for governors and the AO memorandum): www.monitor-nhsft.gov.uk

Internal Audit Standards for the National Health Service, 2002: www.dh.gov.uk/en/ Publicationsandstatistics/Publications/PublicationsPolicyAndGuidance/DH_4110067

The Intelligent Board, Doctor Foster, 2006: www.drfoster.co.uk/

Model Standing Orders, Reservation and Delegation of Powers for SHAs, PCTs and NHS Trusts, Department of Health, 2006: www.dh.gov.uk/en/Publicationsandstatistics/Publications/PublicationsPolicyAndGuidance/DH_4139133

NHS Counter Fraud Service: www.nhsbsa.nhs.uk/fraud

NHS Security Management Service: www.nhsbsa.nhs.uk/security

16. Capital Investment

Introduction

This chapter looks at capital investment under the current regime (2011/12) – what it is and how it is managed across the NHS. It concentrates on capital investment in (non-foundation) NHS trusts and 'public capital' – those assets that have been purchased with public funds. It also looks at capital investment in PCTs, other sources of funding, accounting treatment and alternatives to asset ownership. An alternative to using public funds is the use of public private partnerships – this is covered in chapter 10.

The capital regime followed by foundation trusts (FTs) is covered in chapter 8.

Capital Investment – Definition

Expenditure is classified as either revenue or capital. Where expenditure is significant and is incurred to acquire an asset intended for use on a continued basis then it is classified as capital and is described as capital investment. To ensure that there is consistency in approach across the NHS, capital assets are defined as:

- An individual asset with a cost of £5,000 or more
- Generally having a life greater than one year
- A system or group of functionally interdependent assets of £5,000 or more (for example, IT hardware attached to a network).

The £5,000 includes VAT where this is not recoverable, installation costs and external fees.

The main categories of capital assets are:

- Land
- Buildings
- Dwellings
- Assets in the course of construction
- Equipment (including vehicles)
- Computing and IT equipment.

As the assets purchased are used over a number of years, capital expenditure is charged to the statement of financial position (formerly the balance sheet). Operational (day-to-day or revenue) expenditure is charged to the revenue account and is reported in the statement of comprehensive income (formerly the income and expenditure account) in NHS trusts and the operating cost statement in PCTs and SHAs.

Capital Funding Process

At present, capital investment is funded from one of five sources:

- Internally generated funds
- Borrowing (from the Department of Health)

- Public capital
- Public/private partnerships (see chapter 10)
- Charitable funds where an asset is gifted to an NHS organisation.

The Treasury caps spending on public capital by setting an annual spending limit for the Department of Health – this is referred to as the capital departmental expenditure limit (capital DEL). In order to contain overall expenditure within this limit both PCTs and NHS trusts are set annual capital resource limits (CRLs) by the Department of Health which they must stay within. For NHS trusts there is also a control mechanism called the external financing limit (EFL) which is a control on net cash flows. For further details on CRLs and EFLs see chapters 7 and 14.

Prior to 2007/08, the majority of public capital was allocated on a formulaic basis to trusts and PCTs as 'operational capital' (for buildings and equipment replacement and renewal) and to SHAs as 'strategic capital' (for bigger, more strategic schemes). These allocations took the form of public dividend capital (PDC) which attracted dividend payments. An element of capital funding was also managed centrally to target particular investment objectives.

In 2007/08, the capital allocation process for NHS trusts changed so as to increase the financial rigour of investment decisions and assist trusts in making the transition to foundation status. Through the introduction of an approach similar to that followed by FTs, access to capital and working capital[21] is more closely tied to financial performance and affordability with a 'prudential borrowing limit' or PBL set for each trust each year.

This means that NHS trusts now have two main sources of capital funding:

- Internally generated funds (via retained surpluses, depreciation and proceeds from the sale of capital assets – see below)
- Capital investment loans from the Department of Health (within the PBL).

These are summarised in the table over the page.

The amount of money that an NHS trust can retain following the sale of an asset is capped to match its delegated limit (see chapter 10).

In 2008/09, the approach also changed for PCTs with capital scheme funding allocated to them on the basis of their capital plans as agreed with their SHA. These plans had to be robust and affordable – in other words, sustainable from a revenue consequences perspective. Any unspent capital allocation was not carried forward. Given that the coalition government plans to abolish PCTs from 2013, any PCT capital contracts must now be approved by the relevant SHA and PCTs have a delegated limit of zero (see chapter 10).

---

[21] Working capital is the money and assets that an organisation can call upon to finance its day-to-day operations (it is the difference between current assets and liabilities and is reported in the statement of financial position (balance sheet) as net current assets (liabilities)). If working capital dips too low, organisations risk running out of cash and may need a working capital loan to smooth out the troughs.

Source of capital funding		Description	How NHS trusts use the funding
Internally generated	Based on forecast depreciation	Trusts have to break-even or better (i.e. achieve a surplus) after including a charge for asset depreciation in their revenue expenditure. Depreciation is a notional charge (i.e. it involves no cash payment) and the cash 'generated' can be used for capital investment.	The cash generated and/or any surplus is available unconditionally to invest in building maintenance, replacement equipment and other developments (but subject to capital controls – see later in this chapter and chapter 7).
Borrowing (from Department of Health) in the form of capital investment loans	Based on a prudential borrowing limit – the maximum level of borrowings from all sources that a trust may have (see below for more details).	Enables trusts to invest in locally determined priorities.	Subject to affordability and approval of business case – the size of the scheme dictates the approval mechanism required with SHAs able to approve up to £35m (see chapter 10).

In addition to the capital spending plans of NHS trusts and PCTs, the Department of Health itself invests capital for the overall benefit of the NHS where it is commercially and operationally appropriate. This is accounted for by the Department and costs are borne centrally – for example, the IT structure used across the NHS. For 2011/12, no central capital budget programme is planned.

Prudential Borrowing Limits

The PBL is set by the Department on the assumption that a trust can afford the costs of borrowing to this level both in terms of the interest payments and the principal repayment, and taking into consideration any working capital loans a trust may already have. At present, access to capital investment loans is controlled through both the PBL and the SHA business case approval process. Once SHA approval is secured, the loan must be approved by the Department. The loan interest is set in accordance with the National Loans Fund rate and fixed over the period of the loan, which in the case of a capital investment loan is generally the same as the life of the asset to which it relates. The loan and the associated interest (calculated on the outstanding balance) are repaid in equal instalments in September and March each year. Trusts must generate the cash (for example, through surpluses) to repay the principal and interest on any loans, the interest being charged to revenue expenditure.

The PBL for each trust is not an annual limit – instead it indicates the maximum cumulative borrowing that a trust may take on to fund additional capital investment and to finance operations generally. Using a system that mirrors arrangements for FTs, the PBL is calculated using information from the previous year's financial accounts and financial plan and applying a series of financial ratios to calculate an overall financial risk rating for each trust. PBLs are reviewed at least annually when the latest accounts data becomes available.

The Cost of Capital and Capital Charges

What is the cost of capital?

Any capital investment, whether in the public or private sector, has an 'opportunity cost' (in other words, the money could have been used for alternative purposes or not raised as taxes). The NHS therefore has a system of capital charges to recognise and account for its cost of capital – the money tied up in its assets. Capital charges comprise two key elements – a **return** (similar to debt interest) and **depreciation**. Both elements are explained in greater detail below. They are levied on all capital assets owned by the NHS, except for assets acquired via interest bearing (capital investment) loans, by donation or with a net book value of zero. Capital charges are included in trust revenue costs and budgets.

Capital charges are designed to:

- Ensure that there is a consistent awareness of the costs of capital in the NHS
- Provide incentives to use capital efficiently and dispose of surplus assets
- Ensure that the costs of capital are reflected fully in the costing of healthcare services, so that fair comparisons are possible, both within the NHS and between the NHS and the private sector
- Promote effective planning for the replacement of capital assets.

The system of capital charges ensures that the cost of capital is reflected in the costs of healthcare services so that when alternative service provision options are discussed sound decisions can be made. It also provides an incentive to improve asset utilisation – savings in capital charges arising from better utilisation are 'real' savings available to fund service developments or to meet other cost pressures.

Rate of return

The rate of return is calculated on 'average relevant net assets' – the average of the value of assets held at the beginning and end of the year. Under the 'old' capital system, a trust would buy assets using capital allocations from the Department of Health – public dividend capital as noted above. The asset purchased would attract a rate of return charge (paid through a dividend on that capital allocation) of 3.5%. Under the new system of prudential borrowing, the trust faces direct capital charges through the interest payments it is required to make on the loans it takes out. The loan liability reduces the relevant net assets of the organisation and therefore the trust does not pay the dividend on these assets.

Depreciation

Depreciation is calculated annually to spread the cost of the assets over their expected economic life. Annual depreciation is a revenue cost which is charged to the statement of comprehensive income or operating cost statement.

Capital charges – example

As we have seen above capital charges have two elements:

- The rate of return on average relevant net assets (PDC dividends)
- The depreciation (or wearing out) of those assets.

Consider a simplified example of a trust with average relevant net assets (the average of the assets held at the beginning of the year and at the end of the year) of £158m.

The rate of return or cost of capital is 3.5% of £158m = £5.5m.

Depreciation will be calculated on the mix of non-current assets the trust holds, all of which are depreciated at different rates. In this trust, the depreciation was estimated to be £6m.

Total NHS capital charges (combining rate of return and depreciation) is therefore estimated at £11.5m.

Impact of changes to the rate of return

When capital charges were first introduced to the NHS in 1991, the rate of return was set at 6%. In 2003 this was changed to 3.5%. Changes in the cost of capital are important as they affect:

- The relative attractiveness of public and private financing options
- The attractiveness of leasing options – generally, the higher the cost of public capital the more attractive leasing options are. However, leases classed as finance leases will offer no benefit as these are treated in the same way as any other asset.

Payment of capital charges

Since 2009/10 a trust's PDC dividend payments are made based on the trust's forecast statement of financial position at quarter 1 for the September instalment and quarter 3 for the March instalment. The final PDC dividend payment charge is calculated based on the actual relevant net assets as per the trust's statement of financial position (or operating cost statement) at the end of the financial year with any over and underpayments being matched by a corresponding debtor (for overpayment) and creditor (for underpayment) accrual.

Accounting for Capital Investment

NHS bodies are expected to adhere to the accounting standards issued or endorsed by the International Accounting Standards Board (IASB). However, the government has the final say on how these standards are applied to the public sector (including NHS bodies) and the

Treasury has developed a *Financial Reporting Manual* that sets out details for their implementation. Each year, the Department of Health produces a *Manual for Accounts* for SHAs, PCTs and NHS trusts that is consistent with the requirements of the *Financial Reporting Manual* and which NHS bodies are required to follow.

Of particular relevance in the context of capital spending are the following financial reporting standards:

- IAS 11 Construction Contracts
- IAS 16 Property, Plant and Equipment
- IAS 17 Leases
- IFRS 5 Non-Current Assets Held for Sale
- IAS 36 Impairment of Assets
- IAS 40 Investment Property.

See chapter 14 for more about financial reporting.

Asset Registers

Every NHS body maintains an asset register of all its capital assets. This requirement is set out in the organisation's standing financial instructions (see chapter 15). The register is used in the preparation of annual accounts and to help maintain and improve management control, information and accountability. The asset register is usually kept using the same computer software that is used to calculate depreciation.

The main information recorded in an asset register includes:

- Asset identification, description and location
- Date and method of acquisition and initial capital outlay
- Replacement costs, cumulative depreciation charges and estimated life
- Revaluation and indexation adjustments.

Valuation

On acquisition, capital assets are recorded in the asset register at their fair value (i.e. their market value for existing use). To comply with IAS 16, valuations are revised annually using appropriate indices (see the section on indexation later in this chapter). The indices are applied to tangible assets (i.e. land, buildings etc) and assets under construction so that they reflect their fair value. From 1 April 2010 specialised property such as hospitals, for which a market value cannot be easily determined, is valued on a 'modern equivalent asset' basis. This means that a building is valued at the cost of replacing it with an equivalent, modern one, rather than an exact replica of what is currently there.

Every three to five years, land and buildings must be re-valued by a recognised valuer such as the district valuer (DV), to ensure that local and regional variations in land values and building costs are reflected in the asset registers. Valuation is also required when, for example, trusts merge or there is a major change in use.

Assets transferred between NHS bodies are recorded at the same book value in the receiving trust, as they were valued at in the former trust.

Most intangible assets (i.e. software licences, trademarks etc) are recorded at cost less 'amortisation' (equivalent to depreciation but for intangible assets). However, where a readily ascertainable market value is available then this should be used.

Asset lives and depreciation charges

Depreciation is the mechanism used to reflect the fact that assets wear out over time or are 'consumed' over their useful economic life. Depreciation is an accounting charge only and no cash payment is made by the organisation.

In the past, the Department of Health produced a list of standard lives for various classes of asset and these continue to be used by trusts unless individual asset lives can be justified or the asset does not fit into one of the standard categories. Examples of these standard asset lives are:

- Short life engineering equipment, medical equipment, office and IT equipment – five years
- Medium life medical and engineering equipment and furniture – ten years
- Long life medical and engineering equipment – fifteen years
- Vehicles and soft furnishings – seven years
- Mainframe-type IT installations – eight years.

IAS 16: Property Plant and Equipment specifies that the useful life and the residual value of equipment should be reviewed annually – this usually happens at the year end. The residual value is the amount that an organisation estimates it would receive if it were to dispose of the asset and it was at the end of its useful life. If there is a 'significant' difference between the remaining standard and actual asset life, the relevant accounting entries relating to asset value, life, accumulated depreciation and reserves must be carried out to reflect the current asset life.

Depreciation in the NHS is charged on a straight-line basis over the life of the asset. The following assumptions are used:

- Land is considered to have an infinite life and is not depreciated
- Buildings, installations and fittings are depreciated over their assessed lives, with both the value and the life expectancy determined periodically by a qualified valuer, usually the DV
- Assets in the course of construction are not depreciated until they are in operational use
- Equipment is depreciated over its useful economic life
- Leased assets classified as capital are depreciated over the shorter of the lease term remaining or the asset's remaining economic life.

It is important to note that while the straight line basis of depreciation usually means by equal instalments, because depreciation is calculated on asset values adjusted by indices, the depreciation charged to the statement of comprehensive income (or operating cost statement) each year will not be the same. The difference between this and the calculation without the indices is an annual adjustment between retained earnings (formerly the income and expenditure reserve) or the general fund (in PCTs) and the revaluation reserve.

Indexation

Since April 2008, NHS organisations have used their own indices for calculating asset valuations. In some years the value of the NHS estate may be considered to have reduced – this happened in 2008/09 due to the economic climate. In such instances, reduced indices are used, leading to negative indexation and significant impairments (a loss in asset value).

Although the table below uses the central indices provided by the Department until 2007/08, it gives an idea of the impact that inflation can have in relation to building values.

	Land 2004/05 = 100	Buildings/assets under construction 1985/86 = 100	Equipment (other than IT equipment which has a zero indexation rate) 1992/93 = 100
2005/06	105	222	145
2006/07	111	240	149
2007/08	117	260	153

A simplified example showing how these indices are used is given below:

Indexation – an example for an NHS trust

Assume:

- A building with a book value of £2m and a life of 20 years
- Straight line depreciation is £0.1m per annum.

Using the 2007/08 and 2006/07 indices, indexation is $(260 - 240)/240\% = 8.333\%$

Revised book value is £2.167m

Depreciation for the year is $2.167m/20 = £0.108m$.

Accounting entries

Dr: Building asset: £0.167m

Cr: Revaluation reserve: £0.167m

Dr: Depreciation in the statement of comprehensive income: £0.108m

Cr: Asset book value: £0.108m

Dr: Revaluation reserve: £0.008m (the difference between the straight line depreciation calculated on the original value and the current value)

Cr: Retained earnings: £0.008m

It is worth noting some of the complications that may occur when using indexation and why the example is a simplification:

- When a building is first commissioned its value may be assessed as less than cost
- A building consists of different elements – for example, the outside walls, roof and the doors and walls inside the building. These may all have different life expectancies and therefore depreciation and indexation calculations (the DV uses 26 different elements in its valuation work)
- An asset is unlikely to become operational conveniently on the first day of a financial year. Usual practice is to index an asset the year after it becomes operational and start depreciation the quarter after it becomes operational
- The DV may revise the valuation of the building. Usually this will be an adjustment between the asset's book value and the revaluation reserve – however, there may be circumstances where the change in value affects income and expenditure
- A decision may be taken that a building is surplus. This may lead to an 'impairment' (i.e. a loss in the asset's value) or if the decision is that the building will be surplus in a number of years time give rise to what is termed 'accelerated depreciation'. That is the annual depreciation is adjusted to reduce the value of the building to that expected when it is no longer needed
- When a building becomes surplus, land may also be surplus and this is included when adjusting the accounts.

Indexation adjustments are recorded in the asset register thus providing a clear link between each asset and the revaluation reserve. This is important because accounting for an impairment may include the transfer to retained earnings of any balance relating to the individual asset held in the revaluation reserve.

As each asset is different the appropriate accounting treatment will also vary. It is important that the full texts of relevant accounting standards are referred to. The table below sets out some of the most common accounting transactions:

Dividend payment (in an NHS trust)

The rate of return capital charges calculation becomes the trust's dividend payment:

Dr: Statement of comprehensive income – dividend payment

Cr: Cash

PBL loan – drawdown

Dr: Cash

Cr: Payables (formerly creditors) (Department of Health)

As the loan is repaid these entries are reversed.

PBL loan – interest

Dr: Statement of comprehensive income – interest charges
Cr: Cash

Depreciation

Dr: Statement of comprehensive income – depreciation
Cr: Asset value.

Capital Investment – the Procurement Process

Business cases

Under the current regime (2011/12), NHS trusts and PCTs have rolling programmes of capital investment to ensure that their asset bases are fit for purpose. When additional capital investment is needed to further modernise or develop a new service, the first stage is usually to develop a business case. In the context of capital investment, a business case is a written statement of the need for investment in capital. It sets out the process of selection of the asset (as there are likely to be several options or solutions), and the costs of ownership of the asset.

When preparing business cases it is important to include:

- The strategic 'fit' of the proposed investment within the local health economy, including a clear and concise statement of need
- Effective project management arrangements, clear lines of communication and details of those key individuals who will be personally accountable
- An indication that the proposal has the support and approval of key stakeholders including commissioners, staff and patients
- Quantified analyses of the investment and its lifetime costs, benefits and cash flows (using techniques such as discounted cash flow and net present value where appropriate)
- Evidence-based information supporting the proposal in terms of priority, cost-effectiveness, clinical service management and best use of scarce resources given alternative procurement routes.

Of particular interest to the SHA in their approval process is strategic fit and affordability within the trust's borrowing limit. SHAs also use the Department's checklist of those aspects that need to be tackled before giving approval – this is particularly relevant for larger schemes.

Procurement

The key priority in relation to the procurement process for capital is affordability and value for money. The size and scope of any scheme determines the approval process but regardless of the type, size and funding of capital investment the following procurement principles and processes should be borne in mind:

- The proposed investment should be placed in a strategic context
- Different capital investment options should be evaluated in an outline business case (OBC) using economic appraisals including discounted cash flows to identify the preferred option in financial terms
- The approved option should be prepared for procurement focusing on detailed specifications of outputs, outcomes and risk allocation
- The proposed scheme should be advertised to prospective providers (PFI projects and other large proposed procurements need to be advertised in the Official Journal of the European Union – OJEU – see chapter 10 for details)
- Once a preferred bidder has been chosen, agreement must be reached on contractual arrangements. Under PFI schemes the contracts will cover the facility's useful life (normally between 25 to 30 years for projects that involve building an asset)
- The full business case (FBC) should bring together the arguments for the preferred planned investment including current and future service requirements, affordability, the trust's competitive service position and the ability to complete the project within the specified budget and timescale
- Once the contract is finalised and awarded the contract can be enforced
- The contract will need to be monitored throughout its life
- A post-project evaluation is required to review the procurement procedure from the initial planning and project appraisals to the contract monitoring and actual service outcomes. The purpose is to inform and improve future capital investment decisions.

Capital Investment Control

To give an idea of how the capital investment control mechanisms referred to in this chapter fit together, a simplified example is shown below:

Capital Investment Control Process – example

Assumptions

- Average relevant net assets of £158m
- Depreciation calculated on the mix of property, plant and equipment the trust holds (all of which are depreciated at different rates) is estimated to be £6m
- Income and expenditure budgets are in balance
- An existing rolling programme and other schemes underway total £5m
- Anticipated funding for national objectives is £0.5m
- A risk rating of 2 which gives a PBL of 10% of total assets employed – the trust may therefore borrow up to £15.8m
- A new capital investment is identified that could be completed in year at a cost of £2m
- Depreciation at year end totals £6.2m.

Capital charges estimate	The rate of return or cost of capital = 3.5% of £158m = £5.5m	This determines the trust's dividend payment for the next year generally payable in two equal instalments of £2.75m in September and March.
	Depreciation of £6m	Depreciation is budgeted at £6m. As income and expenditure is in balance the trust has £6m that it may invest in capital assets.
	Total forecast capital charges of £11.5m	
Capital resource limit	£5m is needed for the rolling programme.	As this is less than the budgeted depreciation and the trust's income and expenditure budget is in balance, cash will be available from service agreement and contract income.
	£0.5m is expected for a specific national objective.	The CRL will be increased during the year for any further awards relating to national objectives.
	£2m is needed for the new investment.	CRL will be needed for the new investment.
	The initial capital resource limit (CRL) is set at £7.5m.	The initial CRL is used by the Department to plan the annual position across the NHS enabling early adjustment should the initial assessment exceed the overall capital departmental expenditure limit (DEL).
Prudential borrowing limit	The trust can borrow up to a maximum of £15.8m. This year it has £6m from depreciation and £0.5m from national funding so will need to borrow £1m against its capital expenditure needs of £7.5m. The trust will be keen to keep loans to a minimum as interest is charged at about 4.7%. The trust will ensure the loan is only taken when the cash is needed to fund the scheme.	Where specific sizable capital projects are involved, full business case approval is required from the SHA.

External financing limit	The sources of funding outside of trust operational activities are: £0.5m for central objectives £1.0m towards the new investment (within PBL) **Total EFL = £1.5m**	The next year's EFL will include the first repayment of the loan. Therefore assuming no new schemes or central objectives the EFL for next year will be a minus figure.
Depreciation	Assume the actual depreciation in the year totals £6.2m.	The trust's budget for depreciation will be £0.2m overspent. Assuming no other budget variances the trust accounts for the year will show £0.2m overspending. This has no impact on the trust's capital control limits.

It is worth thinking through some of the complications and risks within the above example:

- The final CRL is unlikely to be that set at the start of the year. There may be changes necessary early on to control the overall NHS total. During the year there may be adjustments for central initiatives
- There may be significant slippage in capital expenditure that may result in the Department withdrawing funds from a trust. Trusts will be aware of this possibility and be prepared to bring forward other future investments
- An approved business case will take a number of months to prepare. The financial position of the trust may change during this period resulting in PBL being withdrawn
- When developing business cases the cost of capital is 3.5% but it is important that trusts plan income and expenditure budgets and cash flow on the basis of interest payments on loans at the national loans fund rate which is likely to be higher. Cash flow planning must also include loan repayments
- Capital investment may be needed to help deliver financial stability to a trust – however, the trust may have a risk rating that does not allow access to PBL
- Trusts may also obtain loans to fund working capital. This affects average relevant net assets and the amount needed to achieve the 3.5% rate of return
- The example takes no account of any working capital loans that exist, which would score against the trust's PBL.

Alternatives to Asset Ownership

The NHS can use assets without legal ownership. The main alternatives are by leasing and PFI schemes.

Leases

A lease may be defined as 'a contract between two parties (the "lessor" and the "lessee") for the hire of a specific asset'. The lessor owns the asset, but conveys the right to use the asset to the lessee for an agreed period of time in return for the payment of specified rentals.

There are two types of lease:

- Where the lessor transfers to the lessee substantially all the economic benefits and risks of asset ownership, the asset should be recorded in the trust's asset register together with a corresponding lease creditor. The asset is in effect treated as if it had been bought outright as soon as it is delivered to the NHS and is operational. It will attract capital charges and be subject to depreciation, indexation and appropriate revaluations as for any owned asset. Such leased assets also count towards the CRL and impact on the EFL. These leases are therefore on the statement of financial position and are often referred to as finance leases
- Any lease which is not a finance lease is an operating lease. These are likely to relate to smaller assets and equipment such as cars and photocopiers. However land can never normally be treated as a finance lease unless it is expected that the title will pass to the lessee at the end of the lease. Rental payments for operating leases are treated as income and expenditure.

Leases are a complex area in accounting terms and are covered by IAS 17. Other relevant standards that need to be considered are IFRIC 4 (Determining whether an arrangement contains a lease) and IFRIC 12 (Service Concession Arrangements). See the IASB website for details.

Private finance initiative (PFI) and local improvement finance trusts (LIFT)

PFI schemes involve creating partnerships between the public and private sectors. Local improvement finance trusts (LIFTs) are also used to develop and improve primary care premises.

At the planning stages of proposed capital investments, schemes should be tested for their suitability for PFI arrangements. For a scheme to be regarded as suitable, it must demonstrate value for money and be affordable. Although the private sector is likely to have a higher cost of capital than the NHS, it may achieve compensating savings – for example, by providing more cost-effective management, efficiency savings or managing risk more effectively.

Assets may be transferred to PFI and LIFT partners. This will normally be at the DV's valuation so that the NHS receives a cash receipt with the costs to the partner being recovered in charges over the agreed contract period.

For more details about PFI and LIFT and their accounting treatment, see chapter 10.

What the future holds for Capital Investment

The coalition government's plans for the NHS do not propose any specific changes to the approach to capital investment. However, the abolition of PCTs and SHAs would clearly have an impact on how current and future capital investments are handled. The reduction in capital monies announced in the 2010 spending review will also have an impact – although total spending on the NHS is set to rise from £104bn in 2010/11 to £114bn in 2013/14, the 0.4% increase includes a 1.3% rise in current (revenue) spending and a 17% cut in the capital budget. It is assumed that the new NHS Commissioning Board will have a role in allocating capital funding to GP consortia but there are no details yet available.

References and Further Reading

NHS Allocations, Department of Health: www.dh.gov.uk/en/Managingyourorganisation/Financeandplanning/Allocations/index.htm

Operating Frameworks, Department of Health: www.dh.gov.uk/en/Managingyourorganisation/Financeandplanning/Planningframework/index.htm

Delegated Limits for Capital Investment, Department of Health, 2010: www.dh.gov.uk/prod_consum_dh/groups/dh_digitalassets/@dh/@en/@ps/documents/digitalasset/dh_122842.pdf

International Accounting Standards Board (for details of accounting standards): www.ifrs.org/Home.htm

Government Financial Reporting Manual, Treasury: www.hm-treasury.gov.uk/frem_index.htm

Public Sector Business Cases using the Five Case Model: a Toolkit, HFMA, 2007: www.hfma.org.uk

Manual for Accounts, Department of Health: www.info.doh.gov.uk/doh/finman.nsf

Public private partnerships guidance (including PFI and LIFT), Department of Health: www.dh.gov.uk/en/Managingyourorganisation/NHSprocurement/Publicprivatepartnership/Privatefinanceinitiative/index.htm

17. NHS Charitable Funds

Introduction

This chapter looks at the management of funds held on trust and is based on the legislative framework as it applies to England and Wales. The key Act is the *Charities Act 2006* – there are different regulatory regimes in Scotland and Northern Ireland.

History and Background

There are just under 300 NHS charities and the overall level of funds held is significant. To a large degree, the accumulation of these funds is a consequence of the historical funding of early health services through charitable sources. More recently these funds have been boosted through capital growth and income from investments, legacies and donations and fundraising appeals.

When the NHS was created, most existing charitable assets were pooled into the Hospital Endowments Fund. The main exceptions to this were teaching and university hospitals, which retained control of their endowments through boards of governors and management committees respectively.

The Nature and Purpose of Charitable Funds

A trust is created when funds are accepted by a trustee to be held and used for the benefit of a beneficiary. The arrangement is usually governed by an instrument that sets out the terms of the trust and the purpose to which funds are to be applied by the trustee. Trustees are not obliged to receive funds on trust and may refuse where conditions imposed by the donor are too onerous. In order to be deemed charitable, funds held on trust must exist to provide public benefit, be exclusively charitable and be used to further the fund's objectives.

The *Charities Act 2006* amended the *Charities Act 1993* in various ways and sets out what can constitute a charitable purpose – there are thirteen categories:

- The prevention or relief of poverty
- The advancement of education
- The advancement of religion
- The advancement of health or saving lives
- The advancement of citizenship or community development
- The advancement of the arts, culture, heritage or science
- The advancement of amateur sport
- The advancement of human rights, conflict resolution or reconciliation or the promotion of religious or racial harmony or equality or diversity
- The advancement of environmental protection or improvement
- The relief of those in need by reason of youth, age, ill-health, disability, financial hardship or other disadvantage
- The advancement of animal welfare
- The promotion of the efficiency of the armed forces of the Crown, or of the efficiency of the police, fire and rescue service or ambulance services
- Other purposes beneficial to the community not falling under any of the other headings.

The Act also provides for the continuing admission of other categories that are analogous to these principal categories. The categories are subject to the overriding requirement of demonstrable public benefit. Funds that do not fall under one or more of the thirteen charitable purposes listed above are likely to be non-charitable but if there is a doubt advice should be sought from the Charity Commission.

Previous guidance from the Department of Health questioned whether non-charitable funds had a place within the NHS and suggested that they should more properly lie in the exchequer accounts as income generation schemes or taken outside the NHS boundary. It is therefore not expected that health service bodies would hold non-charitable trusts. This might, for example, include funds held on trust for the benefit of a single named patient (which has insufficient public benefit to be charitable in law).

There are three main types of charitable funds recognised in law. These are:

- Unrestricted funds – which may be spent at the discretion of the trustees in line with the charity's objectives
- Restricted income funds – which can only be spent in accordance with restrictions imposed when the funds were donated or granted to or raised for the charity
- Endowment funds – where capital funds are made available to a charity and trustees are legally required to invest or retain them. Endowment funds can be 'permanent' (i.e. trustees have no automatic power to spend the capital, only the income generated through its investment. The 2006 Act introduced some flexibility in this area so that it is now possible for a permanent endowment to be spent if consent is given by the Charity Commission) or 'expendable' (here capital can be converted to income).

Funds may also be 'designated' or 'earmarked' which means that trustees can set aside unrestricted funds for a specific purpose. Designating funds can be useful where it is planned to build up funds through periodic transfers from unrestricted funds over time for a significant project or where funds are needed to meet ongoing costs (for example, staffing) to which formal commitments have been made. It may also be a useful way to recognise the apparent 'wishes' of donors (which do not create 'restrictions').

If trustees want to accumulate funds over a longer period (i.e. not for a specific project), they must request a 'power of accumulation' from the Charity Commission (unless the governing document already allows them to do so).

Where Charitable Funds come from

As mentioned above, trustees are not obliged to receive funds on trust and may refuse where the conditions imposed by the donor are too onerous or where they are unlikely to be able to use funds as directed. To avoid criticism and safeguard their own position, trustees are advised to seek advice from the Charity Commission before refusing a donation. Acceptance of all donations should be tested against the general principle that it does not, nor appear to, place an NHS body or the Department of Health/Welsh Assembly Government under an inappropriate obligation.

There are five main sources of new money for charitable funds. These are:

- Donations
- Fundraising
- Legacies
- Grants
- Investment income and interest.

Donations

Donations can be solicited (for example, through posters, leaflets or other appeals) or unsolicited (for example, where, at the end of a hospital stay, a patient asks how they can donate to the ward or hospital charity).

Donations of both types can be unrestricted or restricted. For example, an unrestricted donation would arise when a patient or relative gives money 'for the hospital charity' or 'for the ward funds' without specifying how it should be used. Even if there is a particular use suggested, it will only be a 'restriction' if the terms are strictly limited – for example, 'it must be used' or 'must only be used' – and are formalised in writing. A donation made in response to a fundraising leaflet soliciting donations for a general fund would also be unrestricted.

It is desirable to minimise the proportion of donations received as 'restricted' funds because restricted funds limit spending flexibilities. One way to do this is to use a standard form of receipt that invites donors to record how they 'wish' their donation to be used 'without imposing any trust'. The wishes expressed can be reflected through the designation of donations, but donations on these terms will be 'unrestricted'. The Charity Commission's *NHS Charities Guidance* includes a model receipt form as an appendix. Such a receipting system can also assist with accountability and the receipt can incorporate an invitation to donate under Gift Aid arrangements.

Fundraising

Fundraising income results from events (anything from coffee mornings and sponsored swims through to high profile celebrity events) and targeted appeals. If the money is sought for an explicit purpose (for example, if tickets or a poster for a charity dinner state 'all proceeds from this event will be used to buy monitors for the special care baby unit') then it must be used for that and nothing else. The power of NHS trustees to raise funds is set out in section 222 of the *NHS Act 2006* and the Act does permit funds to be used more flexibly where there is an insufficient response (a failed appeal) or an excess of funds over and above the appeal target, provided certain safeguards are met.

Legacies

Legacies can be restricted or unrestricted depending on the terms on which the bequest is made. The 'wishes' or 'desires' of a donor are normally non-binding designations, however reference should be made to the terms of the gift to ensure that a binding restriction does not mean that the legacy is restricted funds.

If the legacy cannot be fulfilled (for example, if the function it was intended for no longer exists or has been transferred to another body) the NHS trustee(s) concerned should consider whether they received the legacy under section 91 of the *NHS Act 1977* (re-enacted as section 218 of the *NHS Act 2006*), which may provide a power to redirect the funds. Advice may be sought from the Charity Commission. If it appears that section 91/section 218 does not apply then an application must be made to the Charity Commission for a scheme that allows the legacy to be used in another way.

Where a service transfers to another NHS body, the Department of Health or Welsh Assembly Government should be contacted, where appropriate, to organise a transfer of the related charitable funds. This is a separate issue from seeking the Charity Commission's authority to amend the trusts affecting restricted funds. Normally the service transfer (and consequent transfer of charitable funds) authorised by the Department of Health would precede and inform the Charity Commission's decisions on how to amend the trusts of linked restricted funds.

Grants

Grants are usually restricted income given for a specific purpose. As well as the general principles which apply to the use of and accounting for restricted funds, grants often have additional requirements attached. For example, how an acknowledgement is made in the accounts or other public documents.

Investment income and interest

Where charitable funds have surplus monies not needed to fund immediate charitable activities, trustees may invest to generate additional income. However, they must do so in line with legislation and Charity Commission guidance.

Investment income and interest (and any gains or investment losses) must be apportioned to the restricted fund that generates it. Where the trustee(s) administer(s) more than one charity, the income and investment gains and losses must also be apportioned to the respective charities. In the case of designated unrestricted funds of a charity the trustee(s) are permitted to apply investment gains for any of the objects of the charity concerned.

Types of Trustee

The charitable fund's governing documents set out who or what controls, manages and administers the charity – these are the trustees. There are four types of trustee in the NHS:

- **Corporate trustees**: most charitable funds in the NHS are managed by corporate trustees – in other words it is the NHS corporate body (i.e. an NHS trust or special health authority) that is the corporate trustee. The board of the trust or authority acts on behalf of the corporate trustee in the administration of the charitable funds – the members of the board are not themselves individual trustees. NHS trusts derive their power to hold charitable funds from clause 16, part II, schedule 2 of the *NHS and Community Care Act 1990*. Primary care trusts derive their power from schedule 5A, part iii, clause 12(1)(c) of

the *NHS Act 1977* – inserted into that Act by section 2(1) of the *Health Act 1999*. Foundation trusts derive their power from sections 213, 214 and 216 of the *NHS Act 2006*
- **Special trustees**: under section 7 of the *1946 NHS Act* the endowment and trust funds were vested in the Board of Governors of designated teaching hospitals who acted as trustees. Subsequently the *1973 NHS Reorganisation Act* provided for the reorganisation of charitable funds held historically. In particular, section 29 permitted the appointment of bodies of 'special trustees' by the Secretary of State for Health. The terms on which special trustees hold that property are prescribed by sections 93 and 95 of the *NHS Act 1977*, as affected by section 212 of the *NHS Act 2006*. Special trustees are no longer created
- **Section 11 trustees**: under section 11(1–3) of the *NHS and Community Care Act 1990*, (re-enacted under paragraph 10, schedule 4 to the *NHS Act 2006*) the Secretary of State for Health can appoint trustees to hold and administer the charitable funds associated with an NHS trust. Equivalent provision was made in section 7 of the *Health Act 1999* for trustees for a primary care trust
- **Section 51 trustees**: under section 51 of the *NHS Act 2006* the Secretary of State for Health can appoint trustees to hold and administer the charitable funds associated with an NHS foundation trust (section 51 trustees were formerly known as section 22 trustees).

The various provisions of the *NHS Act 2006* mentioned have parallel provisions for Wales, set out in the *NHS (Wales) Act 2006*. In Wales equivalent powers to those of the Secretary of State are exercised by Welsh ministers.

It is important to appreciate that health service bodies are not themselves charities. Only the property they hold on trust for exclusively charitable purposes constitutes a charity. The decision as to which model of trusteeship should apply in any locality (and which NHS body, or body of NHS trustees should hold funds linked to a particular NHS trust or facility) lies with the Department of Health, exercising statutory responsibility (or Welsh ministers in Wales). The Department of Health operates a policy under which charitable funds linked to an NHS body are only allocated to its trusteeship if they total more than £500,000. Below that figure the trusteeship is usually allocated to another NHS body or body of NHS trustees that already holds more than £500,000 of charitable funds.

Trustees – Roles and Responsibilities

In broad terms, trustees have a duty to ensure compliance, a duty of prudence and a duty of care, each of which is discussed below.

Compliance

Trustees must ensure that:

- The charity complies with charity law and with the requirements of the Charity Commission as regulator. As part of this, they must ensure that the charity prepares its annual report, returns and accounts as required by law
- The charity does not breach any of the requirements or rules in its governing document
- Any fundraising activity undertaken by or on behalf of the charity is properly undertaken and funds are properly accounted for. NHS trustees have specific powers to raise funds,

set out in section 222 of the *NHS Act 2006*. Guidance on the proper conduct of fundraising can be found in the Charity Commission's leaflet *CC20: Charities and Fundraising*.

Trustees also have a responsibility to review the charity's objects and ensure that they are still relevant and workable. If they are not, trustees should ask the Charity Commission for advice on how to change them.

Duty of prudence

Trustees must:

- Ensure the charity is and will remain solvent
- Ensure the charity's income and property is applied solely for the purposes set out in its governing document and for no other purpose
- Use charitable funds and assets wisely and only in furtherance of the charity's objects
- Avoid activities that might place the charity, its assets or reputation at risk
- Take special care when investing the charity's funds
- Ensure adequate financial management and control arrangements are in place
- Ensure the charity's expenditure is applied fairly amongst those who are qualified to benefit from it
- Not allow the charity's income to accumulate unless there is a specific power of accumulation and a future use for it in mind
- Have an agreed reserves policy that is reviewed regularly.

Duty of care

Trustees must:

- Exercise such care and skill as is reasonable in the circumstances having particular regard to:
  - any special knowledge or experience that he or she has or professes to have
  - any special knowledge or experience that it is reasonable to expect of a person acting in the course of that kind of business or profession (where he or she acts as a trustee in the course of a business or profession)
- Act with integrity and avoid any personal or organisational conflicts of interest – where trustees are required to make a decision which affects the personal interests of one of their number, that person should not be present at any discussion or vote on the matter
- Ensure they have appropriate risk management plans in place. Trustees of charities with gross annual income over £500,000 must make a statement about this in their annual report
- Consider using external professional advice where there may be a material risk to the charity.

The Charity Commission's guides *The Essential Trustee – an introduction* and *The Essential Trustee – what you need to know* are useful reference sources for all trustees (see the Commission's website).

Regulation – Roles and Responsibilities

The key point to remember in relation to the regulatory framework is that charitable funds are governed by charities (not NHS) legislation. In terms of financial accountability this means that NHS charitable funds submit financial information to the Charity Commission rather than the Department of Health or the Welsh Assembly Government. However, the Department and Assembly do have a role in this area, as set out below.

Department of Health

The Secretary of State for Health is responsible for bringing forward legislation on:

- The appointment and removal of trustees
- The terms of their office
- The transfer of property between trustee bodies – no transfers of charitable funds or trustee responsibilities can be made where NHS bodies are restructured without the Department's authority or agreement
- The preparation and audit of accounts for charitable funds – i.e. the overarching requirement to prepare accounts in line with the relevant charities acts and the SORP (see later in this chapter for details).

These responsibilities are exercised through the Department of Health.

Welsh Assembly Government

In Wales Welsh ministers have equivalent powers to those of the Secretary of State in England, and exercise those responsibilities through the Welsh Assembly Government.

Charity Commission

The Charity Commission is the statutory organisation that regulates charities in England and Wales. It is responsible for regulating the proper conduct and administration of charities. Its aim is to maintain public confidence in the integrity of charity which it does by encouraging better methods of administration, giving advice to trustees and investigating and correcting abuse. The Commission has the power to change the objectives of a charity where this is necessary and where trustees do not have the power to do so themselves. It also keeps a register of charities, which is open to public inspection.

The NHS is required to register charitable funds with the Charity Commission and to file audited accounts in a prescribed form and also to produce an annual report and annual return. The Charity Commission provides advice and guidance to help charities make effective use of their resources and to help trustees fulfil their objectives and obligations.

Charity Tribunal

The 2006 Act established the Charity Tribunal as an independent body to:

- Hear appeals against decisions of the Charity Commission

- Hear applications for review of decisions of the Charity Commission
- Consider referrals from the Attorney General or the Charity Commission on points of law.

The Management of Charitable Funds

Day-to-day management

Trustees are only able to delegate authority that is specified in their governing instrument or section 11 of the *Trustee Act 2000*. However, they cannot delegate their statutory duties and responsibilities. This means that although in practice the day-to-day management of charitable funds may be delegated to a sub-committee and staff, trustees remain accountable for all decisions relating to the charity and its performance. It follows, therefore, that they need to be well informed about the business of the charity if they are to meet their responsibilities effectively. They will need to establish clear reporting lines and ensure that appropriate arrangements exist to enable them to oversee actions taken on their behalf.

This means that there need to be written rules and procedures covering the formal conduct of the charity's business. These will normally be set out in the form of standing orders, standing financial instructions and procedures or guidance notes, in addition to any 'scheme of delegation'. The frequency of corporate trustee meetings or of committee meetings will depend on the size of the charitable funds being administered and the number and complexity of its transactions. Meetings need to be frequent enough to avoid any delays to the charity's administration that might lead to a failure to meet legal and regulatory requirements or to poor management of its resources.

When acting on behalf of corporate trustees, boards of NHS bodies must recognise that:

- The charitable funds they are managing are distinct from the exchequer monies of the NHS body
- In acting on behalf of the corporate trustee they have separate and distinct responsibilities for the administration of the charitable funds.

This is best achieved either by:

- Boards meeting separately to deal with charitable funds business or
- Creating a separate committee to deal with matters relating to the charitable funds, and which reports to the full board of the NHS body acting as corporate trustee.

The Charity Commission also encourages all charities to follow the advice set out in *Good Governance: a Code for the Voluntary and Community Sector*. This Code has been developed by a Steering Group of representatives from the Association of Chief Executives of Voluntary Organisations (ACEVO), the Charity Trustee Network (CTN), the Institute of Chartered Secretaries and Administrators (ICSA) and the National Council for Voluntary Organisations (NCVO) and identifies six key principles that trustees should adhere to in order to provide good governance and leadership. These are:

- Understanding their role
- Ensuring delivery of organisational purpose

- Working effectively both as individuals and a team
- Exercising effective control
- Behaving with integrity
- Being open and accountable.

Reserves policy

As far as the income received by the fund is concerned, trustees are under a legal duty to apply charitable funds within a reasonable time of receiving them. To be able to do this prudently, trustees need to consider, and regularly review, what level of reserves it is appropriate for them to hold (see the 'duty of prudence' earlier in this chapter). Without a sound reserves policy, trustees cannot be content that their reserves are at a level to meet current needs. If reserves are too high, the charity is retaining funds without justification and this could constitute a breach of trust. If reserves are too low, the fund's ability to meet future commitments or needs may be at risk. Trustees are required to have a formal reserves policy, review this regularly and report on it in their annual report.

Investment powers

Under the *Trustee Act 2000*, charity trustees have a general power of investment that can be used in relation to any charity property held on trust (except property of charitable companies) subject to any 'restriction or exclusion' affecting the charity. This power allows a trustee to place funds in any kind of investment, excluding land, as though he or she was the absolute owner of those funds. The *Trustee Act 2000* also gives all charity trustees power to acquire freehold or leasehold land in the UK.

Financial management

Trustees have a duty to use the income of their funds for the purpose for which they were given, unless the charity's governing document gives them the power to accumulate income or they have a specific application in mind. In order to justify the retention of income, trustees need to adopt expenditure plans. Budgets should be set with decision ceilings for fund managers and financial planning should be undertaken.

To be able to discharge their responsibilities effectively, trustees will need relevant management information to inform their decision-making. As well as the more usual financial information relating to budget and spend to date, trustees will need:

- To be informed of significant donations
- A list of large or significant transactions
- A summary investment report
- A report on slow moving or overdrawn funds
- A report on the use of the Chair's discretionary powers.

The Charity Commission booklet (CC60), *The Hallmarks of an Effective Charity*, sets out the standards the Commission believes an effective charity and its trustees will try to uphold and the principles that its regulatory framework exists to support. As such, it provides some useful pointers to trustees when reviewing their governance arrangements.

Risk management

Trustees should maintain a risk register and review it on a regular basis to ensure the effectiveness of actions taken to mitigate identified risks. Detailed guidance is available on the Charity Commission's website.

VAT

VAT applies to charities in the same way that it applies to commercial enterprises. However, the activities of charitable bodies are often carried out on a 'non-business basis' and are therefore not subject to VAT. Conversely, charities may not be able to recover related VAT on expenditure. VAT is a difficult area of tax to deal with – if charities require assistance they should contact the VAT NHS Admin Team. Guidance about what specific charity reliefs are available and how they work is also available via local VAT offices.

Accounting Requirements

The detailed requirements for the preparation, audit and submission of annual accounts of individual charities that are not charitable companies depend upon their level of income and where they are based in the UK. The key document to refer to in England and Wales is *CC15 – Charity Reporting and Accounting: the Essentials*. This is available on the Charity Commission's website. All charities in the UK that prepare accruals accounts must also follow the *Statement of Recommended Practice (SORP) 2005* (also on the Commission's website). Trustees are also required to ensure that the charity keeps proper books and records.

As a minimum, all charities must:

- Prepare and maintain accounting records which must be retained for at least 6 years
- Prepare annual accounts and make these available to the public on request
- Prepare a trustees' annual report and make it available to the public on request.

Charities with a gross annual income of at least £100,000 must prepare their accounts on an accruals basis. Below this threshold, charities may elect to prepare their accounts on a receipts and payments or accruals basis.

Accruals accounts comprise:

- A statement of financial activities (SOFA) for the year that shows all incoming and outgoing resources and reconciles all changes in its funds
- A balance sheet, showing the recognised assets, liabilities and different categories of fund of the charity
- A cash flow statement if at least two of the following apply. the charity has an annual turnover of more than £6.3m; its balance sheet shows more than £3.26m gross assets; it employs an average of 50 or more staff
- Notes explaining the accounting policies adopted.

Where charities have to account for more than one fund under their control, the accounts should provide a summary of the main funds. In particular, they should differentiate between unrestricted income funds, restricted income funds and endowment funds. The columnar format of the SOFA is designed to achieve this.

The Annual Report

The annual report is one of the key tools available to charities to help them communicate with stakeholders including donors, beneficiaries and the wider public. The SORP 2005 provides best practice recommendations, which in England, Wales and Scotland are underpinned by law. The annual report is normally presented along with the accounts but is legally a separate document. It should cover a range of information including, for example:

- Details about how trustees are recruited and trained
- Details about the charity's decision-making processes including, for example, what functions are delegated to sub-committees and staff
- An explanation of the charity's aims and the changes/difference it seeks to make through its work
- Details of the charity's objectives for the year and strategy for meeting these
- Details of significant activities, projects and services that contribute to the achievement of the charity's objectives
- Details about reserves and grant making policies
- Where material investments are held, details of the investment policy and objectives
- Charities with gross annual income of at least £500,000 are required to report on their risk management plans
- Plans for the future.

Guidance on the content of the annual report is available in Charity Commission booklet – CC15, *Charity Reporting and Accounting: the Essentials*.

Consolidation of Charitable Funds

There is ongoing debate about whether or not charitable funds should be consolidated with an NHS organisation's exchequer funds in line with IAS 27 – *Consolidated and Separate Financial Statements*. For 2010/11 HM Treasury gave a dispensation so that IAS 27 did not apply. In 2011/12, the issue remains under review – see the Charity Commission's website for the latest position.

What the future holds for Charitable Funds

The coalition government's proposals for the NHS do not refer to NHS charitable funds. However, there are a number of practical issues that will need to be thought through in relation to the transfer of funds that are associated with any organisations that are abolished.

For charitable funds that relate to community services that are transferred from PCTs (under 'transforming community services'), guidance has been issued by the Department of Health. This makes clear that where possible any such funds should follow the services but if those funds are below the minimum level to 'allow efficient management of the funds', they may need to transfer to another NHS organisation. In such instances, the Department of Health should be consulted. The guidance also specifies the circumstances in which non statutory transfer orders can be used rather than a statutory instrument.

References and Further Reading

Charities Act 2006: www.opsi.gov.uk/acts/acts2006/ukpga_20060050_en_1

Other Acts of Parliament referred to in this chapter can be found via: www.opsi.gov.uk/acts.htm

The Charity Commission offers a range of useful free publications. These can be accessed via www.charity-commission.gov.uk or ordered from its offices. Guidance available from the Charity Commission referred to in this chapter is listed below:

NHS Charities Guidance, Charity Commission (2009)

CC20 – Charities and Fundraising (2008)

CC3 and CC3A – The Essential Trustee: an Introduction (2007) and what you need to know (2008)

CC60 – The Hallmarks of an Effective Charity (2008)

CC15 – Charity Reporting and Accounting: the Essentials (2007)

The Charity Tribunal: www.charity.tribunals.gov.uk/

NHS Charitable Funds: A Practical Guide, HFMA, 2005: www.hfma.org.uk

Good Governance: a Code for the Voluntary and Community Sector: www.charity-commission.gov.uk/Charity_requirements_guidance/Charity_governance/Good_governance/governancecode.aspx

VAT – for NHS connected charities the best contact is the NHS VAT team: nhsvatteam@hmrc.gsi.gov.uk

Information is also available via local VAT offices – see: www.hmrc.gov.uk

SORP 2005: www.charitycommission.gov.uk/investigations/sorp/sorp05docs.asp

IAS 27 – Consolidated and Separate Financial Statements, IASB: www.iasb.org/Home.htm

Funds Held on Trust and Transforming Community Services, FAQ available from the finman site under 'what's new', December 2010: www.info.doh.gov.uk/doh/finman.nsf

18. Health and Social Care in Northern Ireland

Introduction

The primary difference between the NHS in England and services in Northern Ireland is that in Northern Ireland health services and social care are integrated. The Department of Health, Social Services and Public Safety (DHSSPS) is one of the government departments formed to administer the responsibilities devolved to the Northern Ireland Assembly.

A *Review of Public Administration* (RPA) was launched in June 2002 and concluded in March 2006. It was a comprehensive examination of the arrangements for the administration and delivery of public services in Northern Ireland, covering over 150 bodies, including the 26 district councils, the health and social services boards and trusts, the five education and library boards and about 100 other public bodies. The devolved Administration returned in May 2007 and the Executive undertook a comprehensive review of policy and strategic direction in respect of the proposals originally contained in the RPA.

In February 2008, the Health and Social Care Minister launched a full public consultation on his proposals to reform health and social care in Northern Ireland. In July 2008 the Health Minister announced his decision on the outcome of this consultation.

This led to the formation of a single Health and Social Care Board (HSCB), a new multi-professional Public Health Agency (PHA), the establishment of five local commissioning groups (LCGs) to cover the same geographical area as five health and social care trusts (HSC trusts) and a smaller, more sharply focussed Department. A regional Business Services Organisation (BSO) provides a range of support functions for the health and social care service.

Department of Health, Social Services and Public Safety

Health and social care in Northern Ireland are the responsibility of the Minister for Health, Social Services and Public Safety. The Department of Health, Social Services and Public Safety was established by the *Departments (NI) Order 1999* and is the largest of all Northern Ireland Departments. In 2009/10 the Department's budget was £4.3bn, some 48% of the total NI Executive DEL revenue budget. Of this £3.9bn was budgeted for health and social care (including family health services).

The DHSSPS's current remit covers policy and legislation relating to:

- Health and social care (this includes hospitals, family practitioner services, community health and social services)
- Public health (to promote and protect the health and wellbeing of the population of Northern Ireland)
- Public safety (this includes the Fire and Rescue Service, food safety and emergency planning).

The Department's mission statement is to improve the health and social wellbeing of the people of Northern Ireland. It endeavours to do so by:

- Leading a major programme of cross-government action to improve the health and wellbeing of the population and reduce health inequalities. This includes interventions involving health promotion and education to encourage people to adopt activities, behaviours and attitudes which lead to better health and wellbeing. The aim is a population which is much more engaged in ensuring its own health and wellbeing
- Ensuring the provision of appropriate health and social care services, both in clinical settings such as hospitals and GPs' surgeries, and in the community through nursing, social work and other professional services.

The Permanent Secretary of the Department is also Chief Executive of the Health and Social Care system, as well as Principal Accounting Officer for all the Department's responsibilities. Within the Department, the key business groups are the Resources and Performance Management Group, the Healthcare Policy Group, the Social Policy Group, the Health Estates Investment Group (HEIG), the Office of the Chief Medical Officer and the Office of Social Services. The Department also has a Modernisation Directorate and a Human Resources Directorate.

There are five professional groups within the department, each led by a Chief Professional Officer:

- Medical and Allied Services
- Social Services Inspectorate
- Nursing and Midwifery Advisory Group
- Dental Services
- Pharmaceutical Advice and Services.

Health and Social Care Board

As mentioned above, a single Health and Social Care Board replaced the four health and social services boards. The new Board, together with LCGs, are accountable to the Minister for translating his vision for health and social care into a range of services that deliver high quality and safe outcomes for users, good value for the taxpayer and compliance with statutory obligations.

One of the key tasks for the Board is to ensure effective commissioning. Commissioning plans are developed in close partnership with the PHA and through a 'commissioning cycle' that covers:

- Assessing needs
- Strategic planning
- Priority setting
- Securing resources to address needs
- Agreeing with providers the delivery of appropriate services and monitoring that delivery
- Assuring that the safety and quality of services commissioned are improving, that recommendations from the Regulation and Quality Improvement Authority (RQIA) and other reviews have been implemented and that as a minimum, services meet DHSSPS and other recognised standards

- Evaluating impact and feeding back that assessment into the new baseline position in terms of how needs have changed.

A full description of the responsibilities of the HSCB can be accessed from their website at www.hscboard.hscni.net/

Just as the four health and social services boards were replaced by a regional organisation, so the four health and social services councils were replaced by one structure, the Patient Client Council (PCC).

HSC Trusts

As mentioned, there are now five HSC trusts in Northern Ireland, offering a range of acute and community services. The Belfast, Northern, Southern, South Eastern and Western HSC trusts were formed from the merger of eighteen health and social services trusts. A sixth Trust, the Northern Ireland Ambulance Service, manages the ambulance service for Northern Ireland. More information is available from the individual Trust websites which are listed at the end of this chapter.

Other HSC Organisations

A variety of specialist functions are carried out by organisations on a Northern Ireland-wide basis. These include:

- Public Health Agency
- Business Services Organisation
- Northern Ireland Blood Transfusion Service
- Northern Ireland Guardian Ad Litem Agency
- Northern Ireland Practice and Education Council
- Northern Ireland Medical and Dental Training Agency
- Northern Ireland Social Care Council
- Regulation and Quality Improvement Authority.

The new Public Health Agency incorporates and builds on the work of the Health Promotion Agency but has a much wider responsibility for health protection, health improvement and development to address existing health inequalities and public health issues for all the people of Northern Ireland.

Information on all the organisations referred to above can be accessed from the websites listed at the end of this section.

Local Commissioning Groups

There are five LCGs:

- Belfast
- Northern
- South Eastern

- Southern
- Western.

Each LCG is a committee of the HSCB and is co-terminus with their respective health and social care trust area.

LCGs are responsible for the commissioning of health and social care by addressing the care needs of their local population. They also have responsibility for assessing health and social care needs; planning health and social care to meet current and emerging needs; and securing the delivery of health and social care to meet assessed needs.

Funding and Allocations

The process through which resources are allocated to health and social care changed significantly following devolution of responsibilities to the Northern Ireland Assembly.

Overall public sector funding for Northern Ireland is provided via the Northern Ireland block vote, as part of the national spending reviews. Changes to the total provision for Northern Ireland are largely determined through the principle of comparability, whereby the Treasury adjusts the Northern Ireland block vote in line with comparable programmes in England.

The Northern Ireland Assembly has the discretion to allocate devolved resources within the Northern Ireland block across all departmental spending programmes. The DHSSPS sets its proposed allocations in the context of the Minister's overall priorities and objectives for the Department's public expenditure programme. Spending on HSC equates to approximately 40% of the total public expenditure within the control of the Northern Ireland Assembly.

The DHSSPS makes direct revenue allocations to the HSCB and PHA to cover hospital, community health and social care services in the form of a revenue resource limit (RRL). Capital allocations are made directly to the Board, PHA, trusts and smaller non departmental bodies in the form of a capital resource limit (CRL).

The HSCB and PHA use a weighted capitation revenue allocation formula to determine target allocations for hospital, community health and personal social services on a programme of care basis. The formula determines how much each of the five LCGs should receive to purchase services for its residents from trusts. Separate allocations are given for general medical services to cover staffing, IT and premises costs as well as reimbursement for implementing local and direct enhanced services.

Substantial resources are also set aside for primary health services. These areas are subject to indicative budgets (particularly in the area of prescribing) and performance against budget is closely monitored. The intention is to directly relate GP prescribing budgets to their capitation share by 2012/13.

The Commissioning Process

LCGs are committees of the HSCB and were established in Northern Ireland to lead the commissioning process. They have devolved responsibility for addressing the needs of their local populations, working within regional policy and strategy frameworks, available resources and performance targets. They also have responsibility for fully integrated commissioning to deliver better health and wellbeing and improve health outcomes for their local populations as well as reducing health inequalities locally and across the population of Northern Ireland.

As already highlighted these areas are co-terminus with HSC trust boundaries.

A geographical orientation better reflects the needs of natural communities and the organisation of local health and social care economies, including hospitals, community networks and geographically based partners. On the other hand, commissioning around 'communities of interest' or client-groups or 'programmes of care' can ensure that the needs of service users and carers are addressed holistically and services are planned in a coordinated way to meet particular needs.

Both approaches operate within the reformed health and social care commissioning landscape in Northern Ireland. While the establishment of LCGs gives prominence to geography, this is balanced by 'programme of care teams' within LCGs. These teams link across LCG boundaries where necessary, to form regional strategic planning networks relevant to client or 'community of interest' groups.

The HSCB and PHA have separate accountabilities as organisations within the new structure but are required to have a very close working relationship. They are jointly charged with bringing forward an agreed commissioning plan on an annual basis.

Commissioning of services from independent family practitioner contractors continues to reflect the negotiation of contracts by DHSSPS. These arrangements recognise regional priorities, including service framework standards. LCGs will identify local priorities and may use 'local enhanced services' as a mechanism for securing service delivery.

Financial Accounting and Control

The HSCB and HSC trusts prepare annual accounts in formats prescribed by the DHSSPS. Since 2009/10 they have been produced based on guidance in the *Financial Reporting Manual* (FReM) which is based on international financial reporting standards (IFRS).

The annual accounts are audited by the Northern Ireland Audit Office (NIAO), either by their own staff, or by contracting out to private sector firms of accountants and auditors. Each set of accounts is then formally laid before the Northern Ireland Assembly. The Assembly has a Public Accounts Committee (PAC) with a similar role to the committee of the House of Commons of the same name.

The DHSSPS issues a detailed *Manual of Accounts* for all health and social care bodies which is updated annually as required to reflect changes in reporting requirements. If the guidance is not the same for each DHSSPS body, the manual sets out the procedures that each particular body has to follow.

The HSC bodies have financial targets. They must stay within their revenue and capital resource limits and break even.

Corporate Governance and Audit

The corporate governance regime is similar to that in place in the rest of the UK, including codes of conduct, accountability and openness, remuneration committees, audit committees, internal audit, external audit, board reports, annual accounts, annual report and annual public meetings.

External audit of the accounts of the HSCB and HSC trusts is the responsibility of the NIAO. A number of audits are contracted out to private sector accountancy and audit firms.

HSC bodies are required to have in place suitable internal audit arrangements. This service is provided on an in-service basis at present by BSO Internal Audit Unit. Internal audit must comply with HM Treasury's *Government Internal Audit Standards*. The adequacy of the internal audit arrangements is reviewed and reported on each year by the NIAO as part of their report to those charged with governance of each body.

Private Finance Initiative

The private finance initiative in HSC in Northern Ireland follows the same principles as in England with the underlying aim of achieving value for money. Treasury guidance must be adhered to.

Charitable Funds

Charitable funds are held by HSC trusts in Northern Ireland and are derived, for example, from donations by individuals or legacies.

As in England and Wales these funds are used for the purpose for which the original donation was given, or bequest made, where that is known, unless the uses to which the funds can be put is unrestricted. Charitable funds are held and controlled by HSC trusts and boards as corporate trustees.

Northern Ireland's Charity Commission was established on 27 March 2009 and regulates charities, including HSC charitable funds. Details about the Charities Commission Northern Ireland can be found at its website: www.charitycommissionni.org.uk

References and Further Reading

Department of Health Social Services and Public Safety: www.dhsspsni.gov.uk

Health and Social Care Board: www.hscboard.hscni.net/

Public Health Agency: www.publichealth.hscni.net

Patient Client Council: www.patientclientcouncil.hscni.net

Belfast Health and Social Care Trust: www.belfasttrust.hscni.net/

Northern Health and Social Care Trust: www.northerntrust.hscni.net/

Southern Health and Social Care Trust: www.southerntrust.hscni.net/

South Eastern Health and Social Care Trust: www.setrust.hscni.net/

Western Health and Social Care Trust: www.westerntrust.hscni.net/

Northern Ireland Ambulance Service: www.niamb.co.uk/

Review of Public Administration: www.dhsspsni.gov.uk/index/hss/rpa-home

Northern Ireland Agencies: www.n-i.nhs.uk/index.php?link=agencies

Northern Ireland Medical and Dental Training Agency: www.nimdta.gov.uk/

Northern Ireland Social Care Council: www.niscc.info/

Regulation and Quality Improvement Authority: www.rqia.org.uk/home/index.cfm

Health and Social Care in Northern Ireland: www.hscni.net/

Northern Ireland Audit Office: www.niauditoffice.gov.uk

Northern Ireland Public Accounts Committee: www.niassembly.gov.uk/public/accounts.htm

Internal Audit Standards, 2002: www.dfpni.gov.uk/audit_standards.pdf

19. The NHS in Scotland

Introduction

In operational terms much of NHSScotland is similar to England and Wales. However, there are substantial organisational differences, which this chapter looks at. More detailed information regarding the structures and processes of NHS Scotland can be found in the *Introductory Guide to NHS Finance in Scotland* published by HFMA Scotland.

Please note that this chapter has been written during the build up to the May 2011 election for the Scottish Parliament which may result in changes to the way NHSScotland is organised – any such developments will be picked up in the next version of this Guide.

Key Policies

Partnership for Care – Scotland's Health White Paper (2003) was the blueprint for setting in place organisational and policy change within NHSScotland and built on the earlier White Paper – *Our National Health: A Plan for Action, a Plan for Change* (2000). The main changes were to encourage a more collaborative approach to managing and providing health services at both a national and local level.

The main features of the White Paper were:

- Dissolution of NHS trusts as separate legal entities and the transfer of their functions, staff and assets intact to new operating divisions of their area NHS boards
- Introduction of a single local health plan
- A new performance and accountability framework for NHSScotland
- Revised financial framework and financial targets
- Decentralisation of decision-making to front line staff.

More recently the Scottish Executive Health Department issued *Delivering for Health*, as a response to the report from the group led by Professor David Kerr – *Building a Health Service Fit for the Future*. Both reports outlined future models of healthcare which move from acute based, episodic, reactive care to community-based, continuous, integrated and preventative care.

In December 2007, the Scottish government launched *Better Health, Better Care* – this sets out a revised policy to continue the development of the NHS in Scotland. It is based on values of co-operation and collaboration and is aimed at tackling health inequalities, with patients at the centre of the NHS.

Fundamental Differences between England and Scotland

The main differences that exist between the operation of the NHS in Scotland and England are:

- NHSScotland reports to the Scottish Parliament rather than the UK Parliament
- There is no regional tier in Scotland between NHS boards and the Health Department

- There are no NHS trusts in Scotland
- There are very few non-NHS healthcare providers in Scotland.

Statutory Provisions

The following legislation is relevant to the operation of NHSScotland:

- *Public Finance and Accountability (Scotland) Act 2000* – this sets out the rules for the Parliament's budgetary process
- *Community Care and Health (Scotland) Act 2002* – this provides the legislative backing for improvements in care services
- *National Health Service Reform (Scotland) Act 2004* – this allowed for the dissolution of NHS trusts and the establishment of community health partnerships (CHPs); introduced a statutory duty for NHS boards to co-operate with each other with a view to enhancing the health of the nation (for example, through regional and national planning); established powers of intervention on behalf of Scottish ministers in case of service failure; and imposed on NHS boards duties to encourage public involvement and promote health improvement.

Following devolution in Scotland and the subsequent creation of the Scottish Parliament, NHSScotland became accountable to the Parliament, and not as previously to the Secretary of State for Scotland. The *Public Finance and Accountability (Scotland) Act 2000* has five main policy objectives, all of which relate to NHSScotland, concerning procedures for the approval of expenditure, use of resources, management of audit and scrutiny of the outputs obtained from that expenditure. They are:

- To ensure probity in the handling of the public funds under the Scottish Parliament's control
- To help maximise the cost effectiveness of the expenditure under the control of the Parliament
- To provide the information that the Parliament needs to make properly informed and timely decisions and to judge the probity and wider value of the actions of the Executive
- To provide the Scottish people with understandable, consistent, relevant and timely information
- To contain the overhead and compliance costs associated with the procedures.

Organisation of NHSScotland

The First Minister for Scotland has responsibility for NHSScotland and is assisted by the Cabinet Secretary for Health and Well-being. The Scottish Government Health and Community Care Directorate (SGHD) is responsible for NHSScotland and for the development and implementation of health and community care policy. NHSScotland comprises fourteen territorial NHS boards responsible for the planning and delivery of all health services in their own area. In addition, there are eight special health boards in Scotland.

The fourteen NHS boards cover the whole of Scotland with population spans from 20,000 to 1,500,000 over widely differing areas. All NHS boards report to the Chief Executive of the

SGHD. NHS boards are responsible for planning and commissioning hospital and community health services for their resident populations, as well as providing health services.

The roles of the different components of local NHS systems are as follows:

- NHS boards are responsible for strategic planning, governance and performance management
- Operating divisions are part of a single statutory organisation but have the ability to take operational decisions and manage the delivery of healthcare services within the governance framework of their NHS board via a lead Director. However, they must do so with continual reference to the central board of governance
- Community health partnerships (CHPs) are responsible for the planning and delivery of community services, and may report to the NHS board directly (through a CHP director) or via a community or primary care operating division
- Special health boards are national bodies which report directly to the SGHD and are responsible for particular business areas – for example, the Scottish Ambulance Service, National Waiting Times Centre, NHS 24 (similar to NHS Direct in England), NHS Education for Scotland and NHS Quality Improvement Scotland (again similar to NICE in England).

Operating divisions and CHPs have significant management authority at local level with those in the front line empowered to plan and deliver services within a framework of clear strategic direction and rigorous performance management. It is considered vital to the management arrangements that devolution of decision-making does not stop at the operating division level.

The key principles of NHS boards and operating divisions are as follows:

- NHS boards should retain their focus as boards of governance and take a corporate, inclusive approach to collective decision-making based on the principles of partnership working and devolution of powers to the front line of patient care
- NHS boards should support local leadership by delegating financial and management authority as far as possible and encouraging locally responsive approaches to service provision
- As integral parts of local NHS systems, well-defined operating divisions should have specific, delegated authority to act within a defined remit without constant reference to the NHS board, backed up by clear, formal schemes of accountability
- Organisations should recognise the complex interaction between clinicians and other staff who work directly with patients and common services which support them in that task
- Responsibility and decision-making should be devolved to staff who are directly involved in delivering healthcare
- The design and development of services should be grounded firmly in the patient's everyday experience of care at locality level
- NHS boards should continue to develop sustainable frameworks for patient focus and public involvement
- NHS boards should continue to develop CHPs and 'joint future' initiatives (see later in this chapter) in a way that engages with community planning partners and maximises population alignment between CHPs and social care

- Health services should be delivered locally as far as possible, but always consistent with providing safe, sustainable and efficient services to patients. To achieve this, NHS boards should promote, resource and actively manage the development of managed clinical networks and other clinical and care networks, both within and beyond their local boundaries.

Shared services

NHSScotland has elected to develop a shared service approach for payroll and financial services through a number of NHS board consortia. The shared service consortia supply these services to each of the NHSScotland organisations utilising a common chart of accounts and standard processes. It has provided a central service for practitioner services for several years.

Funding Flows

NHSScotland funding forms part of the Scotland vote, which competes in the public expenditure survey (PES) against UK votes such as defence, social security and the environment. The First Minister for Scotland has the task of dividing up the Scottish vote among the various services for which he is responsible including health, prisons, education and social services. Health is one of the major areas of expenditure and allocations tend to mirror the lead given by the Department of Health in England. However, differences in allocation do arise.

Barnett formula

The Barnett formula was introduced in 1978 and forms the basis of the additional changes to expenditure in Scotland (and Wales) and applies to only certain types of expenditure. There are two main components to Scottish public expenditure:

- The inherited expenditure base
- Incremental expenditure changes – this is the part determined by Barnett.

There are three components to the calculation:

- The change in planned spending in departments in England
- The extent to which the relevant English departmental programme is comparable with the services carried out by each devolved administration
- The population proportion of each country.

Spending review process

A bi-annual spending review process is undertaken by Scottish ministers to identify spending plans for the following three-year period. This normally takes place at the same time as other UK spending reviews. The Scottish government finance department manages this process, scrutinising and challenging expenditure proposals and providing advice to departments and ministers.

Arbuthnott formula

The Arbuthnott review was the end product of the national review of resource allocation for NHSScotland. Entitled *Fair Shares for All*, its purpose was to review the methods for allocating funding between the fourteen NHS boards.

The key principles in developing the formula were that it must:

- Be fair
- Be tailored to Scotland's needs and give everyone in Scotland equal access to healthcare
- Take account of the influence of deprivation on healthcare needs and support the aim of tackling inequalities in health
- Take account of the needs of people living in remote and rural areas as well as those in urban areas
- Be based on evidence
- Be clearly explained and open to scrutiny.

The formula recommended using information about population size and the characteristics of each of the fourteen NHS boards to determine the relative funding needs. Four key elements have to be taken into account in the formula:

- The share of the Scottish population living in each NHS board area
- The age/sex structure of the population
- Levels of deprivation
- The proportion of the population living in remote and rural areas.

A revised funding formula has been developed by the NHSScotland Resource Allocation Committee (NRAC). The NRAC was established to refine and extend Arbuthnott, looking in particular at evidence to determine healthcare need in different groups of people. The revised formula has been applied since April 2009. Where boards are above or below parity (the level of funding required for the board to deliver services as per the NRAC formula), movements in allocation are made through applying differential growth rates to boards. All boards receive a minimum uplift. Those below parity receive an additional allocation to move them towards parity. There is no agreed end date to implement fully the revised funding levels.

Cash limited/non-cash limited

Funds allocated for hospital and community health services (HCHS) are distributed via a resource allocation. NHS boards are not allowed to overspend and are highly restricted in their ability to carry forward surpluses or deficits from one year into another. NHS boards are currently permitted to carry forward up to a theoretical 1% of their revenue resource allocations as a surplus into the following year. Since April 2004, general medical services (GMS) have also been included within the resource allocation with the introduction of the 'new' GMS contract.

Funding for family health services (general dental services, general pharmaceutical services and general optical services) forms part of the Scottish government health allocation. Although this is subject to a cash limit nationally much of the expenditure is not subject to cash limits at NHS board level.

Resource accounting

In line with UK government policy, NHSScotland has moved to a resource-based system of public expenditure and control. The main change is the extension of an accruals based approach to accounting with the emphasis on outputs and achievement of aims and objectives rather than accounting on a cash target basis.

Capital planning process

From 2011/12, the approach to managing NHSScotland's capital resources will change. In particular there will be:

- Less capital distributed on a formula basis
- Capital that is allocated by formula will support more routine spending and projects that fall within board delegated limits of between £1.5m and £5m
- All new projects above board delegated limits will be subject to a bidding process for specific project funding.

Full details are set out in CEL 32(2010).

Local and National NHS Plans

In Scotland planning is primarily the function of NHS boards, although an overview is provided by the SGHD.

The role of the NHS board is to:

- Improve and protect the health of local people
- Improve health services for local people
- Focus clearly on health outcomes and people's experience of their local NHS system
- Promote integrated health and community planning by working closely with other local organisations
- Provide a single focus of accountability for the performance of the local NHS system.

The functions of the NHS board are:

- Strategic development through the local health plan
- Resource allocation and addressing local priorities
- Implementation of the local health plan (discharged through the operating divisions)
- Performance management of the local NHS system
- Preparation and implementation of the local health plan.

Each operational division is required to produce local operational plans to achieve the objectives of the local health plan. A performance and accountability framework has also been developed, which takes the reporting focus beyond purely finance-based performance indicators.

Joint Planning

The *NHS and Community Care Act 1990* introduced a fundamental change in the arrangements for encouraging people to be looked after in the community and preventing inappropriate accommodation in hospitals by assigning the lead responsibility for implementing policy to local authorities.

The old Scottish Executive created the 'joint future group' to look into the provision of community care in Scotland and identify practical ways of improving joint working. The main recommendation of this review was to introduce joint resourcing and management.

Since April 2002, NHS bodies and local authorities have been required to bring together all their available resources in the widest sense – including staff, money, equipment and property – under single management. Once the scope of the resources is known and has been agreed, each agency has the option of either aligning their budgets under existing arrangements or pooling them under the flexibility afforded by the *Community Care and Health (Scotland) Act 2002* (see below).

The Scottish government has advocated a partnership approach to be taken by NHS bodies and local authorities. The partnership agreements should outline:

- Joint development priorities and targets for a three-year period, covering key community care client groups and carers
- Developments in joint service management and joint resourcing proposed to support the stated development priorities and targets
- The performance management framework to be used to monitor progress, evaluate impact, and guide corrective action, if necessary
- The governance and accountability framework for the partnership agreement, straddling a number of local agencies.

Joint Future is the name given to the joint planning, assessment and provision of services to ensure that users of the care system receive a coherent and integrated package of care and this is backed by the *Community Care and Health (Scotland) Act 2002*. This Act identifies the practical arrangements for joint working covering:

- Payments by NHS bodies towards certain local authority expenditure
- Payments by local authorities towards expenditure by NHS bodies on prescribed functions
- Delegation between local authorities and NHS bodies
- Transfers of staff.

Costing and Pricing

Costing

Formally known as the *Scottish Health Service Costs Book*, the 'blue book' provides financial and related activity information in sets of published tables, with the information relating mainly to individual hospitals.

The *Costs Book* contains health board and hospital reports, the majority of which relate to hospitals. Hospital reports relate to hospital care and others relate to community care and NHS National Services Scotland.[22] Hospital reports are structured to provide two main dimensions of analysis, one being a care-type/patient-type analysis and the second a functional analysis. The care-type/patient-type analysis forms the bulk of the blue book.

Managers at all levels can use the information as an aid to decision-making, planning and control and it also provides a set of indicators of performance for comparison purposes.

The information contained within the reports is derived from financial and statistical information prepared as part of the annual accounts process. The majority of the information is derived from Scottish financial returns (SFRs). There are a range of these returns detailing costs down to specialty level.

HRG benchmarking service

Healthcare resource groups (HRGs) are a tool developed by the Department of Health in England as a means of categorising hospital patients. The National Services Scotland's information services division (ISD) has used HRGs for several years as a casemix measure for inpatient and day-case datasets.

Costing of hospital patient activity is well established in England but is still under consideration in Scotland. ISD Scotland produces a benchmarking report for acute trusts, in which comparative cost information, taking account of casemix differences, is presented for inpatient and day case activity.

Tariffs

NHSScotland has introduced a tariff system for cross boundary activity flows. The tariff system has the potential to deliver improved benchmarking information and more accurate financial flows. It is expected that a move to a tariff-based system away from locally negotiated service level agreements would result in winners and losers amongst NHS boards; however work is ongoing to mitigate this effect. The tariffs continue to be developed, led by a group of representatives from the Scottish government and NHS boards. The aim is to maximise the benefits from the introduction of tariffs, while improving the quality of the data used in their calculation.

Financial Accounting and Control

Revised financial framework

The financial framework of NHSScotland was historically complex, particularly from the perspective of trusts. As a result of the introduction of the *Scottish Health Plan* changes have been put in place to simplify the financial systems to allow for a patient focused and partnership approach.

---

[22] National Services Scotland is a Non Departmental Public Body that is accountable to the Scottish Government. It provides national strategic support services and expert advice to NHS Scotland.

This approach is an integral part of the accountability, governance and performance frameworks. The focus is intended to be on the whole system, which will, in turn, lead to improved planning and delivery of services.

Financial targets

To recognise the introduction of resource accounting and budgeting (RAB), the financial targets for NHS boards are to operate within their:

- Revenue resource limit
- Capital resource limit
- Cash requirement.

All NHS boards have a responsibility to control their finances throughout the year. Performance is monitored internally and externally. Also, on an annual basis audited accounts must be produced and various statements signed by the Chief Executive, including a statement on internal control. The annual accounts must be published and an extract made available publicly as part of the annual report. The SGHD determines the format of external reporting and the annual accounts so that consolidated accounts can be produced nationally. The principles of financial control and internal monitoring are set out in financial directions. It is left to local discretion to determine the exact nature of internal monitoring but it is sensible that this mirrors the external requirement. Internal financial control is ensured through the adoption of standing financial instructions, standard operating procedures and formal schemes of delegation.

NHS boards meet regularly with the SGHD to monitor and forecast progress against the statutory targets. Where an organisation is forecast not to meet a target, remedial action is expected so that the target can be achieved. In cases where an NHS board fails to operate within the revenue resource limit set, then an adjustment is made in the following year's financial allocation to reflect the amount by which the board has overspent as per RAB rules. The cumulative effect of successive years' failure to meet this target can be crippling for a board, as in the case of the NHS Argyll and Clyde Board, which the then Minister for Health took the decision to dissolve. The functions and services previously within Argyll and Clyde were subsumed within NHS Highland and NHS Greater Glasgow (now called NHS Greater Glasgow and Clyde).

Financial reporting

The revised structure of NHSScotland resulted in a financial reporting system based on unified reporting within NHS board areas.

The introduction of resource accounting (and more recently, international financial reporting standards (IFRS) has led to changes in the prime financial statements used by NHS boards. Under resource accounting, NHS boards are subject to revenue and capital resource limits, and are no longer controlled by cash.

Although the final accounts have changed in line with IFRS (as in the rest of the UK), for monthly monitoring purposes the forms required remain as follows:

- Operating cost statement – this broadly follows the format of the statement of operating costs proposed by the resource accounting manual. It requires similar disclosure to the former income and expenditure account
- Revenue resource analysis – designed to provide the additional information required by the SGHD, this analysis must be completed by all NHS boards and special NHS boards
- Balance sheet – provides an analysis of total assets and liabilities held by each NHS board
- Statement of cash flows – designed to allow the SGHD to review the cash position of each NHS board and NHSScotland as a whole. NHS boards are required to complete their respective cash flows for each period and disclose forecasts for each month up until the year-end
- Capital resource analysis – this is used to monitor the flow of capital funds from source to application by NHS boards. Funds donated for the purchase of capital assets and those purchases should be excluded from the report
- Family health services (FHS) receipts and payments.

Corporate Governance and Audit

Audit Scotland

The audit of NHSScotland is the responsibility of the Auditor General for Scotland (AGS). The AGS is supported by Audit Scotland, which commissions audits from its own staff and commercial firms of auditors.

Audit Scotland is a statutory body set up in April 2000, under the *Public Finance and Accountability (Scotland) Act, 2000*. It provides services to the Accounts Commission and the AGS.

External and internal audit arrangements

NHS boards maintain an internal audit function to carry out more detailed work at local level. NHS boards may provide internal audit themselves, by means of a consortium arrangement with neighbouring boards, or contract out to private firms.

Counter fraud services

Counter Fraud Services (CFS) deters, detects and investigates frauds and other irregularities by FHS contractors and patients against NHSScotland. CFS is hosted within the NHS National Services Scotland, and has links with every NHS board through partnership agreements and nominated fraud liaison officers. As partnership agreements develop, the role of CFS will extend to cover all aspects of boards' service delivery including acute hospitals and NHS staff.

Performance audits

Audit Scotland is responsible for carrying out performance audits (formerly known as value for money audits). The AGS also produces an annual overview of the performance of the NHS in Scotland, which provides information on a range of performance measures – clinical outcomes, waiting times, workforce issues and financial performance.

Risk assessment

The clinical negligence and other risks indemnity scheme (CNORIS) was launched in 2000 with mandatory membership for all health bodies. The scheme has two principal aims:

- Financial efficiency through cost effective risk pooling and claims management
- Effective risk management by encouraging a rigorous approach to the treatment of risk.

Endowment Funds

As with trust or charitable funds in England and Wales, endowment funds are derived from donations by individuals, legacies etc and are used for the purpose for which the original donation was given where that is known. Endowment funds are held and controlled by NHS board directors in their capacity as individual trustees. The board of trustees is an unincorporated body responsible for all matters relating to the charitable funds.

Summary

While there are clearly substantial differences in the organisational structure, governance arrangements and performance management of the NHS in Scotland, the services, beliefs and fundamental principles of the NHS remain the same.

It should be noted that Scotland has the same pay terms and conditions for the majority of its staff, including Agenda for Change, GMS contract and the consultants' contract. The key difference relates to the Executive terms and conditions, which are set by the Scottish Government.

The majority of staff are also covered by the 'knowledge and skills framework' which drives their development and enhances their skills.

References and Further Reading

On line information from NHSScotland: www.show.scot.nhs.uk/

Introductory Guide to NHS Finance in Scotland, HFMA Scotland: www.hfma.org.uk/Branches/Scotland/

Partnership for Care – Scotland's Health White Paper, 2003: www.scotland.gov.uk/Publications/2003/02/16476/18730

Our National Health: A Plan for Action, a Plan for Change, 2000: www.scotland.gov.uk/Publications/2000/12/7770/File-1

Delivering for Health, 2005: www.scotland.gov.uk/Publications/2005/11/02102635/26356

Building a Health Service Fit for the Future, 2005: www.scotland.gov.uk/Publications/2005/05/23141307/13104

Better Health, Better Care, 2007: www.scotland.gov.uk/Publications/2008/01/29152311/0

Public Finance and Accountability (Scotland) Act 2000: www.opsi.gov.uk/legislation/scotland/acts2000/asp_20000001_en_1

Community Care and Health (Scotland) Act 2002: www.oqps.gov.uk/legislation/acts/acts2002/asp_20020005_en_1

National Health Service Reform (Scotland) Act 2004: www.opsi.gov.uk/legislation/scotland/acts2004/asp_20040007_en_1

Fair Shares for All, 2000: www.scotland.gov.uk/Publications/2005/10/19142752/27522

Arrangements for the management of NHSScotland Capital resources after 2010/11 – CEL 32 (2010): www.sehd.scot.nhs.uk/mels/CEL2010_32.pdf

Scottish Futures Trust and Hub Initiative: www.scottishfuturestrust.org.uk/?1=1

The NHS and Community Care Act 1990: www.opsi.gov.uk/acts/acts1990/ukpga_19900019_en_1

Scottish Health Service Costs Book, Information Services Division: www.isdscotland.org/isd/797.html

NHS National Services Scotland: www.nhsnss.org

Counter Fraud Services: www.nhsnss.org/pages/services/counter_fraud_services.php

Audit Scotland, AGS and the Accounts Commission: www.audit-scotland.gov.uk/

Clinical Negligence and other Risks Indemnity Scheme (CNORIS): www.cnoris.com/

20. The NHS in Wales

Introduction

The Welsh Assembly Government has responsibility for health and social care in Wales. It comprises a cabinet of Welsh ministers led by the First Minister who is appointed by the Crown. Cabinet responsibility for the NHS in Wales rests with the Minister for Health and Social Services.

The National Assembly for Wales consists of 60 elected Assembly Members. Its role is to scrutinise:

- How Welsh ministers exercise their executive functions
- The Welsh Assembly Government's budget.

Detailed scrutiny of health matters is undertaken by the Assembly's Health, Wellbeing and Local Government Committee.

Under the *Government of Wales Act 2006*, the National Assembly for Wales has been able to seek powers from the UK Parliament to pass laws for Wales, called *Assembly Measures*, in the areas for which it has devolved responsibility, such as health. However, following the referendum held in March 2011 the National Assembly will in future be able to create laws in all areas of devolved responsibility without the need to seek those powers from the UK Parliament.

While many of the principles underpinning NHS finance in Wales are similar to those in England this chapter looks at the key differences.

Health and Social Care Strategy in Wales

Five-year service, workforce and financial strategic framework for NHS Wales

Following the major reform of the structures of NHS Wales in 2008/09, a five year service, workforce and financial strategic framework was commissioned. This Framework was designed to be a flexible plan that could respond to the challenges faced by one of most complex organisations in the UK. The Framework is a challenge to seize the opportunity of integrated healthcare organisations and implement a plan of action to create world class integrated health, social care and wellbeing services for the people of Wales, within five years, based firmly upon cross public service collaboration. The aim is to improve health, raise system and service performance and quality, and transform health services and in turn transform people's lives.

The overall Framework is a set of documents including the Welsh Assembly Government's 2010 publication *Delivering a Five-Year Service, Workforce and Financial Strategic Framework for NHS Wales,* and seven health board delivery plans which will continue to be developed and refined year on year with partners. These plans will be populated with local service delivery priorities and also with best practice generated by eleven national programmes that also form part of the overall Framework. Other plans prepared with local partners will need to feed into this, particularly Community Strategies, Health Social Care and Well-being Strategies and Children and Young People's Plans.

One Wales

One Wales was the Welsh Assembly Government's progressive agenda for the government of Wales for the third Assembly from 2007 to 2011, and formed the basis of the coalition government. The commitment to health was covered in the chapter on 'a healthy future', and outlines a programme for government on health, including:

- Reviewing NHS reconfiguration
- Strengthening NHS finance and management
- Developing and improving Wales's health services
- Ensuring access to healthcare
- Improving patients' experience
- Supporting social care.

One Wales included a commitment to publicly fund, own and manage health services, and to move purposefully to end the internal market. As a result of this, the structure of the NHS was radically reformed in 2009.

The programme of Government for the fourth Assembly will be published following the Assembly elections in May 2011.

Welsh Assembly Government Health and Social Services Portfolio

Minister for Health and Social Services

The Minister for Health and Social Services has responsibility and accountability to the National Assembly for Wales for the exercise of all the powers in the Health and Social Services portfolio.

National Advisory Board

The National Advisory Board is chaired by the Minister for Health and Social Services, and provides independent advice to the Minister. It assists in discharging ministerial functions, and meeting ministerial accountabilities for the performance of the NHS in Wales.

National Delivery Group

The Director General of Health and Social Services is responsible for providing the Minister with policy advice and for exercising strategic leadership and management of the NHS. The Director General is a member of the Welsh Assembly Government's Strategic Policy and Delivery Board, and is also the Chief Executive for NHS Wales. To support this role, he chairs a National Delivery Group, which forms part of the Health and Social Services Directorate General.

This group is responsible for overseeing the development and delivery of NHS services across Wales and for planning and performance management of the NHS on behalf of Welsh Ministers. This is in accordance with the direction set by the Minister.

Health and Social Services Directorate General

The Health and Social Services Directorate General is the department that supports the Minister and the Director General in discharging their responsibilities. The Chief Medical Officer for Wales is also a member of the Health and Social Services Directorate General.

Organisation of the NHS in Wales

The NHS in Wales comprises seven health boards and three NHS trusts. Specialist services are planned and funded jointly by the health boards through the Welsh Health Specialised Services Committee.

Health boards

The seven health boards are single local health organisations that are responsible for delivering all healthcare services within a geographical area, rather than the trust and local health board system that existed previously.

The seven health boards are formally accountable to the Minister through the Chief Executive, NHS Wales. They are responsible for:

- Planning, designing, developing and securing delivery of primary, community and secondary care services
- Specialist and tertiary services for their areas, to meet identified local needs within the national policy and standards framework set out by the Minister.

The health boards adhere to the standards of good governance set for the NHS in Wales, which are based on the Assembly Government's *Citizen Centred Governance Principles*.

Health boards have a statutory financial duty to keep within their revenue and capital resource limits. In addition they are expected to achieve a 95% compliance rate with the *Better Payment Practice Code*.

NHS trusts

There are three NHS trusts in Wales:

- The Welsh Ambulance Services NHS Trust provides emergency and non-emergency ambulance services and manages NHS Direct in Wales
- Velindre NHS Trust provides specialist cancer services for South Wales, as well as hosting several all-Wales services, including the Welsh Blood Service and the NHS Wales Informatics Service
- Public Health Wales NHS Trust – provides all-Wales screening services and a National Public Health Service.

NHS trusts have a statutory duty to break even, which is measured on an annual basis. They are also expected to keep within their capital resource limits and external financing limits and achieve a 95% compliance rate with the *Better Payment Practice Code*.

Funding and Allocations

Funding

NHS Wales is funded by the Welsh Assembly Government, not the Department of Health. The Welsh Assembly Government receives funds voted by the UK Parliament.

Any changes to the funding provided to the Department of Health for the NHS in England are matched by an increase in the Welsh Assembly Government's funding through the Barnett formula, but it is for the Welsh Assembly Government to determine how this funding is applied. This is done through an annual budget planning round which allocates funding to the sectors for which the Welsh Assembly Government has responsibility. The budget is formally presented to the Assembly for approval in an annual budget motion.

Funding for the NHS in Wales is contained within the Assembly's health and social services main expenditure group, which is the largest expenditure group and comprises approximately 40% of the Assembly's total budget.

Revenue allocation process

Each health board has a unified allocation to fund healthcare for their population. The allocation for hospital and community health services is based on resident populations. Allocations for general medical services and prescribing are based on registered populations, and pharmacy and dental contract allocations are based on provision of services.

The distribution of funding is largely based on historical patterns. A needs based allocation formula was developed by the late Professor Townsend in 2001. Timescale for implementation of the formula is dependent on the availability of growth funding which is allocated on a differential basis to those boards whose current allocations are furthest below target shares.

Health boards contribute to the Welsh Health Specialised Services Committee, which is responsible for planning and funding specialised services on behalf of the health boards.

The Welsh Ambulance NHS Trust and Velindre NHS Trust receive their funding through 'healthcare agreements' with the health boards.

The Public Health Wales NHS Trust receives the majority of its funding directly from the Welsh Assembly Government.

Patient flows between health boards are funded through healthcare agreements between the boards. These are currently based on historic costs, but consideration is being given to introducing an all-Wales standard cost for paying for activity. Healthcare agreements also cover funding allocated by the Welsh Health Specialised Services Committee to specialised services health board providers.

Treatment for some Welsh residents, particularly for specialised services and patients living in North Wales and Powys, is provided by English NHS providers. Treatment for these patients is funded through contracts with the English provider. Where applicable, payment is based on the Payment by Results English tariff (see chapter 13 for more about PbR).

Financial information

In December 2005, the Department for Health and Social Care produced a *Financial Information Strategy*. A programme unit was established in April 2007 to take forward the objectives of the Strategy to improve the quality of NHS cost information so that it is fit for purpose to inform decision-making.

The former NHS trusts were required to produce annual specialty cost returns and healthcare resource group (HRG) cost returns. Until 2008/09, HRG costs were based on the version 3.5 HRG grouper. Since 2009/10 costs have been based on the version 4 HRG grouper.

Costing of provider services became a requirement for the health boards for 2009/10 onwards. Health boards are also required to analyse costs over the 23 programme budget categories, based on version 10 of the *International Classification of Diseases*.

The Welsh Assembly Government has mandated the implementation of service line reporting (SLR) in NHS organisations in Wales.

The development of costing in NHS Wales is overseen by a Financial Information and Costing Group, which is a sub-group of the NHS Wales Directors of Finance Group.

Capital funding

Health boards and NHS trusts are provided with a level of capital they can use for discretionary schemes. Around £50 million is allocated annually for this purpose.

Health boards and trusts are required to submit business cases for funding for major capital schemes using the *Five Case Model*. The Health and Social Services Directorate General has established an Investment Policy and Appraisal Group (IPAG) to provide support to health boards and trusts in the development of business cases, and also to scrutinise cases at all stages of their development.

NHS Trusts are allowed to retain sale proceeds from the disposal of assets up to a maximum of £500,000.

As with other parts of the public sector, the Welsh Assembly Government and NHS Wales are not able to vire funds between capital and revenue allocations.

Strategic Planning and Performance Management

Local health boards inherited from their predecessors joint statutory health, social care and wellbeing strategies prepared in partnership with local authorities, which run to March 2011.

The Health and Social Services Directorate General and NHS organisations in partnership have developed a *Five-Year Service, Workforce and Financial Strategic Framework*. Each health board has prepared an individual *Five Year Strategic Framework* which sets out the medium term direction for the organisation, and describes the key work streams that will deliver transformation and development over the next 5 years.

The Health and Social Services Directorate General has issued an *Annual Quality Framework* for the NHS in Wales for 2011/12. This sets out the ministerial and other priorities that the NHS has to achieve in the year from within the revenue allocation. The *Framework* has been developed within the context of the *Five Year Strategic Framework*. NHS organisations are required to submit annual plans which set out in detail how they will deliver service improvements within available funding.

Performance management of NHS Wales organisations is undertaken by the Health and Social Services Directorate General, and follows six key principles:

- Self-governance
- Proportionality
- Transparency
- Openness
- Minimal duplication
- Minimal information.

The Directorate General is supported by a Delivery and Support Unit and the National Leadership and Innovation Agency in Healthcare in relation to performance management and improvement of NHS Wales organisations.

Financial Accounting and Control

The format and presentation of statutory accounts for the NHS in Wales is similar to that for trusts and primary care trusts (PCTs) in England. The Welsh Assembly Government produces separate *Manuals for Accounts* for health boards (similar to PCT accounts) and NHS trusts.

The individual accounts of local health boards and NHS trusts are summarised into two consolidated NHS accounts that are then subject to independent audit and scrutiny by the Wales Audit Office.

Each NHS organisation is also required to submit monthly monitoring statements reporting on actual financial performance and forecast outturn. This is supplemented by a detailed commentary from the Director of Finance detailing assumptions and risks behind the reported position. The overall position is monitored by the Health and Social Services Directorate General. The Minister will occasionally make a statement to the Assembly on the financial position of the NHS in Wales.

Corporate Governance and Audit

The external audit arrangements in Wales are different to England. The Wales Audit Office was created in April 2005 and the Auditor General for Wales is now responsible for auditing all public accounts and laying them before the Assembly.

Each NHS organisation is responsible for providing an effective internal audit service to meet NHS minimum audit standards. All NHS bodies are required to submit a statement on internal control as part of their annual accounts. Accountable officers (i.e. chief executives) are required to sign the statement on behalf of the board.

In May 2005, the Welsh Assembly Government published the *Healthcare Standards for Wales*. These provided a common framework to support the NHS and partner organisations in providing effective, timely and quality services across all healthcare settings. The standards were used by the Healthcare Inspectorate Wales (HIW) as part of their processes for assessing the quality, safety and effectiveness of healthcare providers and commissioners across Wales. Existing Welsh risk management standards, which were developed by the Welsh Risk Pool, were incorporated into the self-assessment process for the *Healthcare Standards* during 2007. In April 2010, a revised set of standards was issued following a consultation process – the standards, *Doing Well, Doing Better: Standards for Health Services in Wales* replace the *Healthcare Standards for Wales* framework and came into effect from 1st April 2010.

Each NHS body must have an audit committee to oversee the governance and assurance processes for the organisation.

Charitable Funds

Charitable funds are held by NHS trusts and health boards in Wales under the same legislative framework as exists in England. All funds are registered with the Charity Commission and accounts must be submitted to the Charity Commission.

As with the NHS in England, HM Treasury has given dispensation that IAS27 relating to the consolidation of charitable funds with exchequer funds does not apply to the NHS in Wales in 2010/11.

See chapter 17 for more about charitable funds in England and Wales.

References and Further Reading

Welsh Assembly Government Health web pages: http://new.wales.gov.uk/topics/health/?lang=en

Health of Wales Information Service: www.wales.nhs.uk

Delivering a Five-Year Service, Workforce and Financial Strategic Framework for NHS Wales, Welsh Assembly Government, 2010: www.wales.nhs.uk/news/16445

Welsh Assembly Government Ministerial Letters: www.wales.gov.uk/topics/health/publications/health/ministerial/?lang=en

Government of Wales Act 2006: www.opsi.gov.uk/ACTS/acts2006/ukpga_20060032_en_1

Our Healthy Future: http://wales.gov.uk/topics/health/ocmo/healthy/?lang=en

One Wales: http://wales.gov.uk/about/programmeforgovernment/strategy/publications/onewales/?lang=en

Better Payment Practice Code: www.payontime.co.uk/

Programme budgeting (Wales): http://wales.gov.uk/topics/statistics/headlines/health2010/100422/?lang=en

The Five Case Model: www.hm-treasury.gov.uk/data_greenbook_business.htm

National Leadership and Innovation Agency in Healthcare: www.wales.nhs.uk/sitesplus/829

Wales Audit Office: www.wao.gov.uk/

Healthcare Standards for Wales: www.wales.nhs.uk/sites3/home.cfm?OrgID=465

Healthcare Inspectorate Wales: www.hiw.org.uk/

Doing Well, Doing Better: Standards for Health Services in Wales, 2010: www.nhswalesgovernance.com/display/Home.aspx?a=130&s=2&m=0&d=0&p=0

IAS 27 – Consolidated and Separate Financial statements, IASB: www.iasb.org/Home.htm

NHS Wales Governance e-Manual: www.nhswalesgovernance.com/display/home.aspx

Abbreviations

AGS	Auditor General Scotland
ALB	Arm's Length Body
ALE	Auditors' Local Evaluation
AME	Annually Managed Expenditure
ASB	Accounting Standards Board
BSO	Business Service Organisation (NI)
CEDR	Centre for Effective Dispute Resolution
CFISSA	Centrally Funded Initiatives Services and Special Allocations
CFS	Counter Fraud Services
CFSMS	Counter Fraud and Security Management Service
CHMS	Central Health and Miscellaneous Services
CHP	Community Health Partnerships
CNORIS	Clinical Negligence and other Risks Indemnity Scheme (Scotland)
CNST	Clinical Negligence Scheme for Trusts
CPLNHS	Commissioning a Patient-led NHS
CQUIN	Commissioning for Quality and Innovation
CRL	Capital Resource Limit
CSR	Comprehensive Spending Review
CQC	Care Quality Commission
DBFO	Design, Build, Finance, Operate
DEL	Departmental Expenditure Limit
DFT	Distance from Target
DHSC	Directorate of Health and Social Care
DHSSPS	Department of Health, Social Services and Public Safety (NI)
DRG	Diagnosis Related Group
DV	District Valuer
EACA	Emergency Ambulance Cost Adjustment
EBITDA	Earnings before Interest, Taxes and Depreciation
EFL	External Financing Limit
EFR	External Financing Requirement
EPS	Electronic Prescription Service
ESA	European System of Accounts
FBC	Full Business Case
FCE	Finished Consultant Episode
FCF	Free Cash Flow
FESC	Framework for Securing External Support for Commissioners
FHS	Family Health Services
FIMS	Financial Information Management System
FMA	Financial Monitoring and Accounts form
FRAB	Financial Reporting Advisory Body
FRR	Financial Risk Rating
FT	NHS Foundation Trust
FTFF	Foundation Trust Financing Facility
GAAP	Generally Accepted Accounting Practice
GDP	Gross Domestic Product

GDS (nGDS)	General Dental Services Contract
GMS	General Medical Services
nGMS	General Medical Services Contract
GP	General Practitioner
HCAI	Healthcare Associated Infections
HCFHS	Hospital, Community and Family Health Services
HCHS	Hospital and Community Health Services
HEIG	Health Estates Investment Group (NI)
HFMA	Healthcare Financial Management Association
HIW	Healthcare Inspectorate Wales
HPA	Health Protection Agency
HRG	Healthcare Resource Group
HSC	Health Service Circular
HSCB	Health and Social Care Board (NI)
IAS	International Accounting Standards
ICSA	Institute of Chartered Secretaries and Administrators
ICT	Information and Communications Technology
IFRS	International Financial Reporting Standards
IM&T	Information Management and Technology
IPAG	Investment Policy and Appraisal Group
ISD	Information Services Division (Scotland)
ISTC	Independent Sector Treatment Centre
ITN	Invitation to Negotiate
JHWS	Joint Health and Wellbeing Strategy
JSNA	Joint Strategic Needs Assessment
LCG	Local Commissioning Group (NI)
LCFS	Local Counter Fraud Specialist
LDP	Local Delivery Plan
LHB	Local Health Board
LIFT	Local Improvement Finance Trust
LSMS	Local Security Management Specialist
LSP	Local Strategic Partnership
MADEL	Medical and Dental Education Levy
MFF	Market Forces Factor
MPET	Multi Professional Education and Training
MPIG	Minimum Practice Income Guarantee
MUR	Medicine Use Review
NAO	National Audit Office
nGDS	New General Dental Services Contract
nGMS	New General Medical Services Contract
NHSLA	National Health Service Litigation Authority
NIAO	Northern Ireland Audit Office
NICE	National Institute for Health and Clinical Excellence
NMET	Non-Medical Education and Training
NPV	Net Present Value
NRAC	NHSScotland Resource Allocation Committee
NRCI	National Reference Cost Index

NSF	National Service Framework
NSRC	National Schedule of Reference Costs
OBC	Outline Business Case
OCS	Operating Cost Statement
OECD	Organisation for Economic Cooperation and Development
OFR	Operating and Financial review
OGC	Office of Government Commerce
OJEU	Official Journal of the European Union
ONS	Office for National Statistics
PAC	Public Accounts Committee
PASC	Public Administration Select Committee
PBC	Practice Based Commissioning
PBL	Prudential Borrowing Limit
PbR	Payment by Results
PCT	Primary Care Trust
PDC	Public Dividend Capital
PDS (nPDS)	Personal Dental Services Contract
PEC	Professional Executive Committee
PES	Public Expenditure Survey
PfH	Partnerships for Health
PFI	Private Finance Initiative
PHA	Public Health Agency (NI)
PHE	Public Health England
PLICS	Patient Level Information and Costing Systems
PMS	Primary Medical Services
PPP	Public/Private Partnership
PSA	Public Service Agreement
PSS	Personal Social Services
QOF	Quality and Outcomes Framework
RAB	Resource Accounting and Budgeting
RAfDS	Revenue Available for Debt Service
RATE	Regulatory Authority for Tissues and Embryos
RPA	Review of Public Administration
RQIA	Regulation and Quality Improvement Authority (NI)
RRL	Revenue Resource Limit
RS	Reporting Standard
SaFF	Service and Financial Framework
SCG	Specialist Commissioning Group
SFIs	Standing Financial Instructions
SGHD	Scottish Government Health and Community Care Directorate
SHA	Strategic Health Authority
SI	Statutory Instrument
SIC	Statement on Internal Control
SIFT	Service Increment for Teaching
SLM	Service Line Management
SLR	Service Line Reporting
SO	Standing Orders

SOC	Strategic Outline Case
SOCI	Statement of comprehensive income
SOCF	Statement of Cash Flows
SOFA	Statement of Financial Activities
SOFP	Statement of Financial Position
SORP	Statement of Recommended Practice
SPC	Special Purpose Company
SPV	Special Purpose Vehicle
StBOP	Shifting the Balance of Power
SUS	Secondary Uses Service
TME	Total Managed Expenditure
UDA	Unit of Dental Activity
UoR	Use of Resources
VFM	Value for Money
WCC	World Class Commissioning
WGA	Whole of Government Accounts

Glossary of Terms

Accruals
: An accounting concept. In addition to payments and receipts of cash (and similar), adjustment is made for outstanding payments, debts to be collected, and stock (items bought, paid for but not yet used). This means that the accounts show all the income and expenditure that relates to the financial year.

Amortisation
: The process of charging the cost of an intangible asset over its useful life as opposed to recording its cost as a single entry in the income and expenditure records – equivalent to depreciation for a tangible asset. Amortisation is an accounting charge so does not involve any cash outlay.

Assets
: An item that has a value in the future. For example, a debtor (someone who owes money) is an asset, as they will in future pay. A building is an asset, because it houses activity that will provide a future income stream.

Audit
: The process of validating of the accuracy, completeness and adequacy of disclosure of financial records.

Benchmarking
: The process of comparing performance against similar organisations with a view to identifying areas for potential improvement.

Break-even (duty)
: A financial target. Although the exact definition of the target is relatively complex, in its simplest form the break-even duty requires an NHS organisation to match income and expenditure, i.e. make neither a profit nor a loss.

Business cases
: A formal process (in written form) for identifying the financial and qualitative implications of options for changing services and/or investing in capital.

Business plan
: Also known as a service or operational plan, the business plan is the written end product of a process to identify the aims and objectives, and the resource requirements of an organisation over the next three to five year period. Generally business plans cover the forthcoming year in greater detail than those periods further in the future.

Capital
: In most businesses, capital refers either to shareholder investment funds, or buildings, land and equipment owned by a business that has the potential to earn income in the future. The NHS uses this second definition, but adds a further condition – that the cost of the building/equipment must exceed £5,000. Capital is thus an asset (or group of functionally interdependent assets), with a useful life expectancy of greater than one year, whose cost exceeds £5,000.

Capital charges	Capital charges recognise and account for the cost of capital and comprise two key elements – a **return** (similar to debt interest) and **depreciation**. They are levied on all capital assets owned by the NHS, except for assets acquired via interest bearing loans, by donation or with a net book value of zero. Capital charges are included in trust revenue costs and budgets, and recovered through the prices charged to commissioner PCTs and other bodies.
Capital cost absorption	The process whereby the cost of capital (see capital charges above) is taken account of fully ('absorbed') in an organisation's costs.
Capital resource limit (CRL)	The CRL is one of the financial performance targets against which a primary care trust is measured and is set annually by the Department of Health. It is the limit against which the PCT must measure its net capital expenditure in non-current assets. If net capital expenditure is less than the limit, the PCT has met the target.
Comprehensive spending review (CSR)	A cyclical review undertaken by the Treasury to distribute public funding between the main governmental departments.
Cost centre	Rather than record every cost incurred separately costs are categorised into a number of distinct headings referred to as 'cost centres'. Usually cost centres are in line with an organisation's budget heads.
Cost improvement programme	The identification of schemes to reduce expenditure/increase efficiency.
Current assets	Debtors, stocks, cash or similar – i.e. assets that are, or can be converted into, cash within the next twelve months.
Depreciation	The process of charging the cost of an asset over its useful life as opposed to recording its cost as a single entry in the statement of comprehensive income (SOCI) or operating cost statement (OCS). Depreciation is an accounting charge (i.e. it does not involve any cash outlay). Accumulated depreciation is the extent to which depreciation has been charged in successive years' SOCI/OCS accounts since the acquisition of the asset.
Direct costs	Direct costs are costs that can be directly attributed to a particular activity or output. For example, the cost of a radiographer is a direct cost to the radiology department, but an indirect cost to general surgery (as radiology serves several departments).
External financing limit (EFL)	The EFL is a control on a trust's net cash flows. It sets a limit on the level of cash that an NHS trust may:

- draw from either external sources or its own cash reserves (a positive EFL) **OR**
- repay to external sources to increase cash reserves (a negative EFL)

A target EFL is set at the start of the financial year by the Department of Health and the trust is expected to manage its resources to ensure it achieves the target. Trusts must not overshoot their EFL.

Financial reporting standard (FRS)	Issued by the Accounting Standards Board, financial reporting standards govern the accounting treatment and accounting policies adopted by organisations. Generally these standards apply to NHS organisations.
Fixed assets	Land, buildings or equipment that are expected to generate income for a period exceeding one year.
Fixed cost	A cost which does not increase or decrease with changes in activity level.
General medical services	Medical services provided by general practitioners (as opposed to dental, ophthalmic and pharmaceutical services provided by other clinical professions).
Generic cost pressure	An increase in cost that is generally beyond the control of individual health organisations. These may also be referred to as 'national cost pressures', and include items such as national changes to the rate of employers' pension contributions.
Governance	Governance (or corporate governance) is the system by which organisations are directed and controlled. It is concerned with how an organisation is run – how it structures itself and how it is led. Governance should underpin all that an organisation does. In the NHS this means it must encompass clinical, financial and organisational aspects.
Gross domestic product (GDP)	A measure of the value of national economic activity.
Healthcare resource group (HRG)	HRGs are the 'currency' used to collate the costs of procedures/ diagnoses into common groupings to which tariffs can be applied. HRGs place these procedures and/or diagnoses into bands, which are 'resource homogenous', that is, clinically similar and consuming similar levels of resources.
Indexation	A process of adjusting the value, normally of fixed assets, to account for inflation.

Indirect costs | Indirect costs are costs that cannot be attributed directly to a particular activity or cost centre – see direct costs for an example.

Intangible asset | Goodwill, brand value or some other right, which although invisible is likely to generate financial benefit (income) for its owner in future, and for which you might be willing to pay.

International financial reporting standard (IFRS) | A set of standards by which organisations prepare their financial statements. They were applied to the NHS with effect from 1 April 2009 in order to bring consistency and comparability to the financial statements of government departments, facilitating comparisons between and within the public and private sectors therefore enhancing public sector accountability.

Local cost pressure | An increase in cost that, although it may or may not be geographically widespread, is considered to be within the control of individual elements of the NHS.

Marginal cost | The increase/decrease in cost caused by the increase/decrease in activity by one unit.

Net book value | The value of items (assets) as recorded in the balance sheet of an organisation. The net book value takes into consideration the replacement cost of an asset and the accumulated depreciation (i.e. the extent to which that asset has been 'consumed' by its use in productive processes).

Operating cost statement | One of the four primary statements in the accounts of PCTs only. It shows the funding received by the PCT from the Department of Health, and also its day to day revenue and expenditure.

Overheads | Overhead costs are those costs that contribute to the general running of the organisation but cannot be directly related to an activity or service. For example, the total heating costs of a hospital may be apportioned to individual departments using floor area or cubic capacity.

Prudential borrowing limit | The maximum cumulative borrowing that an NHS trust may have to fund additional capital investment.

Payment by results | The system for reimbursing healthcare providers in England for the costs of providing treatment. PbR is based around the use of a national tariff that links a preset price to a defined measure of output or activity.

Private finance initiative | A form of public/private partnership designed to fund major capital investments without immediate recourse to public money. The public sector works with private sector partners who are contracted to design and build the assets needed.

Public dividend capital This is a form of long-term government finance on which the NHS trust pays dividends to the Exchequer. It carries an expected return of 3.5% – this percentage figure is generally regarded as the long-term cost of capital in the public sector.

Public sector payment policy Trusts have to achieve a public sector payment standard of valid invoices paid within 30 days of the receipt of the invoice. A target (currently 95%) is set at the start of the year by the Department of Health for the value and volume of invoices that must be paid within 30 days.

Reference costs NHS organisations are required to submit a schedule of costs of healthcare resource groups to allow direct comparison of the relative costs of different providers. The results are published each year in the National Schedule of Reference Costs.

Revenue resource limit The RRL is one of the financial performance targets against which a PCT is measured and is used to determine whether or not the PCT has met operational financial balance. It is set annually by the Department of Health.

Semi-fixed cost A cost whose magnitude is only partly affected by the level of activity – i.e. although there is a relationship between activity and expenditure, it is not directly proportional. Semi-fixed costs tend to stay the same until an activity increases above a certain level. They are sometimes referred to as 'step costs'.

Statement of cash flows One of the four primary statements in the accounts for all NHS organisations, the SOCF shows the movement in cash and cash equivalents.

Statement of comprehensive income One of the four primary statements in the accounts for NHS trusts and foundation trusts. The SOCI shows the day to day revenue and expenditure for the organisation.

Statement of changes in taxpayers' equity One of the four primary statements in the accounts for all NHS organisations, this statement shows the impact of changes in revenue and expenditure on the organisation's reserves.

Statement of financial position One of the four primary statements in the accounts for all NHS organisations, the SOFP shows the assets, liabilities and equity as at a point in time, normally a month or year end.

Tangible asset A sub-classification of fixed assets, to exclude invisible items such as goodwill and brand values. Tangible fixed assets include land, buildings, equipment, and fixtures and fittings.

Total absorption cost	A process whereby all the costs (including fixed costs/overheads) of an organisation are allocated to cost centres.
Variable cost	A cost that increases/decreases in line with changes in the level of activity.
Variance	The difference between budgeted and actual income and/or expenditure. Variances are an accounting tool used to analyse the cause of over/under spends with a view to proposing rectifying action.
Working capital	Working capital is the money and assets that an organisation can call upon to finance its day-to-day operations (it is the difference between current assets and liabilities and is reported in the statement of financial position (balance sheet) as net current assets (liabilities)). If working capital dips too low, organisations risk running out of cash and may need a working capital loan to smooth out the troughs.